# KOVELS'
## DEPRESSION
## GLASS &
## DINNERWARE
## PRICE LIST

## BOOKS BY
## RALPH AND TERRY KOVEL

American Country Furniture 1780–1875

A Directory of American Silver, Pewter, and Silver Plate

Kovels' Advertising Collectibles Price List

Kovels' American Art Pottery

Kovels' American Silver Marks

Kovels' Antiques & Collectibles Fix-It Source Book

Kovels' Antiques & Collectibles Price List

Kovels' Book of Antique Labels

Kovels' Bottles Price List

Kovels' Collector's Guide to American Art Pottery

Kovels' Collectors' Source Book

Kovels' Depression Glass & American Dinnerware Price List

Kovels' Depression Glass & Dinnerware Price List

Kovels' Dictionary of Marks—Pottery and Porcelain

Kovels' Guide to Selling, Buying, and Fixing Your Antiques and Collectibles

Kovels' Guide to Selling Your Antiques & Collectibles

Kovels' Illustrated Price Guide to Royal Doulton

Kovels' Know Your Antiques

Kovels' Know Your Collectibles

Kovels' New Dictionary of Marks—Pottery & Porcelain

Kovels' Organizer for Collectors

Kovels' Price Guide for Collector Plates, Figurines,
Paperweights, and Other Limited Editions

Kovels' Quick Tips: 799 Helpful Hints on How to Care for Your Collectibles

SIXTH EDITION

# KOVELS'
## DEPRESSION
## GLASS &
## DINNERWARE
## PRICE LIST

Ralph and Terry Kovel

THREE RIVERS PRESS
NEW YORK

Published by Three Rivers Press, a division of Crown Publishers, Inc., 201 East 50th Street, New York, New York 10022. Member of the Crown Publishing Group.

Random House, Inc., New York, Toronto, London, Sydney, Auckland www.randomhouse.com

THREE RIVERS PRESS and colophon are trademarks of Crown Publishers, Inc.

Printed in the United States of America

Library of Congress Cataloging-in-Publication Data
Kovel, Ralph M.
Kovels' depression glass & dinnerware price list / Ralph and Terry Kovel. — 6th ed.
p.   cm.
Rev. ed. of: Kovel's depression glass & American dinnerware price list. 5th ed. 1995.
Includes bibliographical references.
1. Depression glass—Catalogs.   2. Ceramic dinnerware—United States—History—20th century—Catalogs.   I. Kovel, Terry H.
II. Kovel, Ralph M.   Kovel's depression glass & American dinnerware price list.
III. Title.
NK5439.D44K67  1998
738'.0973'075—dc21          97-49034

ISBN 0-517-80310-7

Sixth Edition

# Contents

ACKNOWLEDGMENTS                                    ix


**DEPRESSION GLASS**

INTRODUCTION                                        3
CLUBS AND PUBLICATIONS                              7
COLOR NAMES                                         9
**MAIN LISTING**                                   **11**
REPRODUCTIONS                                       95
FACTORIES, PATTERNS, AND BIBLIOGRAPHY             100
GENERAL REFERENCE BOOKS                           112


**DINNERWARE**

INTRODUCTION                                       115
CLUBS AND PUBLICATIONS                             119
**MAIN LISTING**                                  **121**
FACTORIES, PATTERNS, AND BIBLIOGRAPHY             171
GENERAL REFERENCE BOOKS                           209

# Acknowledgments

Many dealers, collectors, and companies helped with prices and information. Thank you to Antiques World, Backward Glances, Barbara Balin, Diane Brouhle, The Collector's Corner, Depression Delights, Marilyn Emans, Fenner's Antiques, Fiesta Plus, Mary Finegan (Marfine Antiques), First Glass Glass, Ida Fuchs, The Glass Cupboard, Glass Connection, Goldmine Farm Antiques, Grandma's China Closet, Grandma's Cupboard, Grier & Sowden Antiques & Collectibles, Fred Haggert, Helen Hartwick, Alex James, Larry W. Jones, Barry M. Klein, Little Church Ant, Lucky Penny, Stacey Lundy, McLieb's Home Page, Jim Medeiros & Ken Paruti, Moore's Antiques, Christine Nagy, Betty Newbound, Old Things, Olde Loved Things, Nadine Pankow, Past Times Collectibles, Michael E. Pratt, Laird D. Shively, Something Old, Lindy Spinks, T & J's Yesteryear Collectibles, Tickled Pink Antiques, Twentieth Century Designs, Watch World, Larry D. Wells, Ron Whitcomb, Joel Wilson (China Specialties Inc.), Wits' End Antiques, Allen Wutke, Delmer H. Youngen.

Thanks also to Benjamin Margalit who took many of the pictures in this book and to Leo Walter, Jr., and his staff, Jon and Chris, of Stagecoach Antiques who helped us locate dozens of pattern examples for the pictures.

And thank you to the staff at Crown, PJ Dempsey, our editor, Pam Stinson-Bell, and Merri Ann and Dave Morrell. Putting a book like this together takes extra attention to details. Thanks to our staff, Edie and Cherrie Smrekar, Kitty Busher, Grace DeFrancisco, Marcia Goldberg, Karen Kneisley, Eleanore Melzak, Gloria Pearlman, Nancy Saada, Virginia Warner, Anne Wochner, but most of all to Gay Hunter, who reads every word of copy, checks every picture, and then explains all the problems to the rest of us.

# DEPRESSION GLASS

# DEPRESSION GLASS

# Introduction

This book is a price report. Prices are actual offerings in the marketplace last year. They are not an average. The high and low prices represent different sales. Prices reported are not those from garage or house sales or flea markets. They are only from dealers who understand the Depression glass market and who sell at shops, at shows, or through national advertising.

This is a book for beginners as well as for serious collectors of Depression glass. We have included those patterns, both Depression and "elegant" patterns of glass, most often offered for sale at glass shows. The pattern names used are from original catalogs. Most of the patterns included in earlier books are still to be found here because collectors still buy these patterns. Many newly popular patterns are also included. We have made no effort to give an exact definition of the term "Depression glass." If a pattern of American glassware was made between 1925 and 1970 and if it is known to some collectors or dealers as Depression glass, we have included it here.

Opaque glass was popular in the 1930s. Each of the colors was given a special name by the company that produced it. Monax or Ivrene are opaque white glasswares. Opaque green glass was known by a variety of names. Jade green is a generic name used by many companies. Jade-ite was the green used by Anchor Hocking; Jadite was a color of glass and a pattern of green kitchenware made by Jeannette Glass Company. To avoid unnecessary confusion, we have chosen to always spell the word *Jadite* when referring to the color in this book. Delphite, an opaque blue glass, is sometimes spelled "delfite" in the ads, but we have chosen to always use the "Delphite" spelling.

A few rules were followed in the wording of entries. It is always a sugar & creamer, not a creamer & sugar. A pickle dish is listed as a pickle. A relish dish is called a relish. A refrigerator jar is a leftover. An open salt dish is listed as a salt, but a salt shaker has its full name. Some pieces were made for dual use. A champagne (glass) may also be called a high sherbet by some factories. Any glass with a stem is called a goblet in this book. A tumbler can have a flat or footed bottom but not a high stem. A shot glass is listed here as a whiskey. This year we list not only the size of a plate but also what it is commonly called, so it would be a "plate, dinner, 10 in." The size of a dinner plate varies slightly with each pattern and we have used the actual size. If there is a pair of candlesticks or salts or compotes, the word *pair* is included as the last word in the listing.

A bibliography of Depression glass books is included in a new form. It is not a traditional bibliography. Instead we have made it more "user friendly." Look up the factory that made your pattern of glass. (If you don't know the factory name, you will find it in the paragraph listing prices in the main section of the book.) Under the factory name is a list of the most collectible patterns made by that factory. Some factories changed their names. Anchor Hocking changed from Hocking Glass Company to Anchor Hocking Glass Corporation to Anchor Hocking Corporation. We have used the name most in use during the years the glass was made. Some patterns that are listed are priced in this book; some are not. The listing also includes the books that picture or discuss your pattern. General books about Depression glass are listed separately.

This book is not an in-depth study of Depression glass. The beginner who needs more information about patterns, manufacturers, color groups, or how and where to buy should use the improved bibliography-pattern list and the club lists we have included.

This year there is a warning if a reproduction of a pattern is known. It has been added to the paragraphs found in the main listing. There is also a list of known reproductions at the end of the Depression glass section. All of these lists follow the last glass price entries. Hundreds of patterns, many not listed in other price books, are included here. The best way to learn about Depression glass is to attend the regional and national shows devoted to glass. Your local newspaper or the collectors' publications listed in this book will print the dates and locations.

When a dealer says a piece is "Book One," it is a pattern of glassware in the book *Colored Glassware of the Depression Era 1* by Hazel Marie Weatherman, a revision of *A Guidebook to Colored Glassware of the 1920's and 1930's.* "Book Two" refers to patterns in the book *Colored Glassware of the Depression Era 2* by Weatherman. These books are out of print.

Ceramic dinnerware and the prices for these pieces can be found in the second half of this book.

Particular patterns can be found by using either the Depression Glass or Dinnerware main listings, both of which are arranged alphabetically. Depression Glass begins on page 11 and Dinnerware on page 121.

Ralph and Terry Kovel,
Accredited Senior Appraisers,
American Society of Appraisers
March 1998

# Clubs and Publications

## CLUBS

**Akro Agate Collectors Club,** *Clarksburg Crow* (newsletter), 10 Bailey St., Clarksburg, WV 26301-2524.

**Fenton Art Glass Collectors of America, Inc.,** *Butterfly Net* (newsletter), P.O. Box 384, Williamstown, WV 26187.

**Fostoria Glass Collectors, Inc.,** *Glass Works* (newsletter), P.O. Box 1625, Orange, CA 92856.

**Fostoria Glass Society of America, Inc.,** *Facets of Fostoria* (newsletter), P.O. Box 826, Moundsville, WV 26041.

**Heisey Collectors of America,** *Heisey News* (newsletter), 169 W. Church St., Newark, OH 43055.

**Michiana Association of Candlewick Collectors,** *MACC Spyglass* (newsletter), 17370 Battles Rd., South Bend, IN 46614.

**National Cambridge Collectors, Inc.,** *Cambridge Crystal Ball* (newsletter), P.O. Box 416, Cambridge, OH 43725-0416.

**National Candlewick Collectors Club,** *Candlewick Collector* (newsletter), 6534 South Ave., Holland, OH 43528.

**National Depression Glass Association,** *News & Views* (newsletter), P.O. Box 8264, Wichita, KS 67208-0264.

**National Fenton Glass Society,** *Fenton Flyer* (newsletter), P.O. Box 4008, Marietta, OH 45750.

**National Imperial Glass Collectors Society,** *Glasszette* (newsletter), P.O. Box 534, Bellaire, OH 43906.

**National Milk Glass Collectors Society,** *Opaque News* (newsletter), 500 Union Cemetary Rd., Greensburg, PA 15601.

**Tiffin Glass Collectors Club,** *Tiffin Glassmasters* (newsletter), P.O. Box 554, Tiffin, OH 44883.

**Westmoreland Glass Society, Inc.,** *Westmoreland Glass Society, Inc.* (newsletter), P.O. Box 2883, Iowa City, IA 52240-2883.

## PUBLICATIONS

*Antique Trader Weekly* (newspaper), P.O. Box 1050, Dubuque, IA 52004-1050.

*Daze* (newspaper), 10271 State Rd., Box 57, Otisville, MI 48463.

*Fire-King News* (newsletter), PO Box 473, Addison, AL 35540.

*Glass Collector's Digest* (magazine), P.O. Box 553, Marietta, OH 45750-9979.

*Kovels on Antiques and Collectibles (newsletter), P.O. Box 22200, Beachwood, OH 44122.*

*Matching Services: China, Silver, Crystal* (leaflet), **Ralph and Terry Kovel, P.O. Box 22900, Beachwood, OH 44122.**

*The Original Westmoreland Glass Collector's Newsletter* (newsletter), P.O. Box 143, North Liberty, IA 52317.

# Color Names

This is a list of some of the most confusing color names:

| | |
|---|---|
| AMBER | Apricot, Golden Glow, Topaz |
| BLUE-GREEN | Ultramarine |
| CLEAR | Crystal |
| DEEP BLUE | Cobalt, Dark Blue, Deep Blue, Ritz Blue |
| GREEN | Emerald, Forest Green, Imperial Green, Nu-Green, Springtime Green |
| MEDIUM BLUE | Azure, Madonna |
| LIGHT BLUE | Moonlight |
| OPAQUE BLACK | Black |
| OPAQUE BLUE | Delphite |
| OPAQUE GREEN | Jadite |
| OPAQUE OFF-WHITE | Azurite, Chinex, Clambroth, Cremax, Ivrene |
| OPAQUE WHITE | Milk White, Monax |
| PINK | Azalea, Cheri-Glo, Flamingo, Heatherbloom, Nu-Rose, Rose, Rose Glow, Rose Marie, Rose Pink, Rose Tint, Wild Rose |
| PURPLE | Amethyst, Black Amethyst, Burgundy |
| RED | Carmen, Royal Ruby, Ruby Red |
| YELLOW & RED | Lemonade & Oxblood (marbleized colors in Akro Agate) |

# ·A·

**ACCORDION PLEATS,** see Round Robin

## ADAM

Adam, sometimes called Chain Daisy or Fan & Feather, is a glass pattern made from 1932 to 1934 by the Jeannette Glass Company, Jeannette, Pennsylvania. Sets can be found most often in Pink, but Crystal, Delphite, and Green pieces were also made. A few pieces are known in Yellow, but this does not seem to have been a standard production color. Reproductions have been made in Green and Pink. They are listed at the end of the Depression Glass section.

**CRYSTAL**
Tumbler, 4 1/2 In. . . . . . . .27.50
Tumbler, 5 1/2 In. . . . . . . .52.00

**GREEN**
Ashtray,
    4 1/2 In. . . . . . .22.50 to 28.00
Berry Bowl,
    4 3/4 In. . . . . . .15.00 to 18.00
Bowl, 5 3/4 In. . .37.50 to 46.00
Bowl, 7 3/4 In. . .24.00 to 32.00
Bowl, Vegetable, Oval,
    10 In. . . . . . . . . . . . . . .35.00
Butter, Cover . .315.00 to 325.00
Cake Plate, Footed,
    10 In. . . . . . . . .23.00 to 30.00
Coaster, 3 1/4 In. .19.00 to 20.00
Creamer . . . . . . .17.50 to 22.00
Cup . . . . . . . . . . . . . . . .22.00
Cup & Saucer . .28.00 to 36.00
Grill Plate,
    9 In. . . . . . . . .18.00 to 20.00
Pitcher, Square, 32 Oz.,
    8 In. . . . . . . . . . . . . . .45.00
Plate, Dinner,
    9 In. . . . . . . . .26.00 to 30.00
Plate, Salad, Square,
    7 3/4 In. . . . . . .13.50 to 17.50
Plate, Sherbet,
    6 In. . . . . . . . . . .8.00 to 9.50
Platter, 11 3/4 In. . . . . . . .32.00
Punch Bowl, Base . . . . .90.00
Relish, 2 Sections, 8 In. . . .27.00
Saucer . . . . . . . . .4.50 to 7.00
Sherbet, 3 In. . . . .35.00 to 37.50
Sugar . . . . . . . . . . . . . .18.00
Sugar &
    Creamer . . . .37.00 to 39.00
Tumbler,
    4 1/2 In. . . . . . .27.50 to 29.00
Tumbler, Iced Tea,
    5 1/2 In. . . . . . .45.00 to 60.00

**PINK**
Ashtray,
    4 1/2 In. . . . . . .28.00 to 30.00
Berry Bowl, 4 3/4 In.
    . . . . . . . . . . .15.00 to 19.00
Bowl, Cereal,
    5 3/4 In. . . . . .40.00 to 46.00
Bowl, Cover, 9 In. . . . . .65.00
Bowl, Dessert,
    4 3/4 In. . . . . .12.00 to 17.00
Bowl, Square, 9 1/2 In. . . .30.00
Bowl, Vegetable, Oval,
    10 In. . . . . . . .28.00 to 50.00
Butter, Cover . . . . . . . . .85.00

If you live in an earthquake area, a few precautions may help limit damage. Be sure there is a lip on the edge of a shelf that holds dishes and glassware. Use dental wax to stick the objects to the shelf. Keep cabinet doors locked so pieces will not fall out. Magnetic "childproof" locks also help.

Cake Plate, Footed,
    10 In. . . . . . . .22.00 to 28.00
Candlestick, 4 In.,
    Pair . . . . . . .90.00 to 100.00
Candy Jar,
    Cover . . . . . .85.00 to 105.00
Coaster, 3 1/4 In. . . . . . .22.00
Creamer . . . . . . . . . . . . .20.00
Cup & Saucer . .25.00 to 35.00
Grill Plate,
    9 In. . . . . . . . .20.00 to 24.00
Pitcher, 32 Oz., 8 In. . . . .40.00
Plate, Breakfast, Square,
    9 In. . . . . . . . .29.00 to 39.00
Plate, Luncheon, 8 In. . . . .65.00
Plate, Salad, Square,
    7 3/4 In. . . . . .12.50 to 14.00
Plate, Sherbet,
    6 In. . . . . . . . . .7.00 to 12.50
Platter,
    11 3/4 In. . . . . .23.00 to 30.00
Relish, 2 Sections, 8 In. . .30.00
Salt & Pepper, Footed,
    4 In. . . . . . . . .73.00 to 80.00
Saucer . . . . . . . . . . . . . .7.00
Sherbet, 3 In. . . . .26.50 to 35.00
Sugar, Cover . . . . . . . . . .33.00
Tumbler,
    4 1/2 In. . . . . . .26.50 to 30.00
Tumbler, Iced Tea, Footed,
    5 1/2 In. . . . . .52.00 to 70.00
Vase, 7 1/2 In. . . . . . . . .350.00

# AKRO AGATE

Picture a marble cake with the irregular mixture of colors running through the batter. This is what Akro Agate is usually like—a marbleized mixture of clear and opaque colored glass. The Akro Agate Company, Clarksburg, West Virginia, originally made children's marbles. The marbleized dinnerware and other glass children's sets were made in many colors from 1932 to 1951. Lemonade & Oxblood is a marbleized yellow and red glass.

**AMBER**
Bowl, Child's, Interior Panel,
  3 3/8 In. . . . . . .17.50 to 18.00
Creamer, Child's, Interior
  Panel, 1 3/8 In. . . . . . . .28.00
Creamer, Child's, Stippled
  Band . . . . . . . . . . . . . .75.00
Cup, Child's, Stippled
  Band . . . . . . . . . . . . . .12.00
Cup & Saucer, Child's,
  Interior Panel . . . . . . . . .18.50
Plate, Child's, Interior Panel,
  4 1/4 In. . . . . . . . .8.00 to 8.50
Plate, Child's, Stippled Band,
  3 3/4 In. . . . . . . . .6.00 to 7.00
Saucer, Child's, Interior
  Panel, 3 1/4 In. . . .5.00 to 7.00
Saucer, Child's, Stippled
  Band . . . . . . . . . . . . . .5.00
Sugar & Creamer, Child's,
  Interior Panel . . . . . . . .35.00
Teapot, Child's, Interior
  Panel, 2 5/8 In. . . . . . .35.00
Tumbler, Child's, Stippled
  Band . . . . . . . . . . . . .10.00

**BLUE**
Ashtray, 3 3/4 In. . . . . . . .9.00
Ashtray, Leaf, 4 1/8 In. . . . .5.00
Ashtray, Shell . . . . . . . . . .6.00
Bowl, Child's, Concentric
  Ring, 3 1/4 In. . . . . . . .25.00

Bowl, Child's, Interior
  Panel, 3 3/8 In. . . . . . .65.00
Bowl, Graduated Dart,
  3-Footed,
  5 1/4 In. . . . . .10.00 to 22.50
Bowl, Stacked Disc,
  Footed, 5 In. . . . . . . . .20.00
Creamer, Child's, Chiquita,
  1 1/2 In. . . . . .10.00 to 18.00
Creamer, Child's, Chiquita,
  Opaque, 1 1/2 In. . . . . .15.00
Creamer, Child's, Interior Panel,
  1 3/8 In. . . . . .38.00 to 50.00
Creamer, Child's, Stacked
  Disc & Interior Panel . . .50.00
Cup, Child's, Chiquita,
  1 1/2 In. . . . . . .7.00 to 12.00
Cup, Child's, Concentric
  Ring . . . . . . . . . . . . . .16.00
Cup, Child's, Interior
  Panel, 1 1/4 In. . . . . . .28.00
Cup, Child's, Stacked
  Disc & Interior Panel,
  1 3/8 In. . . . . . . . . . . .60.00
Cup & Saucer, Child's,
  Stacked Disc & Interior
  Panel, 1 1/4 In. . . . . . .75.00
Jar, Hat, Cover,
  Mexicali . . . . . . . . . . .20.00
Pitcher, Child's, Stacked
  Disc, 2 7/8 In. .12.00 to 25.00
Planter, Rectangular,
  8 In. . . . . . . . . . . . . . .10.00
Plate, Child's, Chiquita,
  3 3/4 In. . . . . . .7.00 to 10.00
Plate, Child's, Closed
  Handles, Octagonal . . . .16.00
Plate, Child's, Interior
  Panel, 3 1/4 In. . . . . . .28.00
Plate, Child's, Octagonal,
  4 1/4 In. . . . . . .4.00 to 10.00
Plate, Child's, Raised Daisy,
  3 1/4 In. . . . . .16.00 to 21.00
Saucer, Child's, Chiquita,
  3 1/8 In. . . . . . . .4.00 to 5.00
Saucer, Child's, Interior Panel,
  3 1/8 In. . . . . .12.00 to 23.00
Sugar, Child's, Chiquita,
  Opaque, 1 1/2 In. . . . . .15.00
Sugar, Child's, Interior
  Panel . . . . . . . . . . . . . .90.00
Sugar, Cover, Child's,
  Stacked Disc & Interior
  Panel, Large . . . . . . .100.00
Sugar & Creamer, Child's,
  Chiquita . . . . . . . . . . . .20.00

Sugar & Creamer, Child's,
  Stacked Disc, 1 1/4 In. . .12.00
Sugar & Creamer, Interior
  Panel . . . . . . . . . . . . . .50.00
Teapot, Child's, Interior
  Panel, 2 5/8 In. . . . . . .45.00
Teapot, Child's,
  Octagonal . . . . . . . . . .15.00
Teapot, Child's, Stacked
  Disc . . . . . . . . .6.00 to 14.00
Tumbler, Child's, Stacked
  Disc & Interior Panel . . .11.00

**BROWN**
Ashtray, Square, 5 In. . . . . .6.00

**CHARTREUSE**
Cup, Child's, Concentric
  Ring . . . . . . . . . . . . . .35.00

**GRAY**
Cigarette Holder . . . . . . .15.00
Vase, Handles . . . . . . . . . .9.00

**GREEN**
Ashtray, Leaf . . . . . . . . . .5.00
Ashtray, Shell . . . . . . . . . .6.00
Ashtray, Square, 2 7/8 In. . .6.00
Bowl, Child's, Interior Panel,
  3 3/8 In. . . . . .15.00 to 35.00
Bowl, Graduated Dart,
  3-Footed,
  5 1/4 In. . . . . .12.00 to 15.00
Bowl, Utility, Tab Handle,
  9 In. . . . . . . . . . . . . . .50.00
Creamer, Child's, Chiquita,
  Opaque, 1 1/2 In. . . . . . .7.00
Creamer, Child's, Interior Panel,
  1 1/2 In. . . . . .25.00 to 30.00
Creamer, Child's, Stacked
  Disc . . . . . . . . .6.00 to 11.00
Cup, Child's,
  Chiquita . . . . . . .3.00 to 6.00
Cup, Child's, Concentric
  Ring . . . . . . . . . . . . . . .4.00
Cup, Child's, Interior
  Panel . . . . . . .16.00 to 18.00
Cup, Child's, Octagonal,
  Large . . . . . . . . . . . . . .10.00
Cup, Child's, Raised
  Daisy . . . . . . . . . . . . . .25.00
Cup, Child's, Stippled
  Band . . . . . . . . . . . . . .15.00
Cup & Saucer, Child's,
  Chiquita . . . . . . . . . . . . .5.00
Cup & Saucer, Child's,
  Interior Panel . . . . . . . .35.00
Cup & Saucer, Child's,
  Stippled Band . . . . . . .19.50

Flowerpot, Stacked
Disc, Footed,
2 1/4 In. . . . . . . . .6.00 to 8.00

Pitcher, Child's, Interior
Panel . . . . . . . . . . . . . .30.00

Pitcher, Child's, Stacked
Disc . . . . . . . . . .8.00 to 10.00

Pitcher, Child's, Stippled
Band . . . . . . . . . . . . . .28.00

Planter, Lily, 5 1/4 In. . . . .8.00

Planter, Oval, 6 In. . . . . . . .7.00

Planter, Rectangular,
6 In. . . . . . . . . . . . . . . . .8.00

Planter, Rectangular,
8 In. . . . . . . . . . . . . . . . .8.00

Plate, Child's, Chiquita,
Opaque . . . . . . . . . . . . . .5.00

Plate, Child's, Closed
Handles, Octagonal . . . . .5.00

Plate, Child's, Concentric
Rib . . . . . . . . . . .2.00 to 3.00

Plate, Child's, Concentric
Ring, 3 1/4 In. . . . . . . . .10.00

Plate, Child's, Interior
Panel . . . . . . . . .9.00 to 20.00

Plate, Child's,
Otagonal . . . . . . .2.50 to 5.00

Plate, Child's, Stippled
Band . . . . . . . . . . . . . . .7.50

Saucer, Child's, Chiquita,
Opaque . . . . . . . . . . . . . .3.00

Saucer, Child's, Concentric
Ring . . . . . . . . . .2.00 to 3.00

Saucer, Child's, Interior
Panel . . . . . . . . .7.00 to 8.00

Saucer, Child's, Stippled
Band . . . . . . . . . . . . . . .5.00

Soap Dish . . . . . . . . . . .25.00

Sugar, Child's, Chiquita . . .5.00

Sugar & Creamer, Child's,
Stacked Disc . . . . . . . . .12.00

Tea Set, Child's,
Octagonal . . . . . . . . . .170.00

Teapot, Child's, Interior
Panel . . . . . . . . . . . . . .40.00

Teapot, Child's, Stippled
Band . . . . . . . . . . . . . .37.50

Tumbler, Child's, Raised
Daisy . . . . . . . . . . . . . .25.00

Tumbler, Child's, Stippled
Band . . . . . . . . . . . . . .11.00

Urn, Grecian, Beaded Top,
3 1/4 In. . . . . . . . . . . . . .5.50

Urn, White Floral,
3 1/4 In. . . . . . . . . . . . .10.00

### LEMONADE

Cigarette Jar . . . . . . . . .10.00

Creamer . . . . . . . . . . . . .50.00

Cup . . . . . . . . .36.00 to 38.00

Plate . . . . . . . . . . . . . . .30.00

Saucer . . . . . .24.00 to 25.00

Smoker Set, Jar, Square
Ashtray, 5 Piece . . . . . .25.00

Urn, Grecian, 3 1/4 In. . . .12.00

### ORANGE

Ashtray, Leaf . . . . . . . . . .5.00

Ashtray, Shell . . . . . . . . . .6.00

Basket, 2 Handles . . . . . .22.50

Bowl, Utility,
Tab Handle . . . . . . . . .50.00

Flowerpot, Footed,
2 1/2 In. . . . . . . . . . . . . .8.00

Jar, Hat,
Mexicali . . . . .30.00 to 40.00

Urn, Floral . . . . . . . . . . .10.00

Urn, Grecian, 3 1/4 In. . . . .7.00

### PINK

Cup, Child's, Interior
Panel, 1 1/4 In. . . . . . .29.00

Plate, Child's, Interior
Panel, 4 1/4 In. . . . . . .16.00

Saucer, Child's, Concentric
Ring, 2 3/4 In. . . . . . . . .2.50

Saucer, Child's, Interior
Panel, 2 3/4 In. . . . . . .12.00

Saucer, Child's, Octagonal,
2 3/4 In. . . . . . . . . . . . . .8.00

### PUMPKIN

Bowl, Utility, Tab Handle,
9 In. . . . . . . . . . . . . . . .65.00

Cup, Child's, Concentric
Ring, 1 3/8 In. . . . . . . . .22.00

Cup, Child's, Interior
Panel, 1 3/8 In. . . . . . .35.00

Cup, Child's, Octagonal . .25.00

### PURPLE

Cup, Child's, Chiquita,
1 1/2 In. . . . . . . . . . . . .30.00

### WHITE

Bowl, Utility, Tab Handle,
9 In. . . . . . . . . . . . . . . .50.00

Creamer, Stacked Disc,
1 1/4 In. . . . . . . . . . . . .11.00

Mortar & Pestle . . . . . . .10.00

Powder Jar, Colonial
Lady . . . . . . . . . . . . . .90.00

Saucer, Concentric
Ring, 2 3/4 In. . . . . . . . .1.50

**The best time to buy
an antique is when
you see it.**

Saucer,
Octagonal . . . . .3.00 to 10.00

Tumbler, Child's, Stacked
Disc, 2 In. . . . . . .4.00 to 6.00

### YELLOW

Butter, Child's, Cover . . . .75.00

Creamer, Child's, Stacked
Disc, 1 1/4 In. . . . . . . .11.00

Plate, Child's, Concentric
Rib, 3 1/4 In. . . . . . . . . .3.00

Plate, Child's, Interior
Panel, 4 1/4 In. . . . . . . .17.00

Saucer, Child's, Concentric
Rib, 2 3/4 In. . . . . . . . . .2.50

Saucer, Child's, Concentric
Ring, 3 1/8 In. . . . . . . .12.00

Saucer, Child's, Interior
Panel, 2 3/4 In. . . . . . .13.00

Saucer, Child's, Raised
Daisy, 2 1/2 In. . . . . . .13.00

Saucer, Octagonal,
2 3/4 In. . . . . . . . .5.00 to 6.00

## ALICE

An 8 1/2-inch plate, cup, and
saucer were apparently the only
pieces made in the Alice pat-
tern. This 1940s pattern was
made by the Anchor Hocking
Glass Corporation, Lancaster,
Ohio, in Opaque White with a
pink or blue border and in
Jadite. Other related sections in
this book are Charm, Fire-
King, Gray Laurel, Jadite,
Jane-Ray, Peach Lustre, Philbe,
Swirl Fire-King, Turquoise
Blue, and Wheat.

### JADITE

Cup & Saucer . . . . . . . . .6.00

### WHITE

Cup, Blue Trim . . . . . . . .15.00

Cup & Saucer,
Blue Trim . . . . . . . . . .15.00

Plate, Dinner, Blue Rim,
8 1/2 In. . . . . . .20.00 to 25.00

## ALPINE CAPRICE

Caprice and Alpine Caprice
were made from the same
molds. Alpine Caprice has a
satin finish, Caprice is transparent. Alpine Caprice, made by
the Cambridge Glass Company,
Cambridge, Ohio, about 1936,
was made in Blue, Crystal, and
Pink satin-finished glass.

**BLUE**
Bowl, Crimped, Footed,
13 In. . . . . . .150.00 to 175.00
Candlestick, 5 In. . . . . . .62.50
Candlestick, Prisms, 7 In.,
Pair . . . . . . . . . . . . . .160.00
Relish, 3 Sections . . . . . .95.00

**ALPINE CAPRICE,** see also
Caprice

## AMERICAN

American is a pattern made to
resemble the pressed glass of an
earlier time. It was introduced
by Fostoria Glass Company,
Moundsville, West Virginia, in
1915 and remained in production until the factory closed in
1986. Most pieces were made

---

**Rubber cement solvent,
available at art and
office supply stores, has
many uses. Put a few
drops on a paper towel
and use it to rub off ink
smudges, adhesive tape
glue, and label glue
from glass or porcelain.**

---

of clear, colorless glass known
as Crystal. A few pieces are
known in Amber, Blue, Green,
Yellow, and Milk Glass. It is
similar to Cube pattern, but
after looking carefully, you will
soon learn to tell the two patterns apart. Many pieces of
American pattern were re-
produced after 1987. They are
listed at the end of the Depression Glass section.

**CRYSTAL**
Ashtray, Square,
2 7/8 In. . . . . . . . . . . . . .7.50
Bonbon, 3-Footed, 6 In. . .18.00
Bottle, Oil, Stopper . . . . .27.00
Bowl, Almond, 3 3/4 In. . . .9.00
Bowl, Cover, 11 In. . . . .43.00
Bowl, Cupped, 7 In. . . . .50.00
Bowl, Deep, 10 In. . . . . .45.00
Bowl, Float, Low,
11 1/2 In. . . . . . . . . . . .55.00
Bowl, Float, Oval,
10 In. . . . . . . . . . . . . . .36.00
Bowl, Fruit, 3-Footed,
10 1/2 In. . . . . . . . . . . .35.00
Bowl, Fruit, Shallow,
13 In. . . . . . . . . . . . . . .80.00
Bowl, Handles, 8 1/2 In. . .60.00
Bowl, Lemon, Cover,
5 1/2 In. . . . . . . . . . . . .43.00

Bowl, Lily Pond, 12 In. . .65.00
Bowl, Oval, Deep,
11 3/4 In. . . . . . . . . . . .45.00
Bowl, Rolled Edge,
11 In. . . . . . . . . . . . . . .43.00
Bowl, Tricornered, Handle,
5 In. . . . . . . . . . . . . . . .15.00
Bowl, Vegetable, 2 Sections,
Oval, 10 In. . . . . . . . . .32.00
Bowl, Wedding, Cover,
6 1/2 In. . . . . . . . . . . . .90.00
Butter, Cover, 1 Lb. . . . .90.00
Butter, Round, Cover . . . .45.00
Cake Plate, Handles,
10 In. . . . . . . . . . . . . . .24.00
Cake Plate, Round
Pedestal, 10 In. . . . . . . .90.00
Cake Stand, Square,
10 In. . . . . . . . .85.00 to 95.00
Candlestick, 2-Light, 6 1/2 In.,
Pair . . . . . . . .95.00 to 105.00
Candlestick, 3 In.,
Pair . . . . . . . . .22.00 to 30.00
Candlestick, Octagon Base,
6 In., Pair . . . . .50.00 to 55.00
Candlestick, Round Base,
4 3/8 In., Pair . . . . . . . .60.00
Candlestick, Square,
Column, 7 In., Pair . . .190.00
Candy Box, 3 Sections,
Triangular . . . .65.00 to 75.00
Candy Dish, Cover,
Footed . . . . . . . . . . . . .38.00
Cheese & Cracker, With
Bowl, 12 In. . . .45.00 to 55.00
Coaster, 3 3/4 In . . . . . . .12.00
Condiment Bottle,
Stopper . . . . . . . . . . .125.00
Cream & Sugar, Tray,
3 Piece . . . . . . . . . . . .23.00
Creamer, 2 3/8 In. . . . . . .9.00
Cup & Saucer . . .8.00 to 10.00
Cup & Saucer,
Footed . . . . . . .8.00 to 14.00
Decanter, Stopper, 24 Oz.,
9 1/4 In. . . . . .80.00 to 85.00
Decanter Set, Cordial,
Scotch, Gin, Rye, With
Rack, 5 Piece . . . . . . .395.00
Goblet, Cocktail, Cone, Footed,
3 Oz., 2 7/8 In. . . . . . .10.00
Goblet, Cocktail, Oyster,
3 1/2 In. . . . . . .10.00 to 16.00
Goblet, Hexagonal Foot, 10 Oz.,
4 3/4 In. . . . . . . .7.00 to 10.00

Goblet, Low, 9 Oz.,
4 3/8 In. . . . . . . . . . . . . .8.00
Goblet, Water, Hexagonal Foot,
6 7/8 In. . . . . . .11.00 to 14.00
Hat, 3 In. . . . . . . .18.00 to 24.00
Hat, 4 In. . . . . . . .40.00 to 45.00
Ice Bucket, Metal Handle,
6 In. . . . . . . . . . . . . . . .55.00
Ice Tub, Large, 6 1/2 In. . .60.00
Jam Jar, Cover . .55.00 to 60.00
Mayonnaise, Divided,
5 In. . . . . . . . . . . . . . .18.00
Mayonnaise, Footed,
Underplate, Ladle,
3 Piece . . . . . . . . . . . .55.00
Mustard, Footed, Cover . .30.00
Nappy, Cover, 5 In. . . . .25.00
Picture Frame, Oval . . . . .15.00
Pitcher, 1 Pt., 5 3/8 In. . . .33.00
Pitcher, 1/2 Gal., 8 In. . . .60.00
Pitcher, 2 Pt., 7 1/4 In. . . .60.00
Pitcher, 3 Pt. . . . .45.00 to 70.00
Pitcher, No Ice Lip,
1/2 Gal. . . . . . . . . . . .200.00
Plate, Bread & Butter,
6 In. . . . . . . . . . . . . . . .10.00
Plate, Dinner,
9 1/2 In. . . . . . .18.00 to 25.00
Plate, Lemon, Handles,
6 1/2 In. . . . . . . . . . . . .12.00
Plate, Salad,
7 In. . . . . . . . . .8.00 to 10.00
Plate, Salad,
8 1/2 In. . . . . . .11.00 to 15.00
Platter, Oval, 10 1/2 In. . .40.00
Platter, Oval, 12 In. . . . . .60.00
Punch Bowl, Base,
18 In. . . . . . . . . . . . . .325.00
Punch Bowl, Low Base,
14 In. . . . . . .175.00 to 275.00
Punch Bowl,
Tom & Jerry . . . . . . .240.00
Punch Cup, Flared Rim . .12.00
Punch Cup, Straight
Edge . . . . . . . .9.00 to 12.50
Relish, 4 Sections, 9 In. . .45.00
Salt, Individual, 2 In.,
Set Of 12 . . . . . . . . . . .90.00
Salt & Pepper,
3 In. . . . . . . . . .18.00 to 20.00
Salt & Pepper, Individual,
2 In. . . . . . . . . . . . . . . .24.00
Salt & Pepper, Tray,
3 Piece . . . . . . .25.00 to 35.00

Sauceboat, Liner,
2 Piece . . . . . . . . . . . .47.00
Snack Set, 2 Piece . . . . .24.00
Soup, Cream, 5 In. . . . . .50.00
Sugar, Tea, 2 1/4 In. . . . .14.00
Sugar & Creamer, Tea . . .18.00
Sundae, 6 Oz.,
3 1/8 In. . . . . . . . .7.00 to 9.00
Syrup, Dripcut,
6 1/2 Oz. . . . . . . . . . . .55.00
Syrup, Glass Lid,
10 Oz. . . . . . . . . . . . .145.00
Tidbit, Crook Handle . . . .30.00
Tom & Jerry Set, Bowl,
8 Mugs . . . . . . . . . . .340.00
Toothpick . . . . . .19.00 to 25.00
Torte Plate, 14 In. . . . . . .30.00
Torte Plate, 18 In. . . . . . .125.00
Torte Plate, Oval,
13 1/2 In. . . . . .40.00 to 45.00
Tray, 4 Sections,
6 1/2 In. . . . . . . . . . . . .35.00
Tray, 4 Sections,
10 3/4 In. . . . . . . . . . .135.00
Tray, Center Handle,
12 In. . . . . . . . . . . . . .40.00
Tray, For Sugar &
Creamer, 6 3/4 In. . . . . .12.00
Tray, Muffin, 10 In. . . . . .35.00
Tray, Oval, 6 In. . . . . . . .40.00
Tray, Square, 10 In. . . . .110.00
Tumbler, 5 Oz.,
4 3/4 In. . . . . . .10.00 to 13.00
Tumbler, Flared, 8 Oz.,
4 1/4 In. . . . . . . . . . . . .13.00
Tumbler, Flared, Footed,
12 Oz., 6 In. . . . . . . . .14.00
Tumbler, Iced Tea,
12 Oz. . . . . . .16.00 to 20.00
Tumbler, Juice, Hexagonal
Foot, 5 Oz. . . . . . . . . .15.00
Tumbler, Luncheon,
Footed . . . . . . . . . . . . .11.00
Tumbler, Old Fashioned,
6 Oz. . . . . . . . . . . . . . .10.00
Vase, Flared, 6 In. . . . . .23.00
Vase, Flared, 9 1/2 In. . .115.00
Vase, Flared, Footed,
10 In. . . . . . . . . . . . . .90.00
Vase, Square, Footed,
9 In. . . . . . . . . . . . . . .38.00
Vase, Straight Sides,
6 In. . . . . . . . . . . . . . .30.00

Vase, Straight Sides,
10 In. . . . . . . . . . . . . .90.00
Vase, Straight Sides,
12 In. . . . . . . . . . . . .135.00
Vase, Sweet Pea,
4 1/2 In. . . . . . .75.00 to 85.00

**GREEN**
Pitcher . . . . . . . . . . . .450.00

**MILK GLASS**
Bowl, Wedding, Cover . . .95.00

**AMERICAN BEAUTY,** see English
Hobnail

---

## AMERICAN PIONEER

Panels of hobnail-like protrusions and plain panels were used in the design of American Pioneer. It was made by Liberty Works, Egg Harbor, New Jersey, from 1931 to 1934. Crystal, Green, and Pink dishes are easily found. Amber is rare.

**CRYSTAL**
Cup & Saucer . . . . . . . .14.00
Plate, Luncheon, 8 In. . . . .10.00
Sugar & Creamer . . . . . .37.50

**GREEN**
Console, 10 3/8 In. . . . . .69.00
Cup . . . . . . . . .12.00 to 15.00
Cup & Saucer . . . . . . . .17.00
Dish, Mayonnaise,
4 1/4 In. . . . . . . . . . . . .90.00
Ice Bucket, 6 In. . . . . . . .79.00
Pitcher, 5 In. . . . . . . . . .100.00
Plate, Luncheon,
8 In. . . . . . . . . .6.00 to 16.00
Sugar, 3 1/2 In. . . . . . . . .22.00

**PINK**
Bowl, Handle, 9 In. . . . . .22.00
Candy Jar, Footed, 1 Lb. . .95.00
Coaster, 3 1/2 In. . . . . . .30.00
Creamer . . . . . . . . . . . .25.00
Cup & Saucer . . . . . . . .14.00
Plate, 8 In. . . . . . . . . . .14.00

# AMERICAN SWEETHEART

In 1930 Macbeth-Evans Glass Company introduced American Sweetheart. At first it was made of pink glass, but soon other colors were added. The pattern continued in production until 1936. Blue, Cremax, Monax, Pink, and Red pieces were made. Sometimes a gold, green, pink, platinum, red, or smoky black trim was used on Monax pieces. There is a center design on most plates, but some Monax plates are found with plain centers. One of the rarest items in this pattern is the Monax sugar bowl lid. The bowls are easy to find but lids seem to have broken.

### BLUE
Console, 18 In. . . . . . . .1500.00
Sandwich Server,
   15 1/2 In. . . .375.00 to 625.00

### CREMAX
Berry Bowl, Master,
   9 In. . . . . . . . . . . . . . . . .35.00

### MONAX
Berry Bowl, Master,
   9 In. . . . . . . . .65.00 to 70.00
Bowl, Cereal,
   6 In. . . . . . . . .12.00 to 20.00

Bowl, Vegetable, Oval,
   11 In. . . . . . . . . . . . . . .85.00
Chop Plate,
   11 In. . . . . . . .15.00 to 22.00
Console, 18 In. . . . . . . .425.00
Creamer, Footed . .8.50 to 10.00
Cup . . . . . . . . . . . . . . . .10.00
Cup & Saucer . .10.50 to 16.00
Pie Plate, 9 In. . . . . . . . .12.00
Plate, Bread & Butter,
   6 In. . . . . . . . . . .4.00 to 6.50
Plate, Dinner,
   9 3/4 In. . . . . .22.00 to 28.00
Plate, Dinner,
   10 1/4 In. . . . .25.00 to 27.50
Plate, Luncheon,
   9 In. . . . . . . . .11.00 to 13.00
Plate, Salad,
   8 In. . . . . . . . . .7.00 to 10.00
Platter, Oval,
   13 In. . . . . . . .60.00 to 75.00
Salt & Pepper, Footed . . .375.00
Saltshaker . . . . . . . . . . .195.00
Salver, 12 In. . . . .15.00 to 25.00
Saucer . . . . . . . . .3.00 to 4.00
Sherbet, Footed,
   4 1/4 In. . . . . .16.00 to 19.00
Soup, Cream, 4 1/2 In. . .120.00
Sugar, Footed . . . . .7.00 to 9.00
Sugar & Creamer,
   Footed . . . . . . .12.00 to 22.00
Tidbit, 2 Tiers,
   12 In. . . . . . . . . . . . . .100.00

### PINK
Berry Bowl,
   3 3/4 In. . . . . . .70.00 to 80.00
Berry Bowl, Master,
   9 In. . . . . . . . .45.00 to 65.00
Bowl, Cereal,
   6 In. . . . . . . . .12.00 to 20.00
Bowl, Vegetable,
   Oval, 11 In. . . .60.00 to 80.00
Creamer,
   Footed . . . . . . .13.00 to 15.00
Cup . . . . . . . . .15.00 to 18.00
Cup & Saucer . .16.00 to 22.00
Pitcher, 60 Oz.,
   7 1/2 In. . . . . . . . . . . .850.00
Pitcher, 80 Oz.,
   8 In. . . . . . .675.00 to 825.00
Plate, Bread & Butter,
   6 1/2 In. . . . . . . .5.00 to 7.00
Plate, Dinner,
   10 In. . . . . . . .34.00 to 40.00

Plate, Salad,
   8 In. . . . . . . . .10.00 to 16.00
Platter, Oval,
   13 In. . . . . . . .50.00 to 57.00
Salt & Pepper,
   Footed . . . .475.00 to 525.00
Saltshaker,
   Footed . . . .225.00 to 250.00
Salver, 12 In. . . . .19.00 to 30.00
Saucer . . . . . . . . .4.00 to 4.50
Sherbet, Footed,
   3 3/4 In. . . . . .20.00 to 25.00
Sherbet, Footed,
   4 1/4 In. . . . . .17.00 to 22.00
Soup, Cream,
   4 1/2 In. . . . . .60.00 to 95.00
Soup, Dish,
   9 1/2 In. . . . . .60.00 to 65.00
Sugar . . . . . . . . . . . . . . .15.00
Tumbler, 4 3/4 In. . . . . . .150.00
Tumbler, 5 Oz.,
   3 1/2 In. . . . .85.00 to 110.00
Tumbler, Water, 9 Oz.,
   4 1/4 In. . . . . .75.00 to 100.00

### RED
Cup . . . . . . . . . . . . . . .110.00
Plate, Salad,
   8 In. . . . . . . .65.00 to 115.00
Salver, 12 In. . . . . . . . .230.00
Tidbit, 3 Tiers . . . . . . .1150.00

# ANNIVERSARY

Pink Anniversary pattern was made from 1947 to 1949, but it is still considered Depression glass by collectors. Crystal pieces are shown in a 1949 catalog. In the 1970s, Crystal and Iridescent, a carnival-glass-like amber color, were used. The pattern was the product of the Jeannette Glass Company, Jeannette, Pennsylvania.

**CRYSTAL**
Bowl, Fruit, 9 In. . . . . . .10.00
Butter, Cover . . .24.00 to 29.00
Candy Jar, Cover . . . . . .22.00
Creamer . . . . . . . . . . . . .4.00
Cup & Saucer . . . .3.00 to 5.00
Goblet, Wine,
2 1/2 Oz. . . . . . . . . . . . .8.00
Plate, Dinner, 9 In. . . . . . .5.00
Plate, Sandwich,
12 1/2 In. . . . . . . . . . . .13.00
Plate, Sherbet,
6 1/4 In. . . . . . . . .2.00 to 3.50
Sherbet . . . . . . . .5.00 to 6.00
Sugar &
Creamer . . . . .8.00 to 17.50
Vase, 6 1/2 In. . . . . . . . .13.00

**PINK**
Berry Bowl, 4 7/8 In. . . . .11.00
Bowl, Fruit, 9 In. . . . . . .47.00
Creamer, Footed . . . . . . .16.00
Cup & Saucer . . . . . . . .15.00
Goblet, Wine, 2 1/2 In. . . .18.00
Plate, Dinner, 9 In. . . . . .17.00
Sandwich Server,
12 1/2 In. . . . . . . . . . . .25.00
Sherbet, Footed . . . . . . . .16.00
Vase, Ruffled Edge,
6 1/2 In. . . . . . . . . . . . .39.00

**APPLE BLOSSOM,** see Dogwood

## AUNT POLLY

U.S. Glass Company, a firm with factories in Indiana, Ohio, Pennsylvania, and West Virginia, made Aunt Polly glass. Luncheon sets can be found in Blue, Green, and Iridescent. Pink pieces have been reported. The pattern was made in the late 1920s until c.1935.

**BLUE**
Berry Bowl, 4 3/4 In. . . . .15.00
Bowl, Pickle, Handle,
7 1/4 In. . . . . . . . . . . . .28.00
Butter, Cover . .190.00 to 200.00
Candy Dish, 2 Handles,
Footed . . . . . .30.00 to 39.00
Plate, Sherbet,
6 In. . . . . . . . . .7.00 to 15.00
Sherbet . . . . . . .10.00 to 14.00
Sherbet, Footed . . .8.00 to 15.00
Sugar . . . . . . . . . . . . . .25.00
Tumbler,
3 5/8 In. . . . . . .29.00 to 35.00

**GREEN**
Butter, Cover . . . . . . . .220.00
Candy Dish, Handle,
Footed . . . . . . . . . . . . .26.00
Sherbet . . . . . . .8.00 to 11.00
Vase, Footed, 6 1/2 In. . . .25.00

**IRIDESCENT**
Butter . . . . . . . . . . . . . .90.00
Sherbet . . . . . . . . . . . . . .5.00

## AURORA

The Hazel Atlas Glass Company made Aurora pattern glass in the late 1930s. Fewer than ten different pieces were made in Cobalt Blue and Pink; an even smaller quantity in Crystal and Green.

**BLUE**
Bowl, Cereal,
5 3/8 In. . . . . . .15.00 to 18.00
Bowl, Deep,
4 1/2 In. . . . . . .47.00 to 52.00
Creamer . . . . . .18.00 to 23.00
Cup . . . . . . . . .11.00 to 19.50
Cup & Saucer . .18.00 to 22.00
Plate, Sherbet,
6 1/2 In. . . . . . .8.00 to 14.00

Saucer . . . . . . . . . . . . . .5.00
Tumbler,
4 3/4 In. . . . . . .18.00 to 24.00
**CRYSTAL**
Bowl, Cereal, 5 3/8 In. . . .20.00
Bowl, Deep, 4 1/2 In. . . . .60.00
Creamer . . . . . . . . . . . .24.00
Cup & Saucer . . . . . . . .22.00

## AVOCADO

Although the center fruit looks more like a pear, the pattern has been named Avocado. It was made originally from 1923 to 1933 by the Indiana Glass Company, Dunkirk, Indiana, primarily in Green and Pink. Some Crystal pieces were also produced. In 1974, a reproduction line of pitchers and tumblers appeared in Amethyst, Blue, Frosted Pink, Green, Pink, and Red. By 1982, pieces were made in Amber. The pattern is sometimes called Sweet Pear or No. 601.

**CRYSTAL**
Bowl, 2 Handles, Oval . . .17.00
Bowl, Deep,
9 1/2 In. . . . . . .22.00 to 35.00
Bowl, Salad, 7 1/2 In. . . . .12.00

To ship small pieces of glass, try this trick: Put the glass in a Styrofoam cup, then wrap in bubble wrap or several layers of paper. Stuff sides and bottom of a large box filled with breakable antiques with Styrofoam trays. You can usually get extras from your grocery store.

### GREEN

Bowl, 2 Handles,
5 1/4 In. . . . . . 32.00 to 37.00
Bowl, 2 Handles, 8 In. . . .30.00
Bowl,
9 1/2 In. . . . .120.00 to 135.00
Bowl, Preserve, Handle,
7 In. . . . . . . . .15.00 to 20.00
Bowl, Salad,
7 1/2 In. . . . . . 50.00 to 55.00
Cake Plate, Handles,
10 1/2 In. . . . . . . . . . . .50.00
Cup . . . . . . . . . . . . . . .24.00
Plate, 6 3/8 In. . . . 14.00 to 17.00
Plate, Luncheon,
8 1/4 In. . . . . . 15.00 to 16.00
Saucer . . . . . . . . . . . . . .25.00
Sherbet, Footed . .53.00 to 58.00
Sugar & Creamer,
Footed . . . . . . .75.00 to 80.00

### PINK

Bowl, Deep, 9 1/2 In. . . .125.00
Bowl, Handles, 8 In. . . . . .25.00
Cake Plate, Handle,
10 In. . . . . . . . . . . . . .39.00
Cup . . . . . . . . . . . . . . .30.00
Cup & Saucer . . . . . . . .45.00
Plate, Luncheon,
8 1/4 In. . . . . . . . . . . . .18.00
Plate, Sherbet, 6 3/4 In. . .13.00
Sugar & Creamer . . . . . . .85.00

**B PATTERN,** see Dogwood

**BALLERINA,** see Cameo

# ·B·

## BAMBOO OPTIC

Bamboo Optic pattern was made by Liberty Works of Egg Harbor, New Jersey, about 1929. Pink and Green luncheon sets and other pieces were made. The pattern resembles Octagon.

### GREEN
Candlestick, 5 1/2 In. . . . .12.00
Octagon, Cup . . . . . . . . . .5.00

**BANDED CHERRY,** see Cherry Blossom

**BANDED FINE RIB,** see Coronation

**BANDED PETALWARE,** see Petalware

**BANDED RAINBOW,** see Ring

**BANDED RIBBON,** see New Century

**BANDED RINGS,** see Ring

## BAROQUE

Fostoria Glass Company of Moundsville, West Virginia, made Baroque, or No. 2496, from 1936 to 1966. The pattern was made in Crystal, Azure (blue), Gold Tint, Topaz (yellow), and Green. The same molds were used to make other glass patterns decorated with etched designs.

### AZURE
Bowl, 3-Footed, 7 In. . . . .28.00
Bowl, 6 1/2 In. . . . . . . . .25.00
Bowl, Salad, Deep . . . . .95.00
Candlestick, 2-Light,
4 1/2 In. . . . . . . . . . . . .40.00
Candlestick,
4 In. . . . . . . . .25.00 to 35.00
Celery Dish, 11 In. . . . . .54.00
Cup & Saucer . .24.00 to 35.00
Nappy, Handle . . . . . . . .34.00
Plate, Bread & Butter,
6 In. . . . . . . . . . . . . . .12.00
Plate, Salad, 7 1/2 In. . . . .15.00
Salt & Pepper . . . . . . .120.00
Sugar & Creamer, Tray,
Individual . . . . . . . . . .90.00
Torte Plate, 13 In. . . . . . .85.00
Tumbler, Water, Footed,
9 Oz., 5 1/2 In. .36.00 to 38.00
Vase, 7 In. . . . . . . . . . .125.00

### CRYSTAL
Bowl, Handle, 4 In. . . . . .10.00
Candlestick, 7 3/4 In. . . . .50.00
Goblet, Water, 9 Oz.,
6 3/4 In. . . . . . . . . . . . .12.00
Sugar, Individual, 3 In. . . . .4.00
Vase, 7 In. . . . . . . . . . . .40.00

### TOPAZ
Bowl, 4-Footed,
10 1/2 In. . . . . . . . . . . .32.00
Bowl, Flared, 12 In. . . . . .42.00
Bowl, Handle, 10 1/2 In. . .42.00
Bowl, Rolled Edge,
11 In. . . . . . . . . . . . . . .80.00
Candy Dish, Cover,
3 Sections . . . . . . . . .125.00

Compote, 5 1/2 In. . . . . . .39.50
Compote, 6 1/2 In. . . . . . .45.00
Goblet, Water, 9 Oz.,
    6 3/4 In. . . . . . . . . . . .30.00
Ice Bucket, 4 3/8 In. . . . .125.00
Jam Jar, Cover . . . . . . . .85.00
Mayonnaise, Liner,
    5 1/2 In. . . . . . . . . . . .40.00
Mustard, Cover . . . . . . .110.00
Plate, Bread & Butter,
    7 In. . . . . . . . . . . . . . .10.00
Plate, Luncheon,
    8 1/2 In. . . . . . . . . . . .20.00
Relish, 3 Sections,
    10 1/2 In. . . . . .25.00 to 40.00
Rose Bowl, 3 3/4 In. . . . . .95.00
Sugar, Individual, 3 In. . . .16.50
Sugar & Creamer, Footed,
    3 1/2 In. . . . . . . . . . . .20.00
Tidbit, 3-Footed, 8 In. . . . .22.00
Torte Plate,
    14 In. . . . . . . .30.00 to 38.00

**BASKET,** see No. 615

**BERWICK,** see Boopie

**BEVERAGE WITH SAILBOATS,** see
    White Ship

**BIG RIB,** see Manhattan

**BLOCK,** see Block Optic

## BLOCK OPTIC

Block Optic, sometimes called
Block, was made from 1929 to
1933 by the Hocking Glass
Company, Lancaster, Ohio.
Slight variations in the design
of some pieces, like creamers
and sugars, show that the pattern was redesigned at times.
Green is the most common
color, followed by Crystal,
Pink, and Yellow. Amber and
Blue examples are harder to
find. Some pieces were made
with a black stem or a black flat
foot.

### CRYSTAL
Candy Jar, 6 1/4 In. . . . . .49.50
Goblet, Wine, 4 1/2 In. . . .22.00
Pitcher, Bulbous,
    7 5/8 In. . . . . . . . . . . . .26.00
Pitcher, Water, 8 1/4 In. . .28.00
Plate, Breakfast, 9 In. . . . .20.00
Sandwich Tray,
    10 1/4 In. . . . . .11.00 to 17.00
Saucer, 6 1/8 In. . . . . . . . .6.00
Whiskey . . . . . . . . . . . .15.00

### GREEN
Berry Bowl, Master,
    8 1/2 In. . . . . . .22.00 to 32.00
Bowl, 4 1/2 In. . .27.50 to 30.00
Bowl, 4 1/4 In. . . . .7.00 to 8.00
Bowl, Cereal,
    5 1/4 In. . . . . . .13.00 to 16.00
Bowl, Console, Rolled Edge,
    11 3/4 In. . . . .75.00 to 125.00
Bowl, Salad, 7 In. . . . . . .125.00
Butter, Cover . . . . . . . . .19.00
Candlestick, Single . . . . .50.00
Candy Jar, Cover,
    2 1/4 In. . . . . . .25.00 to 50.00
Candy Jar, Cover,
    6 1/4 In. . . . . . .65.00 to 77.50
Cup . . . . . . . . . . .5.50 to 9.00
Cup & Saucer . .12.00 to 17.00
Goblet, Wine, 4 1/2 In. . . .35.00
Ice Bucket . . . . . . . . . . .53.00
Ice Tub . . . . . .40.00 to 66.50
Mug . . . . . . . . . . . . . . .39.50
Pitcher, Bulbous, 54 Oz.,
    7 5/8 In. . . . . . . . . . . . .70.00
Pitcher, Water, 54 Oz., 8
    1/2 In. . . . . . . . . . . . . .38.00
Plate, Dessert, 6 In. . . . . . .2.50
Plate, Dinner,
    9 In. . . . . . . . .22.00 to 27.50
Plate, Luncheon,
    8 In. . . . . . . . . . .3.75 to 7.00

Plate, Sherbet, 6 In. . . . . . .2.00
Salt & Pepper,
    Footed . . . . . . .30.00 to 40.00
Saltshaker,
    Footed . . . . . . .15.00 to 18.00
Saltshaker, Squatty . . . . .42.00
Saucer, 5 1/2 In. . . . . . . .10.00
Sherbet, 3 1/4 In. . .4.50 to 6.00
Sherbet, Thin, 4 3/4 In. . . .17.00
Sugar & Creamer,
    Dark Base . . . . . . . . . .45.00
Sugar & Creamer, Footed,
    3 1/8 In. . . . . . .25.00 to 30.00
Sugar & Creamer,
    Squatty . . . . . . . . . . . .30.00
Sugar & Creamer,
    Tall . . . . . . . . .25.00 to 26.00
Tumbler, 5 Oz.,
    4 5/8 In. . . . . . .20.00 to 24.00
Tumbler, Old Fashioned,
    3 7/8 In. . . . . . . . . . . . .20.00
Tumbler, Water, Footed,
    9 Oz. . . . . . . . . . . . . . .22.00

### PINK
Candleholder, Pair,
    1 3/4 In. . . . . . . . . . . . .75.00
Candy Jar, Cover,
    2 1/4 In. . . . . . . . . . . . .50.00
Candy Jar, Pedestal . . . . .125.00
Console, Rolled
    Edge . . . . . . .85.00 to 155.00
Cup . . . . . . . . . . .5.00 to 7.00
Cup & Saucer . . . . . . . .15.00
Goblet, 5 3/4 In. . . . . . . .25.00
Ice Tub . . . . . .89.00 to 97.00
Pitcher, Water, 54 Oz.,
    1/2 In. . . . . . . . . . . . . .40.00
Plate, Dinner, 9 In. . . . . .30.00
Plate, Luncheon,
    8 In. . . . . . . . . . .5.00 to 6.00
Plate, Sherbet,
    6 In. . . . . . . . . .2.75 to 5.00
Saltshaker, Footed . . . . .38.00
Saucer . . . . . . . . . . . . . .8.00
Saucer, Cup Ring,
    6 1/8 In. . . . . . . . . . . . . .7.00
Sherbet,
    4 3/4 In. . . . . . .12.50 to 15.00
Sherbet, Stem, 3 1/4 In. . . .9.00
Sugar, Cone . . . . . . . . . .12.50
Sugar & Creamer, Cone . .20.00
Sugar & Creamer, Tall . . .23.00
Tumbler, Juice, 5 Oz. . . . .20.00

Tumbler, Water, Footed,
9 Oz., 5 3/4 In. . . . . . .15.00

Tumbler, Water, Footed,
10 Oz., 6 In. . . . . . . . .30.00

### YELLOW

Candy Jar, Cover,
2 1/2 In. . . . . . .60.00 to 64.00

Goblet, 7 In. . . . .34.00 to 35.00

Plate, Dinner,
9 In. . . . . . . . .38.00 to 42.00

Plate, Luncheon, 8 In. . . . . .5.00

Plate, Sherbet, Square,
3 1/4 In. . . . . . . . . . . . . .9.00

Sugar & Creamer . . . . . .22.50

Sugar & Creamer,
Handle . . . . . . . . . . . . .29.50

### BOOPIE

With a name like Boopie, it must have some other attraction. This Anchor Hocking Glass Corporation pattern was made in the late 1940s and 1950s. Only glasses of various sizes are known, including the 3 1/2-ounce, 4-ounce, 6-ounce, and 9-ounce. The pattern came in Crystal, Forest Green, and Royal Ruby.

### CRYSTAL

Sherbet, Footed, 6 Oz. . . . .4.00

### FOREST GREEN

Goblet, Water, 9 Oz. . . . . .10.00

Sherbet, Footed, 6 Oz. . . . .6.50

### ROYAL RUBY

Goblet, Cocktail, 4 Oz. . . .10.00

Goblet, Water, 9 Oz. . . . . .12.00

Sherbet, Footed, 6 Oz. . . . .7.50

Tumbler, Footed, 6 Oz. . . .10.00

**BOUQUET & LATTICE,** see
Normandie

**BRIDAL BOUQUET,** see No. 615

### BUBBLE

Names of Depression glass patterns can be depressingly confusing. Bubble is also known as Bullseye, the original name given by Anchor Hocking Glass Corporation, or as Provincial, the 1960s name. Bubble was made in many colors, originally in Crystal, Pale Blue, and Pink. Dark Green was issued in 1954. Milk White and Ruby Red were made in the 1960s. Recently, Yellow pieces have been seen, possibly made in the 1950s. Reproductions appeared in the 1980s in Green, Jadite, Pink, and Royal Ruby. They usually have an anchor mark on the bottom. They are listed at the end of the Depression Glass section.

### BLUE

Berry Bowl, 4 In. . . . . . . .9.00

Berry Bowl, Master,
8 3/8 In. . . . . .16.00 to 18.00

Bowl, Cereal,
5 1/4 In. . . . . .10.00 to 12.50

Bowl, Fruit,
4 1/2 In. . . . . . .9.00 to 16.00

Creamer . . . . . . . . . . . . .35.00

Cup . . . . . . . . . . . . . . . . .5.00

Cup & Saucer . . . .3.50 to 9.00

Grill Plate,
9 3/8 In. . . . . .20.00 to 22.00

---

Glassware, old or new, requires careful handling. Stand each piece upright, not touching one another. Never nest pieces. Wash in moderately hot water and mild detergent. Avoid wiping gold or platinum banded pieces while glasses are hot. Never use scouring pads or silver polish on glass. With an automatic dishwasher, be sure the water temperature is under 180 degrees.

---

Plate, Bread & Butter,
6 3/4 In. . . . . . . .1.75 to 5.00

Plate, Dinner,
9 3/8 In. . . . . . .5.00 to 12.00

Platter, Oval,
12 In. . . . . . . .14.00 to 17.50

Saucer . . . . . . . . .1.00 to 3.00

Soup, Dish,
7 3/4 In. . . . . .13.00 to 18.00

Sugar . . . . . . . . . . . . . . .18.00

Sugar &
Creamer . . . . .40.00 to 55.00

### CRYSTAL

Berry Bowl, 4 In. . .2.50 to 4.00

Berry Bowl, Master,
8 3/8 In. . . . . . . .6.00 to 9.00

Berry Set, 11 Piece . . . . .25.00

Bowl, Fruit,
4 1/2 In. . . . . . . .2.00 to 5.00

Candlestick, Pair . . . . . . .18.00

Creamer . . . . . . . . . . . . .4.00

Cup & Saucer . . . .4.00 to 5.50

Goblet, Wine . . . . . . . . . .7.00

Nappy, 5 1/2 In. . . . . . . . .7.00

Plate, Bread & Butter,
6 3/4 In. . . . . . . .2.00 to 3.00

Plate, Dinner,
9 3/8 In. . . . . . . .3.00 to 7.00

Salt & Pepper  ........10.00
Sherbet, 5 Oz. ..........10.00
Sugar  ..........4.00 to 6.00
Tumbler, Water, 9 Oz. ....6.00

**GREEN**
Bowl, Cereal,
  5 1/4 In. ......11.00 to 16.00
Bowl, Fruit, 4 1/2 In. .....7.00
Creamer  ......10.00 to 13.00
Creamer, Footed ........13.50
Cup  ..........5.00 to 11.00
Cup & Saucer  ..10.00 to 14.00
Goblet, Water, 9 Oz. .....13.50
Grill Plate, 9 3/8 In. .....25.00
Plate, Bread & Butter,
  6 3/4 In. .............5.00
Plate, Dinner,
  9 3/8 In. ......18.00 to 24.00
Saucer  ..............5.00
Sherbet  ............9.00
Sugar  ........9.00 to 12.00
Sugar & Creamer  ......24.00
Tumbler, Juice, Footed,
  4 1/2 In. ............11.50

**MILK WHITE**
Berry Bowl, 4 In. ........4.00
Berry Bowl, Master,
  8 3/8 In. ............6.50
Bowl, Fruit, 4 1/2 In. .....4.50
Creamer  ............4.00
Sugar & Creamer  ......12.00

**RUBY RED**
Berry Bowl, Master,
  8 3/8 In. ......18.00 to 35.00
Bowl, Fruit,
  4 1/2 In. .......9.00 to 11.00
Cup  ..........4.50 to 11.00
Cup & Saucer  ...9.50 to 12.50
Goblet, Cocktail ........17.00
Plate, Dinner,
  9 3/8 In. ......19.00 to 20.00
Tumbler, Iced Tea,
  12 Oz. ......10.00 to 19.50
Tumbler, Juice,
  6 Oz. ........8.00 to 10.00
Tumbler, Lemonade,
  16 Oz. ......15.00 to 18.00
Tumbler, Old Fashioned,
  8 Oz., 3 1/4 In. ......15.00
Tumbler, Water, 9 Oz.,
  4 1/4 In. .......9.00 to 12.00
Water Set, 7 Piece  ......50.00

**YELLOW**
Goblet, Water, 9 Oz. ......7.00
**BULLSEYE,** see Bubble

# BURPLE

Burple is not a mistype but a real name used by the factory. Anchor Hocking Glass Corporation, Lancaster, Ohio, made Crystal, Forest Green, and Ruby Red dessert sets in this pattern in the 1940s. There are also two sizes of bowls.

**GREEN**
Batter Bowl, Spout ......25.00
Berry Bowl, 8 1/2 In. ....12.00

**BUTTERFLIES & ROSES,** see Flower Garden with Butterflies

**BUTTONS & BOWS,** see Holiday

**CABBAGE ROSE,** see Sharon

**CABBAGE ROSE WITH SINGLE ARCH,** see Rosemary

# ·C·

# CAMEO

Cameo is understandably called Ballerina or Dancing Girl because the most identifiable feature of the etched pattern is the silhouette of the dancer. This pattern must have sold well when made by Hocking Glass Company from 1930 to 1934 because many different pieces were made, from dinner sets and servers, to cookie jars and lamps. The pattern was made in Crystal, sometimes with a platinum trim, and in Green, Pink, and Yellow. In 1981 reproductions were made of both Pink and Green Cameo salt and pep-

per shakers. Children's dishes have recently been made in Green, Pink, and Yellow; but there were never any old Cameo children's dishes.

**CRYSTAL**
Candy Jar, Cover, 4 In. ...80.00
Grill Plate, Closed Handles,
  10 1/2 In. ...........12.00
Plate, Dinner, 9 1/2 In. ...18.00
Plate, Luncheon, 8 In. ....10.00
Plate, Sherbet,
  6 In. ...........4.00 to 5.00
Relish, 3 Sections ......30.00
Sugar ..............20.00
Tumbler, Footed, 9 Oz.,
  5 In. ..............20.00

**GREEN**
Berry Bowl, Master,
  8 1/4 In. ...........35.00
Bowl, Cereal, 5 1/2 In. ...35.00
Bowl, Console, 3-Footed,
  11 In. ........65.00 to 74.00
Bowl, Salad,
  7 1/2 In. ......52.00 to 55.00

Bowl, Soup, Rim, 9 In. . . .68.00
Bowl, Vegetable, Oval,
　10 In. . . . . . . . .30.00 to 35.00
Butter . . . . . . . . . . . . .200.00
Cake Plate,
　10 In. . . . . . . .22.00 to 25.00
Cake Plate, 3-Footed,
　10 In. . . . . . . .12.00 to 22.00
Candlestick, 4 In.,
　Pair . . . . . .105.00 to 135.00
Candy Jar, Cover,
　4 In. . . . . . . . .50.00 to 70.00
Coaster . . . . . . . . . . . . .13.00
Compote, 5 In. . .32.00 to 34.00
Cookie Jar,
　Cover . . . . . . .50.00 to 52.50
Creamer,
　3 1/4 In. . . . . . .20.00 to 25.00
Cup . . . . . . . . . . . . .17.00
Cup, Handle, 6 In. . . . . .20.00
Cup & Saucer . .16.90 to 20.00
Decanter,
　Stopper . . . . .150.00 to 175.00
Dish, Mayonnaise,
　5 In. . . . . . . . .27.50 to 47.50
Goblet, Water, 6 In. . . . .55.00
Goblet, Wine,
　4 In. . . . . . . . .62.00 to 77.50
Grill Plate,
　10 1/2 In. . . . . .8.00 to 15.00
Grill Plate, Closed Handles,
　10 1/2 In. . . . .15.00 to 20.00
Jam Jar, 2 In. . . . . . . . .195.00
Pitcher, Juice, 36 Oz.,
　6 In. . . . . . . . . . . . . . .60.00
Pitcher, Milk, 20 Oz.,
　5 3/4 In. . . . . . . . . . .200.00
Pitcher, Water, 56 Oz.,
　8 1/2 In. . . . . . .52.00 to 60.00
Plate, Dinner,
　9 1/2 In. . . . . . .15.00 to 24.00
Plate, Luncheon,
　8 In. . . . . . . . .10.00 to 14.00
Plate, Sherbet,
　6 In. . . . . . . . . . .4.50 to 5.00
Plate, Square, 8 1/2 In. . . .40.00
Platter, Oval,
　12 In. . . . . . . .20.00 to 27.00
Relish, 3 Sections, Footed,
　7 1/2 In. . . . . . .27.00 to 30.00
Salt & Pepper . . .67.50 to 73.00
Sandwich Server, 10 In. . .15.00
Sherbet,
　3 1/8 In. . . . . . .13.00 to 15.00

Sherbet, 4 7/8 In. . . . . . .35.00
Soup, Cream . . . . . . . . . .165.00
Soup, Dish,
　9 In. . . . . . . . .35.00 to 75.00
Sugar, 3 1/4 In. . . . . . . . .22.00
Sugar, 4 1/4 In. . . . . . . . .25.00
Sugar & Creamer,
　Low . . . . . . . .43.00 to 47.00
Syrup, 20 Oz.,
　5 3/4 In. . . . . . . . . . . .250.00
Tray, Domino . . . . . . . . .190.00
Tumbler, 15 Oz.,
　5 1/4 In. . . . . . . . . . . . .75.00
Tumbler, Footed, 11 Oz.,
　5 3/4 In. . . . . .65.00 to 72.50
Tumbler, Juice, 5 Oz.,
　3 3/4 In. . . . . .22.00 to 29.00
Tumbler, Water, 9 Oz.,
　4 In. . . . . . . . .20.00 to 29.00
Tumbler, Water, 10 Oz.,
　4 3/4 In. . . . . . . . . . . . .30.00
Tumbler, Water, Footed,
　9 Oz., 5 In. . . . .25.00 to 27.00
Vase, 5 3/4 In. . . . . . . . .150.00
Vase, 8 In. . . . . . . . . . . . .40.00

**YELLOW**
Bowl, Cereal,
　5 1/2 In. . . . . . . . . . . . .30.00
Bowl, Vegetable, Oval,
　10 In. . . . . . . . . . . . . . .40.00
Cup . . . . . . . . . . .6.00 to 8.00
Cup & Saucer . . .7.00 to 11.00
Grill Plate,
　10 1/2 In. . . . . .10.00 to 17.00
Grill Plate, Closed Handles,
　10 1/2 In. . . . . . .4.50 to 6.00
Plate, Bread & Butter,
　6 In. . . . . . . . . . . . . . . .4.50
Plate, Dinner, 9 1/2 In. . .8.50 to
12.00
Plate, Luncheon, 8 In. . . . .11.00

◆

**Never allow water to
evaporate in a glass
vase. It will leave a
white residue that may
be impossible to
remove.**

◆

Plate, Sherbet, 6 In. . . . . .2.50
Platter, 12 In. . . . . . . . . .43.00
Sherbet,
　3 1/8 In. . . . . . .35.00 to 40.00
Sugar, Round . . . . . . . . .18.00
Tumbler, Footed, 9 Oz.,
　5 In. . . . . . . . . . . . . . . .18.00

# CANDLEWICK

Candlewick was made by Imperial Glass Company, Bellaire, Ohio, from 1936 to 1982. A few pieces are still being made. Many similar patterns have been made by other companies. The beaded edge is the only design. Although the glass was first made in Crystal, it has also been produced in Black, Nut Brown, Sunshine Yellow, Ultra Blue, and Verde (green). Some pieces of Crystal are decorated with gold. Pieces have been found in Red, Pink, Lavender, and Amber, and with fired-on gold, red, blue, or green beading. Some sets were made with etchings and hand-painted designs. Reproductions have been made. They are listed at the end of the Depression Glass section.

**CRYSTAL**
Ashtray, Bridge . . . . . . . . .6.00
Ashtray, Eagle . . . . . . . . .65.00

Ashtray, Nesting, Square,
   3 Piece . . . . . . . . . . . . .120.00
Basket, 6 1/2 In. . . . . . . .40.00
Bowl, 10 1/2 In. . . . . . . .20.00
Bowl, 2 Handles,
   4 1/2 In. . . . . . . . . . . . .16.00
Bowl, 3-Footed, 6 In. . . . .70.00
Bowl, 5 1/2 In. . . . . . . . .22.00
Bowl, 5 In. . . . . . . . . . . .12.50
Bowl, Belled, 10 1/2 In. . .50.00
Bowl, Belled, 12 In. . . . . .60.00
Bowl, Divided, 6 In. . . . . .22.00
Bowl, Divided, Oblong,
   7 In. . . . . . . . . . . . . . .22.00
Bowl, Footed, Low,
   9 In. . . . . . . . . . . . . . .120.00
Bowl, Heart, 5 1/2 In. . . . .20.00
Bowl, Heart, 9 In. . . . . . .145.00
Bowl, Relish, 12 In. . . . .125.00
Bowl, Square, 5 In. . . . . .125.00
Bowl, Vegetable, Cover,
   8 In. . . . . . . . . . . . . . .250.00
Butter, 5 1/2 In. . . . . . . .32.50
Cake Stand,
   11 In. . . . . . . . .70.00 to 75.00
Canape, Set, 2 Piece . . . . .20.00
Candleholder, 4 In.,
   Pair . . . . . . . . . . . . . . .20.00
Candleholder, Handle,
   5 In., Pair . . . . . . . . . .100.00
Coaster . . . . . . . . . . . . . .6.00
Cocktail, 4 Oz. . .16.00 to 22.00
Compote, Cheese . . . . . . .20.00
Cordial, 1 Oz. . . . . . . . . .70.00
Creamer, Demitasse . . . . .10.00
Creamer, Pedestal . . . . . .15.00
Cruet, Oil, Beaded Base,
   4 Oz. . . . . . . . . . . . . . .60.00
Cruet, Oil, Beaded Base,
   6 Oz. . . . . . . . . . . . . . .70.00
Cup & Saucer . . .8.00 to 15.00
Cup & Saucer, Tea . . . . . . .8.00
Dish, Mayonnaise,
   Sections, 3 Piece . . . . .55.00
Float Bowl, 12 In. . . . . . .40.00
Goblet, 10 Oz. . . . . . . . .18.00
Goblet, Water,
   9 Oz. . . . . . . .16.00 to 24.00
Goblet, Wine, 4 Oz. . . . . .25.00
Goblet, Wine, 5 Oz. . . . . .28.00
Gravy Boat,
   Underplate . . . . . . . . . .180.00

Mustard . . . . . . . . . . . . .35.00
Pitcher, 80 Oz. . . . . . . . .170.00
Plate, 7 In. . . . . . . . . . . . .7.00
Plate, Canape, 6 In. . . . . . .9.00
Plate, Crimped, Handles,
   6 3/4 In. . . . . . . . . . . . .30.00
Plate, Deviled Egg,
   12 In. . . . . . .155.00 to 165.00
Plate, Dinner,
   10 1/2 In. . . . . . . . . . . .37.50
Plate, Luncheon, Gold
   Floral, 8 1/2 In. . . . . . .150.00
Platter, Oval, 16 In. . . . .210.00
Punch Bowl Set,
   19 Piece . . . . . . . . . . .600.00
Punch Bowl Set, Liner,
   15 Piece . . . . . . . . . . .325.00
Relish, 4 Sections,
   Round . . . . . . . . . . . . . .16.50
Relish, Oblong, 10 In. . . .100.00
Relish, Rectangular,
   12 In. . . . . . . . . . . . . . .85.00
Salt & Pepper,
   Individual . . . . . . . . . .12.50
Salt Dip . . . . . . . . . . . . .12.00
Saltshaker, 2 1/4 In. . . . . . .9.00
Sherbet, 5 Oz. . . . . . . . . .12.00
Strawberry Set, 2 Piece . . .95.00
Sugar & Creamer,
   Tray . . . . . . . . . . . . . .28.00
Tray, Oval, 9 In. . . . . . . .40.00
Tumbler, 12 Oz. . . . . . . .12.00
Tumbler, Footed, 5 Oz. . . .24.00
Tumbler, Footed, 9 Oz. . . .20.00
Vase, Miniature . . . . . . . .55.00
Wafer Tray . . . . . . . . . . .25.00

**RED**
Bowl . . . . . . . . . . . . . .250.00
Candleholder . . . . . . . . .450.00
Tumbler, 9 Oz. . . . . . . . .105.00

**VERDE**
Ashtray, Heart . . . . . . . . .35.00

# CAPE COD

Cape Cod was a pattern made by the Imperial Glass Company, Bellaire, Ohio, from 1932. It is usually found in Crystal but was also made in Amber, Azalea (pink), Black, Cobalt Blue, Green, Light Blue, Milk Glass, and Ruby. In 1978 the dinner set was reproduced. The cruet was reproduced in 1986 without the rayed bottom.

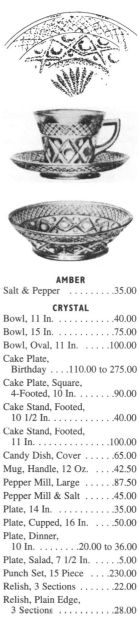

**AMBER**
Salt & Pepper . . . . . . . .35.00
**CRYSTAL**
Bowl, 11 In. . . . . . . . . . .40.00
Bowl, 15 In. . . . . . . . . . .75.00
Bowl, Oval, 11 In. . . . . .100.00
Cake Plate,
   Birthday . . . .110.00 to 275.00
Cake Plate, Square,
   4-Footed, 10 In. . . . . . .90.00
Cake Stand, Footed,
   10 1/2 In. . . . . . . . . . . .40.00
Cake Stand, Footed,
   11 In. . . . . . . . . . . . . .100.00
Candy Dish, Cover . . . . .65.00
Mug, Handle, 12 Oz. . . . .42.50
Pepper Mill, Large . . . . .87.50
Pepper Mill & Salt . . . . .45.00
Plate, 14 In. . . . . . . . . . .35.00
Plate, Cupped, 16 In. . . . .50.00
Plate, Dinner,
   10 In. . . . . . . .20.00 to 36.00
Plate, Salad, 7 1/2 In. . . . . .5.00
Punch Set, 15 Piece . . . .230.00
Relish, 3 Sections . . . . . .22.00
Relish, Plain Edge,
   3 Sections . . . . . . . . . .28.00

Tray, Square, 7 In. . . . . . .48.00
Tumbler, Water, Footed,
    10 Oz. . . . . . .10.00 to 11.00
Whiskey, 2 1/2 Oz. . . . . . .15.00

**RUBY**
Salt & Pepper, Pair . . . . . .15.00

## CAPRICE

Caprice was advertised in 1936 as the most popular crystal pattern in America. It was made until 1953. Over 200 pieces were made in the line. Frosted pieces were called Alpine Caprice, the name given by the maker, Cambridge Glass Company, Cambridge, Ohio. The sets were made in Amber, Amethyst, Blue, Cobalt Blue, Moonlight Blue, Crystal, Emerald Green, Light Green, Pink, and Milk Glass. Reproductions are being made in Cobalt Blue and Moonlight Blue. They are listed at the end of the Depression Glass section.

**AMETHYST**
Pitcher, Ball, 80 Oz. . . . .225.00

**BLUE**
Ashtray, Footed, With
    Place Card . . . . . . . . . .15.00
Ashtray, Round, 4 In. . . . .3.50
Ashtray, Round, 5 In. . . . .24.00

Ashtray, Triangular,
    2 1/2 In. . . . . . . . . . . . .15.00
Bonbon, Footed, Square,
    6 In. . . . . . . . . . . . . . .50.00
Bonbon, Handles,
    4 1/2 In. . . . . . . . . . . . .39.00
Bonbon, Handles, Square,
    6 In. . . . . . . . . . . . . . .48.00
Bowl, 4-Footed,
    10 In. . . . . . .60.00 to 100.00
Bowl, 4-Footed,
    11 1/2 In. . . . . . . . . . . .95.00
Bowl, 7 3/4 In. . . . . . . . .11.50
Bowl, Belled, 3-Footed,
    11 In. . . . . . . . . . . . . .100.00
Bowl, Crimped, 4-Footed,
    9 1/2 In. . . . . . . . . . . . .95.00
Bowl, Crimped, 4-Footed,
    10 1/2 In. . . . . . . . . . . .95.00
Bowl, Crimped, 4-Footed,
    11 In. . . . . . . . . . . . . .115.00
Bowl, Deep, Square,
    5 3/4 In. . . . . . . . . . . . .10.00
Bowl, Fruit, Crimped,
    5 In. . . . . . . . . . . . . . .125.00
Bowl, Square Bottom,
    6 In. . . . . . . . . . . . . . . .7.00
Bowl, Swirl, 4 3/4 In. . . . . .7.00
Candlestick, 2 1/2 In.,
    Pair . . . . . . . . .60.00 to 64.00
Candlestick, 2-Light,
    Pair . . . . . . . . . . . . . .165.00
Candlestick, 3-Light,
    6 In. . . . . . . . . . . . . . .100.00
Candlestick, Prisms,
    Pair . . . . . . . . . . . . . .150.00
Candy Dish, Cover, 3-Footed,
    6 In. . . . . . .100.00 to 125.00
Celery Dish  . . . . . . . . . .85.00

Cigarette Box, With
    4 Shell Ashtrays, Box,
    5 Piece . . . . . . . . . . . .125.00
Compote, 7 In. . . . . . . . .50.00
Cruet, 5 Oz. . . . . . . . . . .350.00
Cup & Saucer  . . . . . . . .45.00
Decanter, 35 Oz. . . . . . .495.00
Goblet, Champagne  . . . .35.00
Jam Jar, 7 In. . . . . . . . . .65.00
Nut Dish, Individual,
    2 1/2 In. . . . . . . . . . . . .60.00
Pitcher, Ball, 80 Oz. . . . .310.00
Plate, 4-Footed,
    14 In. . . . . . . . . . . . . . .65.00
Plate, 4-Footed,
    15 In. . . . . . . . . . . . . .100.00
Plate, Lemon, Handle,
    6 In. . . . . . . . . . . . . . .35.00
Plate, Luncheon,
    8 1/2 In. . . . . . .32.00 to 35.00
Plate, Salad, 7 1/2 In. . . . .32.00
Relish, 3 Sections . . . . . .55.00
Salt & Pepper,
    Individual  . . . . . . . . . .190.00
Saucer  . . . . . . . .6.00 to 15.00
Sugar, 3 3/4 In. . .22.00 to 28.00
Sugar, 3 In. . . . . . . . . . . .10.00
Sugar & Creamer  . . . . . .75.00
Sugar & Creamer,
    Individual . . . . .50.00 to 52.50
Tumbler, 5 Oz. . . . . . . .135.00
Tumbler, 12 Oz. . . . . . . .58.00
Tumbler, 3 1/2 In. . . . . . . .5.00
Tumbler, 4 1/4 In. . . . . . . .5.50
Tumbler, Blown,
    12 Oz. . . . . . . . . . . . . .125.00
Tumbler, Footed, 5 Oz. . . .60.00
Vase, 4 1/2 In. . . . . . . . .275.00
Vase, Sweet Pea, 7 In. . . .75.00

**CRYSTAL**
Bowl, Oval, 7 1/2 In. . . . .14.00
Bowl, Silver Overlay,
    Floral, 10 In. . . . . . . . .35.00
Candlestick, 2 1/2 In.,
    Pair . . . . . . . . . . . . . . .35.00
Candlestick, 2-Light,
    Pair . . . . . . . . . . . . . . .90.00
Candlestick, Prism, 7 In.,
    Pair . . . . . . . . . . . . . .150.00
Cigarette Holder  . . . . . .75.00
Cruet, Handle, 4 Oz.,
    5 In. . . . . . . . . . . . . . . .95.00

Cruet, Oil,
3 Oz. . . . . . . .25.00 to 35.00
Cruet, Oil, Stopper,
5 Oz. . . . . . . . . . . . . . .65.00
Cup & Saucer . .15.00 to 16.50
Decanter, Sherry . . . . . .395.00
Goblet, Water,
9 Oz. . . . . . . .20.00 to 30.00
Goblet, Wine,
2 1/2 Oz. . . . . .27.50 to 47.50
Jug, Ball, 80 Oz. . . . . . . .150.00
Mayonnaise,
2 Sections . . . . . . . . . .57.50
Plate, Anniversary . . . . .40.00
Plate, Dinner, 9 1/2 In. . . .40.00
Plate, Luncheon,
8 1/2 In. . . . . . .13.00 to 15.00
Plate, Salad,
7 1/2 In. . . . . . .12.50 to 16.00
Punch Bowl, Footed . . .2995.00
Salt & Pepper . . . . . . . .35.00
Saltshaker, Handle . . . . .27.50
Sherbet, Tall . . . . . . . . . .16.00
Tray . . . . . . . . . . . . . . .17.50
Tumbler, 12 Oz.,
5 1/4 In. . . . . . . . . . . . .30.00
Tumbler, Footed,
10 Oz. . . . . . . .18.00 to 20.00
Tumbler, Iced Tea, Footed,
12 Oz. . . . . . . .30.00 to 37.50

**LIGHT GREEN**
Whiskey, 2 Oz. . . . . . . . .50.00

**PINK**
Bowl, Salad, Cupped,
13 In. . . . . . . . . . . . . .495.00
Candy Dish, 3-Footed,
Cover . . . . . . . . . . . . .295.00
Mayonnaise, Footed,
Handle . . . . . . . . . . . . .95.00
Plate, Lemon, 6 In. . . . . .50.00

**CAPRICE,** see also Alpine
Caprice

## CARIBBEAN
The rippled design of Caribbean is slick and modern in appearance and has attracted many collectors. It was made by Duncan & Miller Glass Company, Washington, Pennsylvania, from 1936 to 1955.

Sets were made of Crystal, Crystal with ruby trim, Amber, Blue, and Red glass. The Duncan & Miller catalogs identify the line as No. 112.

**AMBER**
Punch Cup . . . . . . . . . . .10.00

**BLUE**
Bowl, 9 In. . . . . . . . . . . .65.00
Bowl, Liner, 12 1/2 In. . . .58.00
Candy Dish, Cover . . . . . .90.00
Celery Dish . . . . . . . . . . .35.00
Cigarette Box, Tray . . . . .75.00
Cocktail Shaker . . . . . . .170.00
Compote, Cheese . . . . . .40.00
Cruet, Stopper . . . . . . . .80.00
Cruet, Tray . . . . . . . . . .195.00
Finger Bowl,
4 1/2 In. . . . . . . . . . . . .32.00
Ice Bucket, 6 1/2 In. . . . .125.00
Nappy, Handles, 6 In. . . . .12.00
Pitcher, Water,
8 1/4 In. . . . . . . . . . . .895.00
Plate, Bread & Butter,
6 In. . . . . . . . . . . . . . .10.50
Plate, Dinner,
10 1/2 In. . . . . . . . . . .100.00
Punch Cup . . . . . . . . . . .12.00
Relish, 5 Sections . . . . . .85.00
Sugar & Creamer . . . . . .45.00
Tumbler, Water, Footed,
9 Oz. . . . . . . . . . . . . . .41.00
Vase, Flared, 6 In. . . . . .48.00
Vase, Straight Sides,
8 In. . . . . . . . . . . . . . .68.00

**CRYSTAL**
Bowl, Tab Handles,
9 1/2 In. . . . . . . . . . . . .35.00
Goblet, 3 Oz.,
4 1/4 In. . . . . . . . . . . . .25.00
Relish, 5 Sections . . . . . .40.00

**RED**
Punch Cup . . . . . . . . . . .12.00

## CENTURY
Century pattern was made by Fostoria Glass Company from 1926 until 1986. It is a plain pattern with a slightly rippled rim. Full dinner sets were made of clear Crystal.

**CRYSTAL**
Bonbon . . . . . . . . . . . . .15.00
Bowl, 8 In. . . . . . . . . . . .20.00
Bowl, 12 In. . . . . . . . . . .35.00
Bowl, Handle,
4 1/2 In. . . . . . .9.00 to 15.00
Bowl, Serving, 2 Handles,
9 1/2 In. . . . . . .28.00 to 35.00
Butter, Red Stripes
On Base, 1/2 Lb. . . . . . .65.00
Cake Plate, Low Pedestal,
12 In. . . . . . . . . . . . . . .35.00
Candlestick, 4 1/2 In.,
Pair . . . . . . . . . . . . . . .28.00
Cruet . . . . . . . . . . . . . . .45.00
Cup . . . . . . . . . . . . . . . .15.00
Cup & Saucer . . . . . . . . .15.00
Pitcher, 16 Oz., 6 1/8 In. . .50.00
Relish, 2 Sections,
7 3/8 In. . . . . . . . . . . . .12.00
Relish, 3 Sections . . . . . .20.00
Sugar & Creamer,
Footed . . . . . . . . . . . . .14.00
Sugar & Creamer,
Large . . . . . . . . . . . . . .18.00
Tidbit, 2 Tiers,
10 1/4 In. . . . . . . . . . . .45.00

Tidbit, 3-Footed,
8 1/8 In. . . . . . . . . . . . .14.00
Tray, Muffin, Handles,
9 1/2 In. . . . . . . . . . . . .25.00
Vase, Bud,
6 In. . . . . . . . .14.00 to 15.00

**CHAIN DAISY,** see Adam

## CHANTILLY

As late as the 1960s the Jeannette Glass Company, Jeannette,
Pennsylvania, made a pattern
called Chantilly that is collected by Depression glass
buffs. It was made in Crystal
and Pink.

### CRYSTAL
Bowl, Flared, 4-Footed,
12 In. . . . . . . . . . . . . .50.00
Candy Dish, 3 Sections,
Sterling Knob Cover . . .75.00
Cocktail Shaker, Sterling
Knob, 32 Oz. . . . . . . .150.00
Mayonnaise Set, 3 Piece . .40.00
Relish, 5 Sections . . . . . .50.00
Salt & Pepper, Silver
Top, Handles . . . . . . . .35.00

### PINK
Decanter, Sherry . . . . . .395.00
Goblet, Iced Tea, Footed,
12 Oz. . . . . . . . . . . . . .30.00
Goblet, Water, 10 Oz. . . . .30.00
Shaker, Handle . . . . . . . .27.50

## CHARM

Charm is a pattern of Fire-King
dinnerware made from 1950 to
1954. The square-shaped dishes
were made by Anchor Hocking
Glass Corporation of Lancaster, Ohio. The dinnerware was
made of Forest Green, Royal
Ruby, Jadite (opaque green),
and Azurite (opaque blue-
white). Collectors often refer to

the color name rather than the
pattern name when describing
these pieces. It is sometimes
called Square. Other related
sections in this book are Alice,
Fire-King, Gray Laurel, Jadite,
Peach Lustre, Philbe, Swirl
Fire-King, Turquoise Blue, and
Wheat.

### AZURITE
Cup & Saucer . . . . . . . . .3.00
Plate, Dinner,
9 1/4 In. . . . . . .15.00 to 20.00
Plate, Luncheon,
8 3/8 In. . . . . . . . . . . . . .5.00
Saucer . . . . . . . . .1.00 to 2.50
Sugar . . . . . . . . . .4.00 to 6.00

### FOREST GREEN
Berry Bowl,
4 3/4 In. . . . . . . .4.00 to 5.50
Bowl, Salad, 7 3/8 In. . . . .10.00
Bowl, Vegetable, Oval,
8 1/2 In. . . . . . . . . . . . .22.00
Cup & Saucer . . . .5.00 to 6.50
Mixing Bowl, No. 3,
6 In. . . . . . . . . . . . . . . .7.00
Plate, Dinner, 9 1/4 In. . . .35.00
Plate, Luncheon,
8 3/8 In. . . . . . . .5.00 to 7.00
Plate, Salad,
6 5/8 In. . . . . . . .5.00 to 7.00
Platter, 11 In. . . . . . . . . .25.00
Saucer . . . . . . . . .1.00 to 2.00
Soup, Dish,
6 In. . . . . . . . .15.00 to 23.00
Sugar & Creamer . . . . . .11.00

---

❖

**Antique glass should be
handled as if it has been
repaired and might fall
apart. Hold a pitcher by
the body, not the han-
dle. Pick up stemware
by holding both the
stem and the bowl. Hold
plates in two hands, not
by the rim.**

❖

---

### JADITE
Cup . . . . . . . . . . . . . . .9.00
Cup & Saucer . . . . . . . .12.00
Plate, Luncheon, 8 3/8 In. . .9.00

### ROYAL RUBY
Cup & Saucer . . . . . . . . .9.00
Plate, Luncheon,
8 3/8 In. . . . . . . . . . . . .11.00
Saucer . . . . . . . . . . . . . .3.00

## CHEROKEE ROSE

The Tiffin glass factory can be
traced back to the 1840s, when
Joseph Beatty made glass in
Steubenville, Ohio. The factory
failed and was purchased by
Alexander Beatty in 1851. He
was joined by his sons and
moved to Tiffin, Ohio, in 1888.
The company became part of
U.S. Glass Company in 1892
and was still operating in 1963
when U.S. Glass went bank-
rupt. Employees bought the
plant and it went through several changes of ownership until
it closed in 1980. Cherokee
Rose was one of the popular
glass patterns made by Tiffin in
the 1940s and 1950s. The glass
was made only in Crystal.

### CRYSTAL
Cordial, 1 Oz. . . . . . . . . .47.50
Goblet, Cocktail,
3 1/2 Oz. . . . . .12.00 to 22.50
Goblet, Water, 8 Oz. . . . . .17.50
Plate, Luncheon, 8 In. . . . .16.00
Plate, Sherbet, 6 In. . . . . . .2.00
Sherbet, Stemmed . . . . . .20.00
Tumbler,
Iced Tea . . . . . .29.00 to 35.00
Vase, Bud, 8 In. . . . . . . . .30.00

**CHERRY,** see Cherry Blossom

## CHERRY BLOSSOM

Cherry Blossom is one of the most popular Depression glass patterns. It has been called Banded Cherry, Cherry, or Paneled Cherry Blossom by some collectors. The pattern was made by the Jeannette Glass Company, Jeannette, Pennsylvania, from 1930 to 1939. Full dinner sets, serving pieces, and a child's set were made in a wide range of colors. Pieces were made in Crystal, Delphite (opaque blue), Green, Jadite (opaque green), Pink, and Red. During the course of production, molds were changed, resulting in several shapes and styles for some pieces. Many reproductions of Cherry Blossom pieces have been made and sold in recent years. They are listed at the end of the Depression Glass section.

### CRYSTAL
Plate, Dinner, 9 In. . . . . . .20.00

### DELPHITE
Berry Bowl,
4 3/4 In. . . . . .14.00 to 15.00

Berry Bowl, Master,
8 1/2 In. . . . . . . . . . . .50.00
Bowl, Vegetable, 2 Handles,
9 In. . . . . . . . .22.00 to 30.00
Child's Set,
14 Piece . . . .310.00 to 325.00
Creamer . . . . . . . . . . . . .22.00
Cup & Saucer . .22.00 to 24.00
Cup & Saucer, Child's . . .42.00
Plate, Child's, 6 In. . . . . .13.00
Plate, Dinner,
9 In. . . . . . . . .17.00 to 22.50
Sandwich Server, 2 Handles,
Round, 10 1/2 In. . . . . . .20.00
Saucer, Child's . . . . . . . . .7.00
Sugar, Child's . . . . . . . . .45.00
Sugar & Creamer . . . . . .29.00
Tumbler, Water, Footed,
9 Oz. . . . . . . . .16.00 to 25.00

### GREEN
Berry Bowl,
4 3/4 In. . . . . . .17.50 to 19.00
Berry Bowl, Master,
8 1/2 In. . . . . . .56.00 to 58.00
Bowl, 2 Handles,
9 In. . . . . . . . .55.00 to 65.00
Bowl, Cereal, 5 3/4 In. . . .46.00
Bowl, Fruit, 3-Footed,
10 1/2 In. . . . . . . . . . . .90.00
Bowl, Oval, 9 In. . . . . . .37.00
Bowl, Round, 8 1/2 In. . . .48.00
Butter, Cover . . .85.00 to 98.00
Cake Plate . . . . .35.00 to 39.00
Coaster, 6 In. . . . .12.00 to 14.00
Creamer . . . . . .20.00 to 22.00
Cup . . . . . . . . . . . . . . . .23.50
Grill Plate, 9 In. .22.00 to 26.00
Mug, 7 Oz. . . . . . . . . . .185.00
Pitcher, Footed, 36 Oz.,
8 In. . . . . . . . .55.00 to 65.00
Pitcher, Juice, Scalloped Base,
6 3/4 In. . . . . .62.00 to 65.00
Pitcher, Water, Flat,
42 Oz., 8 In. . . . . . . . . .57.00
Plate, Dinner,
9 In. . . . . . . . .23.00 to 26.00
Plate, Salad,
7 In. . . . . . . . .15.00 to 22.00
Plate, Sherbet, 6 In. . . . . .8.00
Platter, 11 In. . . . . . . . . .47.00
Platter, 2 Sections,
13 In. . . . . . . . .30.00 to 65.00

Sandwich Server, 2 Handles,
10 1/2 In. . . . . .25.00 to 30.00
Saucer . . . . . . . . .5.00 to 6.00
Sherbet, Footed . .17.00 to 18.00
Soup, Dish . . . . . . . . . . .86.00
Sugar, Cover . . . . . . . . . .34.00
Sugar & Creamer,
Cover . . . . . . . . . . . . .52.00
Tumbler, 9 Oz.,
4 1/2 In. . . . . . .18.00 to 22.00
Tumbler, Footed,
3 3/4 In. . . . . . .20.00 to 22.00
Tumbler, Juice, 3 1/2 In. . .30.00
Tumbler, Juice, Footed,
4 1/2 In. . . . . . . . . . . . .18.00
Tumbler, Juice,
Scalloped, Footed,
4 1/2 In. . . . . . .35.00 to 44.00

### PINK
Berry Bowl,
4 3/4 In. . . . . . .10.00 to 22.00
Berry Bowl, Master,
8 1/2 In. . . . . . .45.00 to 50.00
Bowl, 2 Handles, 9 In. . . .48.00
Bowl, Cereal,
5 3/4 In. . . . . . .30.00 to 40.00
Bowl, Fruit, 3-Footed,
10 1/2 In. . . . . .85.00 to 90.00
Bowl, Vegetable, Oval,
9 In. . . . . . . . . . . . . . . .50.00
Butter, Cover . . .85.00 to 95.00
Cake Plate, Footed,
10 1/4 In. . . . . .26.00 to 31.00
Child's Set, 14 Piece . . . .300.00
Coaster . . . . . . . .15.00 to 19.50
Creamer . . . . . . .17.00 to 22.50
Cup . . . . . . . . .19.50 to 20.00
Cup & Saucer . .21.00 to 27.00
Grill Plate,
9 In. . . . . . . . .25.00 to 29.50
Pitcher, 36 Oz.,
6 3/4 In. . . . . . .55.00 to 65.00
Pitcher, Cone, Footed,
8 In. . . . . . . . . . . . . . . .85.00
Plate, Dinner,
9 In. . . . . . . . .22.00 to 28.00
Plate, Salad,
7 In. . . . . . . . .18.00 to 27.00
Plate, Sherbet,
6 In. . . . . . . . . .8.00 to 10.00
Platter, Oval,
11 In. . . . . . . . .40.00 to 45.00
Sandwich Server,
10 1/2 In. . . . . .25.00 to 30.00

Saucer . . . . . . . . . . . . . . .5.50
Sherbet . . . . . . .14.00 to 20.00
Soup, Dish,
7 3/4 In. . . . . .85.00 to 90.00
Sugar, Cover . . . .28.00 to 43.00
Sugar & Creamer . . . . . . .32.00
Sugar & Creamer,
Cover . . . . . . .49.00 to 55.00
Tumbler, Juice, Footed, 4 Oz.,
3 3/4 In. . . . . .20.00 to 27.50
Tumbler, Scalloped Foot,
8 Oz., 4 1/2 In. . . . . . .32.50

## CHERRY-BERRY

Two similar patterns, Cherry-Berry and Strawberry, can be confusing. If the fruit pictured is a cherry, then the pattern is called Cherry-Berry. If the strawberry is used, then the pattern has that name. The dishes were made by the U.S. Glass Company in the early 1930s in Crystal, Green, Iridescent Amber, and Pink.

**GREEN**
Berry Bowl, Deep,
7 1/2 In. . . . . . .18.00 to 19.00
Bowl, 6 1/4 In. . . . . . . . .55.00
Butter, Cover . . . . . . . . . .75.00
Plate, Sherbet, 6 In. . . . . .11.00
Sugar . . . . . . . . . . . . . . .25.00
Sugar, Cover . . . . . . . . . .55.00

❖

**Shallow nicks and rough edges on glass can sometimes be smoothed off with fine emery paper.**

❖

**PINK**
Creamer, Small . . . . . . . .25.00
Plate, Salad, 7 1/2 In. . . . .15.00
Sherbet . . . . . . .9.00 to 13.50

**CHERRY-BERRY,** see also
Strawberry

## CHINEX CLASSIC

Chinex Classic and Cremax are very similar patterns made by Macbeth-Evans Division of Corning Glass Works from about 1938 to 1942. *Chinex* and *Cremax* are both words with two meanings. Each is the name of a pattern and the name of a color used for other patterns. Chinex is ivory-colored, Cremax is a bit whiter. Chinex Classic, the dinnerware pattern, has a piecrust edge, and just inside the edge is an elongated feathered scroll. It may or may not have a decal-decorated center and colored edging. The Cremax pattern has just the piecrust edge. The decals used on Chinex Classic are either floral designs or brown-toned scenics.

**IVORY**
Plate, Bread & Butter . . . . .4.00
Plate, Dinner,
9 3/4 In. . . . . . . .4.00 to 6.00
Saucer . . . . . . . . .1.50 to 4.00
Sherbet, Footed, Low . . . . .6.00
Soup, Dish . . . . . . . . . . . .8.00
Sugar & Creamer . . . . . . .16.00

**IVORY WITH DECAL**
Bowl, Cereal, Scenic,
5 3/4 In. . . . . . . . . . . . .17.00

Bowl, Vegetable, Scenic,
9 In. . . . . . . . . . . . . . . .35.00
Cup & Saucer,
Scenic . . . . . . . . . . . . .21.50
Plate, Dinner, Scenic,
9 3/4 In. . . . . . . . . . . . .20.00
Plate, Sherbet, Scenic,
6 1/4 In. . . . . . . . . . . . . .7.50
Sandwich Server, Scenic,
11 1/2 In. . . . . . . . . . . .25.00
Sherbet, Scenic . . . . . . . .25.00
Soup, Dish, Scenic,
7 3/4 In. . . . . . . . . . . . .35.00

**CHINEX CLASSIC,** see also
Cremax

## CHINTZ

Several companies made a glass named Chintz. To identify Chintz pattern pieces, remember the design is named for the etched pattern, not the shape, of the glass. Fostoria Glass Company made Baroque, a glass shape that included molded fleur-de-lis–shaped handles and ridges. This glass blank was then etched with design No. 338 and then sold as Chintz pattern. The etched design pictures branches of leaves and flowers. It was also used on some vases and other pieces that were not Baroque blanks. Only Crystal pieces were made. Pieces were made from 1940 to 1972. To confuse this even more, the company made other etched designs (Navarre) on the Baroque blanks. Other Chintz patterns were made by A. H. Heisey & Company from 1931 to 1938. They both had etched designs of butterflies and encircled flowers. These Chintz patterns were made in Crystal, Flamingo (pink), Moongleam (green), Sahara (yellow), and Alexandrite (orchid), a glass that turned from blue to purple depending on the lighting source. Pieces listed in this book are for Fostoria Chintz.

**CRYSTAL**

Bowl, Vegetable, Oval,
9 1/2 In. . . . . . . . . . . .195.00

Candlestick, 2-Light,
Pair . . . . . . . . . . . . . . .60.00

Compote . . . . . . . . . . . .40.00

Cup & Saucer . . . . . . . . .25.00

Goblet,
Champagne . . .10.00 to 20.00

Goblet, Sherbet, Low, 6 Oz.,
4 3/8 In. . . . . . . . . . . . .145.00

Tumbler, Juice, Footed,
5 Oz. . . . . . . . . . . . . . .200.00

## CHRISTMAS CANDY

Christmas Candy, sometimes
called Christmas Candy Ribbon or No. 624, was made by
the Indiana Glass Company,
Dunkirk, Indiana, in 1937. The
pattern, apparently only made
in luncheon sets, was made in
Crystal, a light green called
Seafoam Green, a bright blue
called Teal Blue, and dark
Emerald Green.

**CRYSTAL**

Creamer . . . . . . . . . . . . .9.00

Plate, Luncheon, 8 In. . . . . .7.00

Sugar . . . . . . . . . . . . . . .9.00

**TEAL BLUE**

Plate, Luncheon, 8 In. . . . .12.50

---

Sandwich Server,
11 1/4 In. . . . . . . . . . . .40.00

Saucer . . . . . . . . . . . . .7.00

Sugar, Footed . . . . . . . . .20.00

**CHRISTMAS CANDY RIBBON,**
see Christmas Candy

## CIRCLE

Circles ring the Circle pattern
made by Hocking Glass Company, Lancaster, Ohio, in the
1930s. It is found in Green,
Crystal, and Pink. It can be distinguished from the similar
Hocking pattern called Ring by
the number of groupings of
rings—Circle has only one set,
Ring has several sets with four
rings in each group.

**GREEN**

Bowl, 4 1/2 In. . . . . . . . .15.00

Cup . . . . . . . . . . . . . . .5.00

Cup & Saucer Set . . . . . .7.50

Goblet, Water, 8 Oz. . . . . .11.00

Goblet, Wine,
4 1/2 In. . . . . . .12.50 to 15.00

Goblet, Wine, Gold Trim,
4 1/2 In. . . . . . . . . . . . .12.00

Pitcher, 60 Oz. . .32.00 to 35.00

Plate, Luncheon,
8 1/4 In. . . . . . . . . . . . .11.00

Plate, Sherbet,
6 In. . . . . . . . . . .2.00 to 3.00

Plate, Sherbet, Gold Trim,
6 In. . . . . . . . . . . . . . . .1.50

Saucer . . . . . . . . . . . . .2.50

Sherbet, 3 1/8 In. . . . . . . .4.00

---

Sherbet, 4 3/4 In. . . . . . . .11.00

Sherbet, Gold Trim,
4 3/4 In. . . . . . . . . . . . .6.00

Tumbler, Iced Tea, 10 Oz.,
5 In. . . . . . . . .16.00 to 17.00

Tumbler, Water, 8 Oz. . . . .9.00

**PINK**

Plate, Luncheon, 8 In. . . . . .8.00

Sherbet, 3 1/8 In. . . . . . . .6.00

**CIRCULAR RIBS,** see Circle

**CLASSIC,** see Chinex Classic

## CLEO

In 1930 the Cambridge Glass
Company, Cambridge, Ohio,
introduced an etched pattern
called Cleo. Many pieces are
marked with the Cambridge C
in a triangle. Sets were made in
Amber, Blue, Crystal, Green,
Pink, and Yellow.

**AMBER**

Candy Dish, Cover,
3 Sections . . . . . . . . .105.00

Ice Tub . . . . . . . . . . . . .40.00

**BLUE**

Cup & Saucer, Decagon . .33.00

Mayonnaise, Liner . . . . . .13.00

Plate, Decagon, 6 In. . . . .14.00

Plate, Decagon, 8 In. . . . .32.00

## GREEN

Cocktail, Insert & Liner . .95.00

## PINK

Berry Bowl, Belled,
5 In. . . . . . . . . . . . . . .55.00
Bowl, Vegetable, Oval,
10 3/4 In. . . . . . . . . . .125.00
Candlestick, 4 In., Pair . . .95.00
Cup & Saucer . . . . . . . .18.00
Gravy Boat, Double . . . .220.00
Ice Tub . . . . . . . . . . . . .95.00
Tumbler, Flat, 11 Oz. . . . .48.00
Tumbler, Footed, 6 Oz. . . .25.00

## CLOVERLEAF

Three-leaf clovers form part
of the border of Cloverleaf pattern made by Hazel Atlas
Glass Company from 1930 to
1936. It was made in Black,
Crystal, Green, Pink, and Topaz (yellow).

## BLACK

Creamer . . . . . . .18.00 to 18.50
Cup . . . . . . . . . . . . . . .16.00
Cup & Saucer . .22.50 to 25.00
Plate, Luncheon,
8 In. . . . . . . . . .14.50 to 17.00
Plate, Sherbet,
6 In. . . . . . . . . .37.00 to 38.00
Salt & Pepper . . .80.00 to 85.00
Saltshaker . . . . . . . . . . .40.00

Saucer . . . . . . . . .6.50 to 7.00
Sherbet, Footed . .18.00 to 20.00
Sugar . . . . . . . .15.00 to 20.00
Sugar &
Creamer . . . . .35.00 to 36.00

## GREEN

Bowl, Dessert,
4 In. . . . . . . . . .24.00 to 25.00
Bowl, Salad,
7 In. . . . . . . . . .38.00 to 45.00
Candy Dish, Cover . . . . . .72.00
Cup . . . . . . . . . . . . . . . .8.00
Cup & Saucer . . .9.00 to 14.00
Grill Plate, 10 1/4 In. . . . .25.00
Plate, Luncheon,
8 In. . . . . . . . . .8.00 to 12.00
Salt & Pepper . . . . . . . .35.00
Saucer . . . . . . . . .3.00 to 4.50
Sherbet, Footed . . .7.00 to 12.00
Sugar . . . . . . . . . . . . .10.00
Tumbler, 10 Oz.,
5 3/4 In. . . . . . .25.00 to 39.00

## PINK

Cup . . . . . . . . . . .7.00 to 9.00
Plate, Luncheon,
8 In. . . . . . . . . .7.00 to 11.00
Saucer . . . . . . . . . . . . . .4.00
Sherbet, Footed . . . . . . .10.00

## TOPAZ

Bowl, Dessert, 4 In. . . . .32.00
Candy Dish, Cover . . . .145.00
Cup . . . . . . . . . . . . . . .10.00
Plate, Luncheon, 8 In. . . . .14.00
Plate, Sherbet,
6 In. . . . . . . . . . .7.00 to 8.00
Saucer . . . . . . . . . . . . . .5.00
Sherbet . . . . . . .10.00 to 11.00
Sugar . . . . . . . .17.50 to 20.00

## COLONIAL

Sometimes this pattern is called
Knife & Fork, although Colonial is the more common
name. It was made by Hocking
Glass Company, Lancaster,
Ohio, from 1934 to 1938. Crystal, Green, and Pink pieces are
more common than Opaque
White.

## CRYSTAL

Butter . . . . . . . . . . . . . .30.00
Cup . . . . . . . . . . . . . . . .6.00
Goblet, Cocktail, 3 Oz.,
4 In. . . . . . . . . . . . . . .12.00
Goblet, Wine, 2 1/2 Oz.,
4 1/2 In. . . . . . . . . . . . .12.00
Pitcher, 68 Oz., 7 3/4 In. . .35.00
Plate, Bread & Butter,
6 In. . . . . . . . . . . . . . . .3.00
Plate, Dinner, 10 In. . . . .20.00
Spooner . . . . . . . . . . . . .60.00
Sugar, Cover . . . .9.00 to 20.00
Tumbler, Juice, 5 Oz.,
3 In. . . . . . . . . . . . . . . .8.00
Tumbler, Juice, Footed,
5 Oz. . . . . . . . . . . . . . .15.00
Tumbler, Water, 9 Oz.,
4 In. . . . . . . . . . . . . . .10.00

## GREEN

Berry Bowl,
4 1/2 In. . . . . . . .6.00 to 20.00
Berry Bowl, Master,
9 In. . . . . . . . . . . . . . . .28.00

Bowl, Vegetable, Oval,
10 In. . . . . . . . . .10.00
Butter, Cover . . .55.00 to 85.00
Cheese Dish, Cover . . . .500.00
Cup & Saucer . . . . . . . .15.00
Goblet, Claret, 4 Oz.,
5 1/4 In. . . . . . .25.00 to 29.00
Goblet, Cocktail, 3 Oz.,
3 1/4 In. . . . . . .19.00 to 29.00
Goblet, Cordial, 1 Oz.,
3 3/4 In. . . . . . .25.00 to 27.00
Goblet, Water, 8 Oz.,
5 3/4 In. . . . . . .25.00 to 32.00
Goblet, Wine, 2 1/2 Oz.,
4 1/2 In. . . . . . .22.00 to 28.00
Grill Plate,
10 In. . . . . . . . .25.00 to 30.00
Pitcher, 54 Oz.,
7 In. . . . . . . . . .62.00 to 75.00
Plate, Dinner, 10 In. . . . . .45.00
Plate, Sherbet,
6 In. . . . . . . . . . .6.00 to 8.00
Platter, Oval, 12 In. . . . . .30.00
Salt & Pepper . . . . . . .145.00
Sherbet . . . . . . . .16.00 to 17.00
Soup, Cream,
4 1/2 In. . . . . . .65.00 to 71.00
Spooner . . . . .125.00 to 135.00
Sugar . . . . . . . . .18.00 to 19.00
Sugar, Cover . . . . . . . . . .35.00
Sugar & Creamer,
Footed . . . . . . . . . . . . .56.00
Whiskey, 1 1/2 Oz.,
2 1/2 In. . . . . . . . . . . . .15.00

**OPAQUE WHITE**
Plate, 8 In. . . . . . . . . . . .10.00
Saucer . . . . . . . . . . . . . .3.00

**PINK**
Berry Bowl,
4 1/2 In. . . . . . .15.00 to 16.00
Cup . . . . . . . . . . . . . . .12.00
Cup & Saucer . . . . . . . .17.00
Goblet, Claret, 4 Oz.,
5 1/4 In. . . . . . . . . . . . .38.00
Grill Plate, 10 In. . . . . . .25.00
Pitcher, 68 Oz., 7 3/4 In. . .75.00
Plate, Dinner, 10 In. . . . . .50.00
Sherbet . . . . . . . . . . . . .12.00
Soup, Dish . . . . .75.00 to 90.00
Soup Cream, 4 1/2 In. . . . .65.00
Spooner . . . . .133.00 to 135.00
Tumbler, Footed, 10 Oz.,
5 1/4 In. . . . . . .46.00 to 48.00

Tumbler, Juice, 5 Oz.,
3 In. . . . . . . . .19.00 to 20.00
Tumbler, Juice, Footed, 3 Oz.,
3 1/4 In. . . . . . .17.00 to 21.00
Tumbler, Water, 9 Oz.,
4 In. . . . . . . . .18.00 to 21.00
Tumbler, Water, Footed,
5 Oz., 4 In. . . . . . . . . .32.00
Whiskey, 1 1/2 Oz.,
2 1/2 In. . . . . . . . . . . . .11.00

## COLONIAL BLOCK
A small set of dishes, mostly
serving pieces, was made in
Colonial Block pattern by
Hazel Atlas Glass Company, a
firm with factories in Ohio,
Pennsylvania, and West Virginia. The dishes were made in
the 1930s in Black, Crystal,
Green, and Pink and in the
1950s in White.

**CRYSTAL**
Bowl, 4 In. . . . . . . . . . . . .6.00
Bowl, 7 In. . . . . . . . . . . .16.00
Butter, Cover . . . . . . . . .30.00
Creamer . . . . . . . . . . . . .7.00
Goblet, Water, 8 1/2 Oz.,
6 In. . . . . . . . . . . . . . . .9.00
Sherbet . . . . . . . . . . . . . .6.00
Sugar . . . . . . . . . . . . . . .6.00

**GREEN**
Bowl, 7 In. . . . . . . . . . . .15.00
Butter, Cover . . .29.00 to 60.00
Candy Jar,
Cover . . . . . . .35.00 to 40.00

Goblet . . . . . . .10.00 to 13.00
Sherbet . . . . . . . . . . . . . .9.00
Sugar . . . . . . . . . . . . . . .10.00
Sugar & Creamer . . . . . . .20.00

**PINK**
Sherbet . . . . . . . . . . . . . .9.00

## COLONIAL FLUTED
Federal Glass Company made
Colonial Fluted or Rope pattern
from 1928 to 1933. Luncheon
sets were made primarily in
Green, although Crystal pieces
were also produced.

**CRYSTAL**
Cup . . . . . . . . . . . . . . . .5.00
Plate, Luncheon, 8 In. . . . . .4.00
Plate, Sherbet, 6 In. . . . . . .2.50
Sugar . . . . . . . . . . . . . . .5.00

**GREEN**
Berry Bowl, 4 In. . . . . . . . .6.50
Creamer . . . . . . . . . . . . .7.00
Grill Plate . . . . . . . . . . .14.00
Plate, Luncheon, 8 In. . . . . .5.00
Plate, Sherbet, 6 In. . . . . . .2.50
Sherbet . . . . . . . . . . . . . .6.00
Sugar, Cover . . . . . . . . . .24.00
Sugar & Creamer,
Cover . . . . . . . .28.00 to 30.00

## COLONY

Colony was made by Fostoria Glass Company from the 1920s to the 1970s. Red candlesticks and bowls were sold after 1982 under the Maypole name, and matching vases and other pieces were made by Viking. Colony was originally made in Amber, Blue, Crystal, Green, and Yellow. Red was made in the 1980s. Another pattern, also named Colony, was made by Hazel Atlas Glass Company in the 1930s in Crystal, Green, and Pink. Colony is a pattern that has also been called Elongated Honeycomb or Hexagon Triple Band because of the features in the molding. Colony made by Fostoria is listed here. Reproductions have been made. They are listed at the end of the Depression Glass section.

**CRYSTAL**
Ashtray, Round, 3 In. . . . .10.00
Ashtray, Round, 6 In. . . . .19.00
Bowl, 11 In. . . . . . . . . . .25.00
Bowl, Ice Cream, Square,
   5 1/2 In. . . . . . . . . . . . .25.00
Bowl, Oval, Footed,
   11 In. . . . . . . . . . . . . . .65.00
Cake Plate, Footed,
   12 In. . . . . . . . . . . . . . .75.00

---
❖
---

**Tired of scrubbing and scrubbing glass to remove marks from masking tape and labels? Pat some commercial hand cleaner on the stain; wait 30 minutes. Then rub off the stain with a cloth and wash the glass.**

---
❖
---

Candlestick, 2-Light,
   6 1/2 In., Pair . . . . . . . .55.00
Candlestick, 3 1/2 In.,
   Pair . . . . . . . . . . . . . . .15.00
Candlestick, Prisms,
   7 1/2 In., Pair . . . . . . . .120.00
Candy Dish, Cover . . . . . .95.00
Compote, Cover,
   6 1/2 In. . . . . . .42.00 to 45.00
Creamer, Footed, 7 Oz. . . . .9.00
Cup & Saucer . . . . . . . . .8.00
Goblet, Water, 9 Oz.,
   5 1/8 In. . . . . . .10.00 to 14.50
Jelly Dish, Cover, 6 In. . . .42.00
Nappy, Round, 4 1/2 In. . .10.00
Pickle . . . . . . . . . . . . . .16.00
Pitcher, Ice Lip,
   8 1/2 In. . . . . . . . . . . .100.00
Plate, Luncheon, 8 In. . . . .10.00
Platter,
   12 1/2 In. . . . . .27.00 to 50.00
Punch Cup . . . . . . . . . . .20.00
Relish, 2 Sections, Oval . .20.00
Salt & Pepper . . . . . . . .16.00
Sherbet, 5 Oz. . . . .7.00 to 9.00
Sugar, Footed, Open . . . . . .9.00
Sugar & Creamer,
   Footed . . . . . . . . . . . . .13.00
Sugar & Creamer, Individual,
   2 3/4 In. . . . . . .13.00 to 16.00
Tray, Center Handle,
   11 1/2 In. . . . . . . . . . . .30.00
Tray, Muffin, 8 3/8 In. . . .30.00
Wine, 3 1/4 In. . .20.00 to 22.00

**PINK**
Candy Jar, Cover,
   6 1/2 In. . . . . . . . . . . . .45.00

## COLUMBIA

Columbia pattern can be found in Crystal but is rare in Pink. It was made by Federal Glass Company, Columbus, Ohio, from 1938 to 1942.

**CRYSTAL**
Bowl, Cereal,
   5 In. . . . . . . . .16.00 to 19.00
Bowl, Ruffled,
   10 1/2 In. . . . . .18.00 to 20.00
Bowl, Salad,
   8 1/2 In. . . . . . .14.00 to 20.00
Butter, Cover . . .16.00 to 25.00
Chop Plate,
   11 In. . . . . . . . .10.00 to 12.00
Cup . . . . . . . . . . . . . . . .8.00
Cup & Saucer . .10.00 to 15.00
Plate, Bread & Butter,
   6 In. . . . . . . . . .4.00 to 12.00
Plate, Luncheon,
   9 1/2 In. . . . . . .9.00 to 10.00
Plate, Snack . . . .30.00 to 42.00
Soup, Dish, 8 In. . . . . . . .20.00
Sugar & Creamer,
   Cover . . . . . . . . . . . . . .20.00

**PINK**
Cup & Saucer . . . . . . . .30.00
Plate, Bread & Butter,
   6 In. . . . . . . . . . . . . . .13.00
Plate, Luncheon,
   9 1/2 In. . . . . . . . . . . . .30.00

## CORONATION

Coronation was made, primarily in berry sets, by Anchor Hocking Glass Corporation, Lancaster, Ohio, from 1936 to 1940. Most pieces are Crystal or Pink, but there are also Dark Green and Ruby Red sets. The pattern is sometimes called Banded Fine Rib or Saxon. Some of the pieces are confused with those in Lace Edge pattern.

### PINK
Berry Bowl, 4 1/4 In. . . . . .8.00
Cup . . . . . . . . . . . . . . . .6.00
Plate, Sherbet,
    6 In. . . . . . . . . . .2.00 to 4.00
Sherbet, Footed . . . . . . . .10.00
Tumbler, Footed, 10 Oz.,
    5 In. . . . . . . . .22.00 to 34.00

### ROYAL RUBY
Berry Bowl,
    4 1/4 In. . . . . . . .4.50 to 6.75
Berry Bowl, Master,
    8 In. . . . . . . . .14.00 to 15.00
Bowl, Nappy,
    6 1/2 In. . . . . . .10.00 to 15.00

❖

**Don't use ammonia on glasses with gold or silver decorations.**

❖

## CRACKED ICE

Cracked Ice is an Art Deco-looking geometric pattern made by Indiana Glass Company in the 1930s. It was made in Green and Pink.

### GREEN
Salt & Pepper, Pair . . . . .38.00
Sugar & Creamer . . . . . .59.00

### PINK
Plate, Bread & Butter,
    6 1/2 In. . . . . . . . . . . . .20.00
Sherbet, 3 In. . . . . . . . . .20.00

## CREMAX

Cremax and Chinex Classic are confusing patterns. There is an added piece of molded design next to the fluted rim trim on Chinex Classic. Also the names Cremax and Chinex refer to colors as well as patterns. Cremax, made by Macbeth Evans Division of Corning Glass Works, was made from 1938 to 1942. It is a cream-colored opaque glass, sometimes decorated with floral or brown-tinted decals or with a colored rim.

Plate, Dinner, 9 3/4 In . . . .5.00
Plate, Sandwich, Pink
    Border, 11 1/2 In. . . . .13.00

CREMAX, see also Chinex Classic

CUBE, see Cubist

## CUBIST

Cubist, or Cube, molded with the expected rectangular and diamond pattern, was made by Jeannette Glass Company from 1929 to 1933. It was made first in Pink and Crystal. Later, Green replaced Crystal, and Amber, Blue, Canary Yellow, Pink, Ultramarine, and White were added. Various shades of some of the colors were made. It has been made recently in Amber, Opaque White, and Avocado.

### CRYSTAL
Creamer . . . . . . . . . . . . .3.00
Tumbler, Juice, 9 Oz.,
    4 In. . . . . . . . . . . . . . .67.00

### GREEN
Bowl, Dessert,
    4 1/2 In. . . . . . .6.00 to 10.00
Bowl, Salad, 6 1/2 In. . . . .18.00
Butter, Cover . . . . . . . . .60.00
Candy Jar, Cover,
    6 1/2 In. . . . . . .20.00 to 32.00
Coaster, 3 1/4 In. . .8.00 to 9.00
Creamer, Large . . .8.00 to 13.00
Cup . . . . . . . . . . . . . . . .9.00
Cup & Saucer . . . . . . . .11.00

Pitcher, Water, Applied
Handle, 9 In. . . . . . . . . .25.00
Plate, Luncheon,
8 In. . . . . . . . . .8.00 to 11.00
Plate, Sherbet, 6 In. . . . . .4.00
Powder Jar, Cover . . . . . .28.00
Salt & Pepper . . .30.00 to 35.00
Saucer . . . . . . . . . . . . . . .3.00
Sherbet . . . . . . . .7.00 to 8.00
Sherbet, Footed . . . . . . . .8.00
Sugar, 3 In. . . . . . . . . . . . .6.00
Sugar & Creamer Set,
3 In. . . . . . . . . . .9.00 to 33.00
Tumbler, Water, 9 Oz.,
4 In. . . . . . . . . . . . . . .70.00

**PINK**
Bowl, Dessert,
4 1/2 In. . . . . . . . .5.00 to 8.00
Bowl, Salad, 6 1/2 In. . . . .12.00
Butter, Cover . . .57.00 to 70.00
Candy Jar,
Cover . . . . . . . .22.00 to 27.00
Coaster, 3 1/4 In. . . . . . . .7.00
Creamer, Large,
3 9/16 In. . . . . . . . . . . . .6.00
Cup . . . . . . . . . . . . . . . .8.00
Cup & Saucer . . . . . . . .10.00
Pitcher, 45 Oz.,
8 1/4 In. . . . . . . . . . . .245.00
Plate, Luncheon, 8 In. . . . . .6.00
Powder Jar, Cover . . . . . .25.00
Salt & Pepper,
Pair . . . . . . . .25.00 to 30.00
Saucer . . . . . . . . . . . . . . .3.00
Sherbet, Footed . . . .7.00 to 8.00
Sugar, 3 In. . . . . . . . . . . . .5.00
Sugar & Creamer,
Cover . . . . . . . .23.00 to 25.00

---

If you are going to dis-
play a large bowl on a
wooden table, apply self-
adhesive green felt pads
to the bottom of the
bowl. This will keep the
table from being
scratched and the bowl
from chipping.

---

Tumbler, Water, 9 Oz.,
4 In. . . . . . . . . . . . . . .70.00

**DAISY,** see No. 620

**DAISY PETALS,** see Petalware

**DANCING GIRL,** see Cameo

## ·D·

## DECAGON
Decagon, named for its 10-
sided outline, was made by the
Cambridge Glass Company of
Cambridge, Ohio. The pattern,
dating from the 1930s, was
made in Amber, Black, Cobalt
Blue, Green, Moonlight Blue
(light blue), Pink, and Red.

**AMBER**
Bottle, Salad Dressing . .110.00
Cruet . . . . . . . . . . . . . .32.50

**BLACK**
Bowl, Flared, 12 In. . . . .65.00
Goblet, Wine . . . . . . . . .30.00
Tray, For Sugar &
Creamer . . . . . . . . . . . .45.00

**COBALT BLUE**
Goblet, 8 Oz. . . . . . . . . .24.00
Sherbet . . . . . . . . . . . . .20.00

**GREEN**
Bowl, Cupped, Deep,
5 1/2 In. . . . . . . . . . . . .55.00
Bowl, Footed, 6 In. . . . . .24.00
Bowl, Fruit, Belled,
5 1/2 In. . . . . . . . . . . . .16.00
Celery Dish . . . . . . . . . .37.00
Creamer . . . . . .15.00 to 25.00
Cruet, 3-Spout . . . . . . .165.00

Cup & Saucer . .10.00 to 11.00
Goblet, Cocktail,
3 1/2 Oz. . . . . . . . . . . . .24.00
Goblet, Water, 9 Oz. . . . . .20.00
Mug, Lemonade,
Handle . . . . . . . . . . . . .55.00
Nut Dish, Footed,
2 1/2 In. . . . . . . . . . . . .30.00
Pickle, 8 1/2 In. . . . . . . .35.00
Plate, Bread & Butter,
7 1/2 In. . . . . . . . . . . . .10.00
Plate, Salad,
8 1/4 In. . . . . . .10.00 to 18.50
Relish, 2 Sections,
8 1/2 In. . . . . . . . . . . . .35.00
Salt & Pepper, 3 In. . . . . .50.00
Sandwich Server, Center
Handle . . . . . . . . . . . . .22.00
Sherbet . . . . . . . . . . . . .10.00
Soup, Cream, With Liner .35.00
Soup, Dish, 6 3/4 In. . . . . .24.00
Sugar & Creamer . . . . . . .20.00
Tumbler, Juice, 5 Oz. . . . .11.00
Whiskey, Footed,
2 1/2 Oz. . . . . . . . . . . . .12.00

**MOONLIGHT BLUE**
Basket, 6 1/4 In. . . . . . . .45.00
Bouillon, Footed . . . . . . .20.00
Candlestick, 5 In. . . . . . .42.00
Creamer & Sugar . . . . . .40.00
Cruet, 6 Oz. . . . . . . . . .195.00
Cup & Saucer . . . . . . . .15.00
Goblet, Champagne,
6 Oz. . . . . . . . . . . . . . .24.00
Goblet, Water, 9 Oz. . . . . .33.00
Goblet, Wine, 2 1/2 Oz. . .35.00
Plate, 2 Handles, 7 In. . . . .24.00
Plate, Salad, 7 1/2 In. . . . .15.00
Sandwich Server, Center
Handle . . . . . . . . . . . . .35.00
Sherbet, Low . . . .19.00 to 20.00
Soup, Cream, Liner . . . . .45.00
Tray, For Sugar &
Creamer . . . . . . . . . . . .45.00
Tray, Oval, 9 In. . . . . . . .35.00
Tumbler, Iced Tea, Footed,
12 Oz. . . . . . .35.00 to 45.00
Tumbler, Water, Footed,
10 Oz. . . . . . . . . . . . . .28.00

**PINK**
Ice Bucket . . . . . . . . . . .85.00
Sherbet, Low . . . . . . . . .16.00

## DELLA ROBBIA

Della Robbia is a heavy glass with raised pears and apples as part of the design. It was made by the Westmoreland Glass Company, Grapeville, Pennsylvania, from 1926 to the 1960s. The pattern was made in Crystal, Roselin, Green, and Amber. Crystal pieces often have fruit stained in natural colors.

### CRYSTAL

Bowl, Heart Shape,
  8 In. . . . . . . . . . . . . . .125.00
Box, Chocolate, Cover . . .75.00
Candlestick, 4 In.,
  Pair . . . . . . . . .45.00 to 55.00
Plate, Luncheon,
  9 In. . . . . . . . .30.00 to 35.00
Plate, Salad, 7 1/4 In. . . . .22.00
Punch Bowl Set,
  13 Piece . . . . . . . . . . .700.00
Salver, Footed, 14 In. . . .120.00
Sherbet, Low Foot, 5 Oz.,
  4 3/4 In. . . . . . .19.00 to 26.00
Torte Plate, Crystal,
  14 In. . . . . . .85.00 to 125.00
Tumbler, Iced Tea,
  12 Oz. . . . . . . . . . . . . .35.00

---

**Never run an ad that
says to call after
6:00 p.m. It is an
announcement that
you are away from
the house during
the day.**

---

Tumbler, Water,
  8 Oz. . . . . . . .28.00 to 30.00

**DIAMOND,** see Windsor

**DIAMOND PATTERN, see** Miss
  America

## DIAMOND QUILTED

Imperial Glass Company, Bellaire, Ohio, made Diamond Quilted, sometimes called Flat Diamond, in the 1920s and early 1930s. It was made in Amber, Black, Blue, Crystal, Green, Pink, and Red. Dinner sets, luncheon sets, and serving pieces, including a large punch bowl, were made, but not all items were made in all colors.

### BLACK

Cup . . . . . . . . . . . . . . . .20.00
Soup, Cream, 4 3/4 In. . . .20.00

### BLUE

Candlestick, Pair . . . . . . .48.00
Plate, Luncheon, 8 In. . . . .16.00
Plate, Sherbet, 6 In. . . . . . .9.00
Sherbet . . . . . . . . . . . . .13.00
Soup, Cream . . . . . . . . . .19.00
Sugar . . . . . . . . . . . . . . .20.00
Sugar & Creamer . . . . . . .45.00

### GREEN

Candlestick,
  Pair . . . . . . . . .24.00 to 25.00
Plate, Luncheon, 8 In. . . . . .6.00
Plate, Sherbet, 6 In. . . . . . .4.00

### PINK

Basket, Cookie . . . . . . .150.00
Bowl, Handle, 5 1/2 In. . .15.00
Candlestick . . . . . . . . . .12.00
Candy Jar, Cover . . . . . .150.00
Cup . . . . . . . . . .8.00 to 10.00
Plate, Luncheon,
  8 In. . . . . . . . . . . . . . .11.00
Sherbet . . . . . . . . . . . . . .5.00
Sugar . . . . . . . . .8.00 to 13.00

## DIANA

Diana is one of the many Depression glass patterns with swirls in the glass, which often cause confusion. Federal Glass Company, Columbus, Ohio, made this pattern, sometimes called Swirled Sharp Rib, from 1937 to 1941. It was made in Amber, Crystal, Green, and Pink and can be distinguished from other swirled patterns by the two sets of swirls used— one in the center of the piece, another on the rim. A Pink bowl was reproduced in 1987.

### AMBER

Bowl, Cereal,
  5 In. . . . . . . . . .10.00 to 12.00
Bowl, Console, Fruit,
  11 In. . . . . . . . .10.00 to 18.00
Bowl, Salad, 9 In. . . . . . .20.00
Coaster, 3 1/2 In. . . . . . .16.00
Creamer . . . . . . . . . . . . .9.00
Cup & Saucer . . . . . . . . .8.00
Plate, Luncheon,
  9 1/2 In. . . . . . . . . . . . .8.00
Platter, Oval, 12 In. . . . . .13.00
Salt & Pepper . . . . . . . .100.00
Saucer . . . . . . . . . . . . . .2.00
Shaker . . . . . . . . . . . . . .49.00
Sherbet . . . . . . . .7.00 to 9.00
Soup, Cream,
  5 1/2 In. . . . . . . . . . . . .16.00
Sugar & Creamer . . . . . .15.00

Tumbler, 9 Oz.,
   4 1/2 In. . . . . . . . . . . . .26.00

### CRYSTAL
Bowl, Cereal, 5 In. . . . . . .4.00
Cup & Saucer . . . . . . . . .12.00
Cup & Saucer, After
   Dinner . . . . . . .10.00 to 13.00
Goblet, Cordial,
   1 1/2 Oz. . . . . . . . . . . .65.00
Salt & Pepper . . . . . . . .20.00
Saucer . . . . . . . . . . . . . .1.50
Soup, Cream, 8 1/2 In. . . . .6.00
Tea Set, Child's, Metal
   Holder . . . . . . . . . . . . .90.00
Tumbler, 9 Oz. . . . . . . . .32.00

### PINK
Bowl, Cereal,
   5 In. . . . . . . . . .3.00 to 11.00
Bowl, Console, Fruit,
   11 In. . . . . . . . . . . . . .40.00
Bowl, Salad,
   9 In. . . . . . . . .20.00 to 22.00
Candy Jar,
   Cover . . . . . . .30.00 to 45.00
Creamer . . . . . .12.00 to 20.00
Cup . . . . . . . . . .9.00 to 14.00
Cup, After
   Dinner . . . . . .10.00 to 30.00
Cup & Saucer . .13.00 to 19.00
Plate, Bread & Butter,
   6 In. . . . . . . . . . . . . . . .3.00
Plate, Dinner, 9 1/2 In. . . .16.00
Platter, Oval, 12 In. . . . .30.00
Salt & Pepper . . . . . . . .75.00
Soup, Cream,
   5 1/2 In. . . . . . .25.00 to 30.00
Tumbler, 9 Oz. . . . . . . . .30.00

---

## DOGWOOD
Dogwood is decorated with a strange flower that has been given many names. Collectors have called this pattern Apple Blossom, B pattern, Magnolia, or Wildrose. It was made from 1930 to 1934 by Macbeth-Evans Glass Company. It is found in Cremax, Crystal, Green, Monax, Pink, and Yellow. Sometimes the Pink pieces were trimmed with gold.

Some pieces were made with such thin walls the factory redesigned the molds to make the pieces thicker.

### GREEN
Cake Plate, 13 In. . . . . . .110.00
Cup . . . . . . . . .35.00 to 40.00
Cup & Saucer, Thin . . . .40.00
Plate, Luncheon, 8 In. . . . .8.00
Saucer . . . . . . . . . . . . . .7.00

### MONAX
Cup . . . . . . . . . . . . . . . .36.00

### PINK
Ashtray, Square . . . . . . . .5.00
Berry Bowl, Master,
   8 1/2 In. . . . . . .58.00 to 60.00
Bowl, Cereal,
   5 1/2 In. . . . . . .25.00 to 32.50
Bowl, Cereal, Rolled Edge,
   5 1/2 In. . . . . . .55.00 to 80.00
Cake Plate,
   13 In. . . . . . .125.00 to 150.00
Creamer, Thick . .19.00 to 27.50
Creamer, Thin . . .15.00 to 19.50
Cup, Thick . . . . . . . . . . . .15.00
Cup & Saucer,
   Thick . . . . . . .20.00 to 25.00
Cup & Saucer,
   Thin . . . . . . . . .18.00 to 25.00
Grill Plate . . . .20.00 to 22.00
Pitcher . . . . . .220.00 to 230.00
Plate, Bread & Butter,
   6 In. . . . . . . . . .6.50 to 10.00
Plate, Dinner,
   9 1/4 In. . . . . . .22.50 to 40.00
Plate, Luncheon,
   8 In. . . . . . . . . . .5.50 to 9.00
Platter, 12 In. . . . . . . . .500.00
Salver, 12 In. . . . .28.00 to 40.00
Saucer . . . . . . . . . . . . . .7.00
Sherbet, Footed . .30.00 to 40.00
Sugar, Thick,
   3 1/4 In. . . . . . .16.00 to 21.00
Sugar, Thin,
   2 1/2 In. . . . . . .15.00 to 18.00
Sugar & Creamer, Thick,
   Footed . . . . . . .35.00 to 38.00
Sugar & Creamer,
   Thin . . . . . . . . .30.00 to 36.00
Tumbler, 12 Oz.,
   5 In. . . . . . . . .43.00 to 77.50
Tumbler, Decorated, 12 Oz.,
   Box, 6 Piece . . . . . . . .425.00
Tumbler, Iced Tea, Decorated,
   12 Oz. . . . . . .58.00 to 60.00

---

## DORIC
Doric was made by Jeannette Glass Company, Jeannette, Pennsylvania, from 1935 to 1938. The molded pattern has also inspired another name for the pattern, Snowflake. It was made in Delphite (opaque blue), Green, Pink, and Yellow. A few White pieces may have been made.

### DELPHITE
Candy Dish, 3 Sections . . . .8.00
Candy Dish, Cover . . . . . . .5.00
Sherbet, Footed . . .6.00 to 10.00

### GREEN
Berry Bowl,
    4 1/2 In. . . . . . .7.00 to 11.00
Berry Bowl, Master,
    8 1/4 In. . . . . . . . . . . . .26.00
Bowl, Handles, 9 In. . . . . .24.00
Creamer . . . . . .13.00 to 17.00
Pitcher, 36 Oz., 6 In. . . . . .45.00
Plate, Salad,
    7 In. . . . . . . . .22.00 to 28.00
Plate, Sherbet, 6 In. . . . . . .5.00
Relish, 4 x 4 In. . . . . . . . .16.50
Sherbet . . . . . . . . . . . . . .14.00
Sugar & Creamer,
    Cover . . . . . . . . . . . . .50.00

### PINK
Berry Bowl,
    4 1/2 In. . . . . . .8.00 to 12.00
Berry Bowl, Master,
    8 1/4 In. . . . . .14.00 to 35.00
Bowl, 2 Handles, 9 In. . . .20.00
Bowl, Vegetable, Oval,
    9 In. . . . . . . . .35.00 to 36.00
Cake Plate,
    3-Footed . . . .22.00 to 30.00
Candy Dish, 3 Sections . . .12.50
Candy Dish,
    Cover . . . . . . .35.00 to 39.00
Creamer . . . . . .10.00 to 12.00
Cup & Saucer . .11.00 to 14.50
Grill Plate . . . . . . . . . . .20.00
Pitcher, 32 Oz.,
    5 1/2 In. . . . . .41.00 to 45.00
Pitcher, 48 Oz.,
    7 1/2 In. . . . . . . . . . . .695.00
Plate, Dinner,
    9 In. . . . . . . . .12.00 to 17.50
Plate, Salad,
    7 In. . . . . . . . . . . . . . .10.00
Plate, Sherbet,
    6 In. . . . . . . . . . .3.50 to 6.50
Platter, Oval,
    12 In. . . . . . . .22.00 to 35.00
Salt & Pepper . . . . . . . .40.00
Saltshaker . . . . . . . . . . .16.00
Sherbet . . . . . . . . . . . . .11.00
Sugar, Cover . . . . . . . . . .13.00
Sugar & Creamer,
    Cover . . . . . . .25.00 to 38.00

❖

**Moving is a collector's nightmare. Best for wrapping are the rolls of paper used in schools to cover lunch tables. Cut the paper to different sizes before starting to pack. Put paper plates between plates. Wrap saucers in stacks of 10 to 16.**

❖

Tray, 8 x 8 In. . . . . . . . . . .36.00
Tray, Handle,
    10 In. . . . . . . .12.50 to 17.00
Tumbler, 9 Oz.,
    4 1/2 In. . . . . . . . . . . . .66.00
Tumbler, Footed, 10 Oz.,
    4 In. . . . . . . . .60.00 to 69.00

## DORIC & PANSY
The snowflake design of Doric alternates with squares holding pansies, so, of course, the pattern is named Doric & Pansy. It, too, was made by Jeannette Glass Company, but only in 1937 and 1938. It was made in Crystal, Pink, and Ultramarine. The Ultramarine varied in color from green to blue. Collectors pay more for the blue shades. A set of child's dishes called Pretty Polly Party Dishes was made in this pattern.

### CRYSTAL
Cup & Saucer . . . . . . . . .13.00
Tray, 2 Handles, 10 In. . . .45.00

### PINK
Creamer, Child's . . . . . .37.00
Saucer, Child's . . . . . . . . .7.00

### ULTRAMARINE
Butter, Cover . .450.00 to 525.00
Creamer, Child's . . . . . .46.00
Cup, Child's . . . . . . . . . .45.00
Cup & Saucer . .21.00 to 22.00
Cup & Saucer, Child's . .50.00
Plate, Child's . . . . . . . . .13.00
Plate, Salad, 7 In. . . . . . .40.00
Saucer . . . . . . . . . . . . . . .5.00
Tumbler,
    4 1/2 In. . . . . . .85.00 to 90.00

**DORIC WITH PANSY,** see Doric & Pansy

**DOUBLE SHIELD,** see Mt. Pleasant

**DOUBLE SWIRL,** see Swirl

**DRAPE & TASSEL,** see Princess

**DUTCH,** see Windmill

**DUTCH ROSE,** see Rosemary

## ◆E◆

**EARLY AMERICAN HOBNAIL,** see Hobnail

**EARLY AMERICAN ROCK CRYSTAL,** see Rock Crystal

**EARLY AMERICAN SANDWICH GLASS,** see Sandwich Duncan & Miller

**ELONGATED HONEYCOMB,** see Colony

# ENGLISH HOBNAIL

Westmoreland Glass Company, Grapeville, Pennsylvania, made English Hobnail pattern from the 1920s through 1983. It is similar to Miss America except for more rounded hobs and the absence of the typical Hocking sunburst ray on the base. English Hobnail was made in Amber, Cobalt Blue, Crystal, Green, Ice Blue, Opaque White, Pink, Red, and Turquoise. There is much variation in the shading, and a darker amber was made in the 1960s. Red and Pink reproduction pieces were made in the 1980s.

### AMBER
Candlestick, 3 1/2 In.,
   Pair . . . . . . . . . . . . . . .18.00
Candy Dish, Cone . . . . .20.00
Cologne Bottle . . . . . . .47.00
Creamer, Footed . . . . . . .24.00
Nappy, 4 1/2 In. . . . . . . . .8.00
Plate, Dinner, 10 In. . . . . .18.00
Salt & Pepper . . . . . . . .75.00
Sherbet, Footed . . . . . . . .15.00
Vase, 7 1/4 In. . . . . . . . .85.00

### COBALT BLUE
Bottle, Toilet, Stopper,
   5 Oz. . . . . . . . . . . . . . .69.00
Candlestick, 3 1/2 In.,
   Pair . . . . . . . . . . . . . . .15.00
Goblet, Claret,
   5 Oz. . . . . . . . .18.00 to 27.00

### CRYSTAL
Bowl, Grapefruit,
   6 1/2 In. . . . . . .12.00 to 14.00
Compote, Square Foot . . .24.00
Cup & Saucer . .10.00 to 26.00
Finger Bowl, Square
   Foot, 4 1/2 In. . . . . . . . .8.00
Goblet, Claret, Square
   Foot, 5 Oz. . . . . .8.00 to 12.00
Goblet, Cocktail, Square
   Foot, 3 Oz. . . . . . . . . .12.00
Goblet, Round Foot,
   6 In. . . . . . . . . .10.00 to 11.00
Goblet, Water, 8 Oz.,
   6 1/4 In. . . . . . . . . . . . .70.00
Lamp, Electric,
   6 1/2 In. . . . . . . . . . . . .45.00
Lamp, Electric,
   9 1/2 In. . . . . . .40.00 to 75.00
Plate, Bread & Butter,
   Round, 5 1/2 In. . .6.00 to 7.00
Plate, Luncheon,
   8 In. . . . . . . . . . .5.00 to 6.00
Salt & Pepper . . .18.00 to 30.00
Sherbet, Round Foot . . . . .9.00
Sherbet, Square Foot . . . .8.00
Torte Plate, Handle,
   10 In. . . . . . . . . . . . . . .10.00
Tumbler, Iced Tea,
   10 Oz., 5 In. . . . . . . . .12.00
Tumbler, Iced Tea, Footed,
   12 Oz. . . . . . . .11.00 to 16.00
Tumbler, Juice, 5 Oz.,
   3 3/4 In. . . . . . . . . . . . .10.00

### GREEN
Ashtray . . . . . . . . . . . . .22.00
Bowl, Hexagonal, Footed,
   8 In. . . . . . . . . . . . . . .29.00
Candlestick, 3 1/2 In.,
   Pair . . . . . . . . . . . . . . .28.00
Cup & Saucer . . . . . . . .35.00

Goblet, Water, Square
   Foot, 8 Oz. . . . . . . . . .25.00
Jam Jar, Cover . . . . . . . .35.00
Nappy, 4 1/2 In. . . . . . . .12.00
Plate, Luncheon, Round,
   8 In. . . . . . . . . . . . . . .11.00
Plate, Sherbet,
   6 1/2 In. . . . . . . . . . . . .4.00
Powder Box, Cover . . . . .35.00
Relish, Oval, 8 In. . . . . . . .25.00
Salt & Pepper, Round
   Foot . . . . . . . . .75.00 to 85.00
Sherbet, Footed . . . . . . . .18.00
Soup, Cream, 4 3/4 In. . . .20.00
Tumbler, Iced Tea,
   12 Oz., 6 In. . . . . . . . .18.00
Vase, 7 1/4 In. . . . . . . . .55.00

### ICE BLUE
Goblet, Water, Square Foot,
   8 Oz., 6 1/4 In. . . . . . . .50.00
Plate, Luncheon, Round,
   8 In. . . . . . . . . . . . . . .25.00
Sherbet, Footed . . . . . . . .25.00
Tumbler, Iced Tea,
   10 Oz., 4 1/2 In. . . . . . . .50.00

### PINK
Basket, 6 In. . . . . . . . . . .80.00
Bowl, 6 In. . . . . . . . . . . .23.00
Cup & Saucer . . . . . . . .20.00
Finger Bowl, 4 1/2 In. . . . .15.00
Goblet, Champagne, 6 Oz.,
   6 1/4 In. . . . . . .18.00 to 26.00
Goblet, Water, 8 Oz. . . . . .36.00
Goblet, Wine, 2 Oz. . . . . .36.00
Nappy, 4 1/2 In. . .9.00 to 15.00
Plate, Luncheon, Round,
   8 In. . . . . . . . . . . . . . .9.00
Sherbet, Low Footed . . . . .18.00
Sugar, Footed . . . . . . . . .22.00
Sugar & Creamer . . . . . .25.00
Tumbler, Iced Tea,
   12 Oz., 5 In. . . . . . . . . .13.00
Tumbler, Juice, 5 Oz. . . . .15.00
Vase, 7 1/4 In. . . . . . . .100.00

### RED
Basket, 6 In. . . . . . . . . .125.00

### TURQUOISE
Candlestick, 3 1/2 In.,
   Pair . . . . . . . . . . . . . . .67.00
Goblet, Champagne,
   6 Oz., 6 1/4 In. . . . . . . .44.00

Nappy, 4 1/2 In. . . . . . . .18.00
Salt &
  Pepper . . . . .112.00 to 195.00

## FAIRFAX

Fairfax was made by Fostoria Glass Company, Fostoria, Ohio, from 1927 to 1960. The name Fairfax refers to a glass blank and to an etching pattern. The same glass blanks were used for other etched designs including June, Trojan, and Versailles. The undecorated blank, also known as No. 2375, is popular with collectors. The same shapes were used to make other patterns with etched designs. The glass was made in Amber, Azure (blue), Crystal, Gold Tint, Green, Orchid, Red, Rose (pink), and Topaz.

**AMBER**
Ice Bucket . . . . . . . . . . .12.00
Nut Cup,
  Footed . . . . . . .14.00 to 15.00
Plate, Mayonnaise . . . . . .25.00

**AZURE**
Ashtray . . . . . . . . . . . . . .15.00
Bowl, Whipped Cream . . .75.00
Cheese & Cracker . . . . . .42.00
Goblet, Water, 10 Oz. . . . .25.00
Goblet, Wine . . . . . . . . . .45.00
Ice Bucket . . . . . . . . . . .50.00
Nut Cup . . . . . . . . . . . . . .25.00
Pitcher, Water, 48 Oz.,
  9 1/2 In. . . . . . . . . . . . .250.00
Plate, Dinner, 10 In. . . . . .58.00
Plate, Luncheon,
  9 1/2 In. . . . . . . . . . . . . .15.00
Saucer . . . . . . . . . . . . . . .9.00
Shaker, Footed . . . . . . . .40.00
Sherbet, Footed . . . . . . . .22.00
Sugar Pail . . . . . . . . . . .95.00

Tray, Service . . . . . . . . .150.00
**CRYSTAL**
Cup & Saucer . . . . . . . . .7.00
Saucer, After Dinner . . . . .5.00

**GREEN**
Bouillon, Liner . . . . . . . . .17.50
Bowl, Fruit,
  5 In. . . . . . . . . .15.00 to 20.00
Candlestick, 3 In., Pair . . .42.00
Compote, 7 In. . . . . . . . .95.00
Compote, Footed,
  5 1/2 In. . . . . . .42.00 to 60.00
Cup . . . . . . . . . . . . . . . .16.00
Cup, After Dinner . . . . . .10.00
Cup & Saucer . . . . . . . . .11.50
Cup & Saucer, After
  Dinner . . . . . . . . . . . . .22.00
Finger Bowl . . . .15.00 to 25.00
Gravy Boat . . . . . . . . . .55.00
Pitcher, Water, 48 Oz.,
  9 1/2 In. . . . . . . . . . . . .175.00
Plate, Dinner,
  10 1/4 In. . . . . .35.00 to 48.00
Plate, Luncheon,
  9 1/2 In. . . . . . . . . . . . . .20.00
Plate, Salad, 7 In. . . . . . . .4.00
Platter, Oval, 10 1/2 In. . .58.00
Platter, Oval,
  12 In. . . . . . . .45.00 to 68.00
Platter, Oval, 15 In. . . . .145.00
Relish, 2 Sections,
  8 1/2 In. . . . . . . . . . . . . .9.00
Relish, 3 Sections,
  11 1/2 In. . . . . .15.00 to 28.00
Salt & Pepper . . . . . . . . .55.00
Sauceboat, Liner . . . . . . .110.00
Soup, Cream . . . . . . . . . .19.00
Sugar, Cover . . . . . . . . . .33.00

❖

**When the weather is bad, the auction will probably be good. Brave the storm and cold to attend an auction in bad weather, when the crowd will be small and the prices low.**

❖

Torte Plate . . . . . . . . . . .30.00
Vase, Footed,
  7 In. . . . . . . . .46.00 to 75.00
**ORCHID**
Compote, Footed . . . . . .48.00
Cup & Saucer . . . . . . . . .17.00
Cup & Saucer, Footed . . .24.00
Pitcher, Water, 48 Oz.,
  9 1/2 In. . . . . . . . . . . . .350.00
Plate, Bread & Butter,
  6 In. . . . . . . . . . . . . . . .7.00
Plate, Luncheon,
  8 1/2 In. . . . . . . . . . . . .14.00
Plate, Salad, 7 1/2 In. . . . .12.00
Saucer, After Dinner . . . . . .8.00

**ROSE**
Bowl, Fruit, 5 In. . . . . . . .12.00
Cheese & Cracker . . . . . .40.00
Creamer, Footed . . . . . . .18.00
Creamer, Tea . . . . . . . . .35.00
Cup & Saucer . . . . . . . . .12.50
Pitcher, Water, 48 Oz.,
  9 1/2 In. . . . . . . . . . . . .210.00
Plate, 7 In. . . . . . . . . . . . .5.00
Sugar, Footed . . . . . . . . .17.00

**TOPAZ**
Bowl, Fruit,
  5 In. . . . . . . . . .7.00 to 15.00
Compote, 7 In. . . . . . . . .24.00
Compote, Round, 5 In. . . .65.00
Creamer, Footed . . . . . . .10.00
Cup & Saucer . . . . . . . . .10.00
Cup & Saucer,
  After Dinner . . . . . . . . .17.50
Dish, Sweetmeat,
  2 Handles . . . . .11.00 to 18.50
Goblet, Cordial . . . . . . . .32.00
Pitcher, Water, 48 Oz.,
  9 1/2 In. . . . .100.00 to 135.00
Plate, Bread & Butter,
  6 In. . . . . . . . . . . . . . . .2.50
Plate, Dinner, 10 In. . . . . .38.00
Plate, Luncheon,
  9 1/2 In. . . . . . . . . . . . .12.50
Plate, Salad, 7 1/2 In. . . . .5.50
Plate, Salad, 8 3/4 In. . . . .8.00
Relish, 2 Sections . . . . . . .17.00
Salt & Pepper,
  Individual . . . . . . . . . . .24.00
Sugar & Creamer . . . . . . .28.00
Whiskey, Footed . . . . . . .25.00

# ·F·

**FAN & FEATHER,** see Adam

**FINE RIB,** see Homespun

## FIRE-KING

Fire-King or Fire-King Oven Glass, Fire-King Oven Ware, and Fire-King Dinnerware were all made by Anchor Hocking Glass Corporation, Lancaster, Ohio, from 1941 through 1976. Fire-King Oven Glass is a transparent, pale blue glassware with a lacy decoration. A matching dinnerware set is called Philbe. It was made in Crystal and Pale Blue. Philbe is listed under its own name in this book. Fire-King Oven Ware is an opaque glass made by Anchor Hocking in the 1950s. It was made in Blue, Crystal, Ivory, Jadite, and Pink, or Ivory with gold or colored trim. Some mixing bowls and kitchen sets were made with tulips or red kitchen objects pictured on the sides. Fire-King Dinnerware sets were made in patterns named Alice, Charm, Fleurette, Game Bird, Gray Laurel, Jadite, Jane-Ray, Peach Lustre, Philbe, Primrose, Square, Swirl Fire-King, Turquoise Blue, and Wheat. These are listed in this book in their own sections.

**BLUE**
Bowl, Cereal,
5 3/8 In. . . . . . .12.00 to 22.00
Bowl, Measuring,
16 Oz. . . . . . . . . . . . . .25.00

Bowl, Utility, 8 3/8 In. . . .16.00
Bowl, Utility, 10 1/8 In. . .20.00
Casserole, Cover, Individual,
10 Oz. . . . . . . . .9.50 to 12.00
Casserole, Individual,
10 Oz. . . . . . . . .6.50 to 9.00
Casserole, Knob Cover,
1 Pt. . . . . . . . .10.00 to 15.00
Casserole, Knob Cover,
1 Qt. . . . . . . . .11.25 to 15.00
Casserole, Knob Cover,
2 Qt. . . . . . . . . . . . . .15.00
Custard Cup,
5 Oz. . . . . . . . . .3.00 to 5.00
Custard Cup,
6 Oz. . . . . . . . . .3.00 to 4.50
Hot Plate,
Tab Handles . . .10.00 to 20.00
Loaf Pan,
9 x 5 In. . . . . . .18.00 to 22.00
Measuring Cup, 8 Oz. . . . .40.00
Measuring Cup, 16 Oz. . . .25.00
Mug, 7 Oz. . . . . . . . . . . .30.00
Nurser, 8 Oz. . . . . . . . . .30.00
Percolator Top, 2 1/8 In. . . .5.00
Pie Plate, 8 3/8 In. . .6.00 to 9.00
Pie Plate,
9 5/8 In. . . . . . . .8.00 to 11.00
Pie Plate, 9 In. . . . .8.00 to 20.00
Pie Plate, Juice Saver,
10 3/8 In. . . . . . . . . . .170.00
Roaster,
8 3/4 In. . . . . . .25.00 to 90.00
Roaster, 10 3/8 In. . . . . .45.00
Utility Pan,
10 1/2 x 2 In. . . . . . . . .14.00

**CRYSTAL**
Baker, Individual, 6 Oz. . . .5.50
Custard Cup, 6 Oz. . . . . . .2.00
Grease Jar, Cover, Black
Dot . . . . . . . . . . . . . . .35.00
Hot Plate, Tab Handles . . .16.00

**IVORY**
Batter Bowl, Handle,
1-In. Band . . . . . . . . . .18.00
Bowl, 5 3/8 In. . . . . . . . . .8.00
Casserole, Knob Cover,
1 1/2 Qt. . . . . .8.00 to 15.00
Casserole, Knob Cover,
2 Qt. . . . . . . . . . . . . .15.00
Cup & Saucer, St. Dennis . .7.00
Custard Cup, 6 Oz. . . . . . .2.50

Glasses decorated
with colorful comic or
sports figures are often
given away as promotions. But be careful—
they may fade in
sunlight or when washed
in the dishwasher.

Grease Jar,
Tulip . . . . . . .20.00 to 25.00
Hot Plate, Tab Handles . . .18.00
Mixing Bowl, 8 In. . . . . . .12.00
Mixing Bowl, Blue
Gazelle, Large . . . . . . .35.00
Mixing Bowl Set, Apple,
4 Piece . . . . . . . . . . . .100.00
Mixing Bowl Set, Brown
Dots, 7, 6 & 4 1/2 In.,
3 Piece . . . . . . . . . . . .35.00
Mixing Bowl Set, Red
Dot, 4 Piece . . . . . . . . .100.00
Pie Plate, Individual,
4 3/8 In. . . . . . . . . . . . .16.00
Refrigerator Jar, Cover,
4 1/8 x 4 1/8 In. . . . . . . .9.00

**JADITE**
Batter Bowl . . . .20.00 to 35.00
Mixing Bowl, 8 3/8 In. . . . .9.00
Refrigerator Jar, Crystal
Cover, 4 x 4 In. . . . . . .12.00
Skillet . . . . . . . . . . . . . .20.00

**FLAT DIAMOND,** see Diamond Quilted

## FLEURETTE

Fleurette is a white Fire-King pattern with decal decoration.
Bowl, Dessert, 4 3/8 In. . . .3.00
Creamer . . . . . . . . . . . . .2.00
Plate, Bread & Butter,
6 1/4 In. . . . . . . . . . . . .2.00
Plate, Dinner, 9 1/8 In. . . . .5.00
Plate, Salad, 7 3/8 In. . . . .3.00
Saucer . . . . . . . . . . . . . . .75
Serva-Snack Set, 2 Piece . .2.50

## FLORAGOLD

The iridescent marigold color of carnival glass was copied in this 1950s pattern made by Jeannette Glass Company, Jeannette, Pennsylvania. The pattern is called Floragold or Louisa, the name of the original carnival glass pattern that was copied. Pieces were made in Crystal, Iridescent, Ice Blue, Shell Pink, and Reddish Yellow.

**CRYSTAL**

Berry Bowl, Square,
4 1/2 In. . . . . . . . .3.50 to 8.00

Bowl, Cereal, 5 1/2 In. . . . .6.00

Bowl, Deep,
9 1/2 In. . . . . . .38.00 to 42.50

Bowl, Fruit, Ruffled,
5 1/2 In. . . . . . . . .7.00 to 8.00

Bowl, Fruit, Ruffled,
12 In. . . . . . . . .8.00 to 10.00

Bowl, Salad, Ruffled,
9 1/2 In. . . . . . .8.00 to 10.00

Butter, Cover,
1/4 Lb. . . . . . .22.00 to 38.00

Butter, Cover,
Round . . . . . .40.00 to 42.50

Candlestick, 2-Light,
Pair . . . . . . . . . . . . . .47.50

Candy Dish, Cover,
5 1/4 In. . . . . . .45.00 to 50.00

Candy Dish, Cover,
6 3/4 In. . . . . . . . . . . . .50.00

Coaster, 4 In. . . . .4.75 to 10.00

Creamer . . . . . . .7.00 to 22.00

Cup . . . . . . . . . . .4.75 to 6.00

Cup & Saucer . .15.00 to 18.00

Pitcher, Water,
64 Oz. . . . . . . .33.00 to 40.00

Plate, Bread & Butter,
5 3/4 In. . . . . . .10.00 to 12.00

Plate, Dinner,
8 1/2 In. . . . . . .22.00 to 40.00

Plate, Sherbet, 5 1/2 In. . .11.00

Platter,
11 1/4 In. . . . . .22.00 to 28.00

Salt & Pepper, White
Plastic Cover . .45.00 to 52.00

Saucer . . . . . . .11.00 to 12.00

Sherbet, Footed . .13.00 to 14.00

Sugar, Cover . . . .17.00 to 22.00

Sugar & Creamer,
Cover . . . . . . . .23.00 to 25.00

Tray, 13 1/2 In. . .20.00 to 22.00

Tray, With Indentation,
13 1/2 In. . . . . . . . . . . .55.00

Tumbler, Iced Tea, Footed,
15 Oz. . . . . .90.00 to 100.00

Tumbler, Water, Footed,
10 Oz. . . . . . . .15.00 to 18.00

Tumbler, Water, Footed,
11 Oz. . . . . . . . . . . . . .16.00

Water Set, 7 Piece,
Box . . . . . . . . . . . . . .135.00

**IRIDESCENT**

Bowl, Fruit, Ruffled,
5 1/2 In. . . . . . . . . . . . . .7.00

Bowl, Ruffled, 9 1/2 In. . .35.00

Bowl, Square, 4 1/2 In. . . . .4.00

Butter, Cover,
1/4 Lb. . . . . . .16.50 to 22.00

Candlestick, 2-Light,
Pair . . . . . . . . .43.00 to 45.00

Candy Dish, Cover,
6 3/4 In. . . . . . . . . . . . .65.00

Candy Dish, Footed,
5 1/4 In. . . . . . . . . . . . . .8.50

Cup . . . . . . . . . . .5.00 to 8.00

Cup & Saucer . . . . . . . .13.00

Platter,
11 1/4 In. . . . . .19.00 to 22.00

Saucer, 5 1/4 In. . . . . . . .10.00

Sherbet, Footed . . . . . . . .15.00

Sugar, Cover . . . . . . . . . .14.00

Tray, 13 1/2 In. . .50.00 to 60.00

Tumbler, Water, Footed,
10 Oz. . . . . . . . . . . . . .11.00

**PINK**

Tumbler, Water, Footed,
10 Oz. . . . . . . . . . . . . .15.00

## FLORAL

Poinsettia blossoms are the decorations on Floral patterns made by Jeannette Glass Company from 1931 to 1935. Green is the most common color, although the pattern was also made in Amber, Crystal, Delphite, Green, Jadite, Pink, Red, and Yellow. Reproductions have been made. They are listed at the end of the Depression Glass section.

**CRYSTAL**

Candy Dish, Cover . . . . .22.00

Lemonade Set, 48 Oz.
Pitcher, 6 Piece . . . . .425.00

Sugar, Cover . . . . . . . . . .13.00

Tumbler, Juice, Footed,
5 In. . . . . . . . . . . . . . .19.00

**GREEN**

Bowl, 7 1/2 In. . .16.00 to 32.50

Bowl, Cover,
8 In. . . . . . . . .42.00 to 50.00

Bowl, Ruffled,
4 In. . . . . . . . .18.00 to 25.00

Bowl, Salad, Ruffled,
7 1/2 In. . . . . . . . . . . . .20.00

Bowl, Vegetable, Cover,
8 In. . . . . . . . . . . . . . .50.00

Butter, Cover . . . . . . . . .90.00

Candy Dish,
Cover . . . . . . .35.00 to 45.00

Candy Jar, Cover . . . . . .40.00

Coaster, 3 1/4 In. .7.00 to 10.00

Creamer . . . . . . . . . . . .15.00

Cup . . . . . . . . .13.00 to 16.00

Cup & Saucer . .22.00 to 28.00

Ice Tub, 3 1/2 In. . . . .1300.00

Pitcher, Juice, Cone,
32 Oz., 8 In. . . .33.00 to 39.00

Pitcher, Lemonade,
10 1/4 In. . . . . . . . . . .275.00
Pitcher, Milk, 24 Oz.,
5 1/2 In. . . . . . . . . . . .585.00
Plate, Dinner, 9 In. . . . . . .12.00
Plate, Salad, 8
In. . . . . . . . . .10.00 to 15.00
Plate, Sherbet,
6 In. . . . . . . . . . .7.50 to 9.00
Platter,
10 3/4 In. . . . . .18.00 to 25.00
Relish,
2 Sections . . . .19.00 to 20.00
Salt & Pepper, 6 In. . . . . .50.00
Salt & Pepper, Footed,
4 In. . . . . . . . . . . . . . . .52.00
Saucer . . . . . . . . .7.00 to 12.00
Sherbet . . . . . . . .18.00 to 22.00
Sugar, Cover . . . .29.00 to 34.00
Sugar & Creamer,
Cover . . . . . . . .37.00 to 43.00
Tumbler, Juice, Footed,
5 Oz., 4 1/4 In. . . . . . . .21.00
Tumbler, Juice, Footed, 7 Oz.,
4 3/4 In. . . . . . .21.00 to 23.00
Tumbler, Water, 9 Oz.,
4 1/2 In. . . . . . . . . . . .260.00
Tumbler, Water, Footed, 9 Oz.,
5 1/4 In. . . . . .47.50 to 55.00
Tumbler, Whiskey, Footed,
3 Oz., 3 1/2 In. . . . . . .400.00
Vase, 8 Sides, 6 7/8 In. . .500.00

### PINK
Berry Bowl,
4 In. . . . . . . . . .16.00 to 22.50
Bowl, Vegetable, Cover,
8 In. . . . . . . . .43.00 to 60.00
Butter, Cover . . . . . . . . .95.00
Candy Jar,
Cover . . . . . . .40.00 to 43.00
Coaster . . . . . . . . . . . . .16.50
Creamer . . . . . . .10.00 to 20.00
Cup . . . . . . . . . . . . . . . .12.50
Cup & Saucer . .23.00 to 33.00
Pitcher, Juice, Cone, 32 Oz.,
8 In. . . . . . . . .32.50 to 39.00
Plate, Salad,
8 In. . . . . . . . .11.00 to 17.00
Plate, Sherbet,
6 In. . . . . . . . . .6.00 to 10.00
Platter, Inner Rim,
9 In. . . . . . . . . . . . . . .195.00

Platter, Oval,
10 3/4 In. . . . . .12.00 to 24.00
Relish,
2 Sections . . . .12.00 to 17.00
Salt & Pepper,
4 In. . . . . . . . .45.00 to 50.00
Salt & Pepper,
6 In. . . . . . . . .45.00 to 59.00
Sherbet . . . . . . .15.00 to 20.00
Sugar, Cover . . . .15.00 to 26.00
Sugar & Creamer,
Cover . . . . . . . .40.00 to 50.00
Tray, Square, Closed
Handles, 6 In. . . . . . . . .75.00
Tumbler, Juice, Footed, 7 Oz.,
4 3/4 In. . . . . . .18.00 to 45.00
Tumbler, Water, Footed, 9 Oz.,
5 1/4 In. . . . . . .42.00 to 45.00

## FLORAL & DIAMOND BAND

Floral & Diamond Band was
made by the U.S. Glass Company from the late 1920s until
c.1937. It features a large center flower and pressed diamond
bands of edging. Luncheon sets
were made in varying shades of
Pink and Green, but Black,
Crystal, and Yellow colors
were also used. Some pieces
are Iridescent Marigold and are
considered carnival glass, called
Mayflower by the collectors.

### CRYSTAL
Tumbler, Iced Tea, 5 In. . .35.00

### GREEN
Berry Bowl,
4 1/2 In. . . . . . .7.00 to 11.00
Bowl, 8 In. . . . . .13.00 to 17.00
Butter, Cover . .120.00 to 125.00
Creamer, 4 3/4 In. . . . . . .26.00

Creamer, Small . . . . . . . .12.00
Pitcher, Water, 42 Oz.,
8 In. . . . . . . . . . . . . . .115.00
Plate, Sherbet, 6 In. . . . . .4.00
Sherbet . . . . . . . . . . . . . .7.00
Sugar, Small . . . . . . . . . .12.00
Tumbler, Water,
4 In. . . . . . . . .25.00 to 28.00

### PINK
Plate, Luncheon, 8 In. . . . .35.00
Sherbet . . . . . . . . . . . . . .9.00

**FLORAL RIM,** see Vitrock

## FLORENTINE NO. I

Florentine No. 1, also called
Poppy No. 1, is neither Florentine in appearance nor decorated with recognizable poppies.
The plates are hexagonal and
have scalloped edges, differen-
tiating them from Florentine
No. 2 which has round pieces.
The pattern was made by the
Hazel Atlas Glass Company
from 1932 to 1935 in Cobalt
Blue, Crystal, Green, Pink, and
Yellow. Reproductions have
been made. They are listed at
the end of the Depression Glass
section.

### COBALT BLUE
Sugar & Creamer,
Ruffled . . . . . . . . . . .125.00

## CRYSTAL

Bowl, Cover, Vegetable, Oval,
9 1/2 In. . . . . . .20.00 to 25.00
Creamer . . . . . . . .6.50 to 10.00
Cup . . . . . . . . . . . . . . . .6.50
Pitcher, Juice, Footed,
36 Oz., 6 1/2 In. . . . . . .40.00
Pitcher, Water, 48 Oz.,
7 1/2 In. . . . . . . . . . . . .70.00
Plate, Dinner,
10 In. . . . . . . . .10.00 to 15.00
Plate, Salad, 8 1/2 In. . . . . .7.00
Plate, Sherbet, Footed,
3 Oz. . . . . . . . . . . . . . . .4.00
Salt & Pepper . . .30.00 to 40.00
Soup, Cream . . . . . . . . . .15.00
Sugar . . . . . . . . . . . . . . .10.00
Sugar & Creamer . . . . . . .50.00

## GREEN

Ashtray,
5 1/2 In. . . . . . .21.00 to 22.00
Berry Bowl,
5 In. . . . . . . . . . .5.00 to 11.00
Berry Bowl, Master,
8 1/2 In. . . . . . .22.00 to 35.00
Bowl, Cereal, 6 In. . . . . . .33.00
Bowl, Vegetable, Cover,
Oval, 8 1/2 In. . . . . . . .36.00
Cup . . . . . . . . . . .6.00 to 10.00
Cup & Saucer . . . . . . . .12.00
Grill Plate, 10 In. . . . . . .12.00
Pitcher, 48 Oz., 7 1/2 In. . .63.00
Pitcher, Footed, 36 Oz.,
6 1/2 In. . . . . . .45.00 to 59.00
Plate, Dinner,
10 In. . . . . . . . .16.00 to 18.00
Plate, Salad,
8 1/2 In. . . . . . .6.00 to 12.00
Platter, Oval, 11 1/2 In. . .18.00
Punch Bowl, Base . . . . . .75.00
Salt & Pepper,
Footed . . . . . . .35.00 to 40.00
Saltshaker, Footed . . . . . .17.00
Saucer . . . . . . . . . . . . . . .3.00
Sherbet, Footed, 3 Oz. . . . .9.00
Sugar, Cover . . . . . . . . . .35.00
Sugar & Creamer,
Cover . . . . . . . .12.00 to 36.00
Tumbler, Juice, Footed, 5 Oz.,
3 1/4 In. . . . . . .15.00 to 18.00

## PINK

Berry Bowl, Master,
8 1/2 In. . . . . . . . . . . . .36.00

Butter, Cover . .160.00 to 225.00
Grill Plate,
10 In. . . . . . . . .16.00 to 18.00
Nut Cup, Ruffled . . . . . .20.00
Pitcher, Footed, 36 Oz.,
6 1/2 In. . . . . . . . . . . . .44.00
Plate, Dinner, 10 In. . . . .27.00
Platter, Oval, 11 1/2 In. . .21.00
Salt & Pepper, Footed . . . .65.00
Sherbet . . . . . . . . . . . . . .9.50
Sugar, Cover . . . . . . . . . .42.00
Sugar & Creamer . . . . . .20.00
Tumbler, Water, Footed,
9 Oz., 5 1/4 In. . . . . . . .25.00

## YELLOW

Berry Bowl, Master,
8 1/2 In. . . . . . . . . . . . .14.00
Bowl, Cereal, 6 In. . . . . .35.00
Butter, Cover . .140.00 to 170.00
Creamer . . . . . . . . . . . . .18.00
Gravy Boat,
Underplate . . . . . . . . .119.00
Grill Plate,
10 In. . . . . . . . .10.00 to 13.00
Pitcher, Juice, Footed, 36 Oz.,
6 1/2 In. . . . . . .40.00 to 45.00
Pitcher, Water, 48 Oz.,
7 1/2 In. . . . . . . . . . . . .154.00
Pitcher, Water, Footed,
48 Oz., 7 1/2 In. . . . . . .49.00
Plate, Dinner, 10 In. . . . .13.00
Plate, Salad,
8 1/2 In. . . . . . .9.00 to 13.00
Platter, Oval, 11 1/2 In. . .28.00
Sherbet . . . . . . . . . . . . .16.00
Sugar, Cover . . . . . . . . . .32.00
Tray, Condiment . . . . . . .95.00
Tumbler, Juice, Footed,
5 Oz., 3 3/4 In. . . . . . . .19.00
Tumbler, Water, Footed,
9 Oz., 5 1/2 In. . . . . . . .35.00

❖

**Never put hot glass in
cold water, or cold glass
in hot water. The tem-
perature change can
crack the glass.**

❖

# FLORENTINE NO. 2

Florentine No. 2, sometimes
called Poppy No. 2 or Oriental
Poppy, was also made by Hazel
Atlas Glass Company from
1934 to 1937. It has round
plates instead of the hexagonal
pieces of Florentine No. 1, and
larger and more prominent
flowers. It was made in Amber,
Cobalt Blue, Crystal, Green,
Ice Blue, and Pink. Reproductions have been made. They are
listed at the end of the Depression Glass section.

## AMBER

Berry Bowl, 4 1/2 In. . . . .20.00
Berry Bowl, Master,
8 In. . . . . . . . . .29.00 to 32.00
Bowl, 5 1/2 In. . . . . . . . .52.00
Bowl, Cereal,
6 In. . . . . . . . . .36.00 to 49.00
Bowl, Vegetable, Cover,
Oval, 9 In. . . . .70.00 to 78.00
Butter, Cover .129.00 to 160.00
Candlestick, 2 3/4 In. . . . .30.00
Candlestick, 2 3/4 In.,
Pair . . . . . . . . .60.00 to 72.00

Coaster,
3 1/4 In. . . . . . .21.00 to 27.50

Coaster, 5 1/2 In. . . . . . . .35.00

Creamer . . . . . . .10.00 to 20.00

Cup . . . . . . . . . . . . . . .10.00

Cup & Saucer . .12.00 to 15.00

Custard Cup . . . . . . . . . .108.00

Grill Plate,
10 1/4 In. . . . . .13.00 to 16.00

Parfait, 6 In. . . . .60.00 to 66.00

Pitcher, Juice, Cone, 28 Oz.,
7 1/2 In. . . . . . .25.00 to 36.00

Pitcher, Milk, Cone, 24 Oz.,
6 1/4 In. . . . . . . . . . . .185.00

Pitcher, Water, 48 Oz.,
7 1/2 In. . . . .150.00 to 206.00

Plate, Dinner,
10 In. . . . . . . . .10.00 to 17.00

Plate, Salad,
8 1/2 In. . . . . . .7.00 to 10.00

Plate, Sherbet,
6 In. . . . . . . . . . .3.00 to 8.00

Platter, For Gravy Boat,
12 In. . . . . . .95.00 to 100.00

Platter, Oval,
11 In. . . . . . . .16.00 to 22.00

Relish, 3 Sections,
10 In. . . . . . . .28.00 to 30.00

Salt & Pepper . . .48.00 to 55.00

Saucer . . . . . . . . . . . . . .5.00

Sherbet, Footed . .10.00 to 13.00

---❖---

**Having trouble with a stain in a glass bottle or vase? Fill the bottle with water, drop in an Alka-Seltzer, and let it soak for about 24 hours. Then rub the ring with a brush or a cloth. If the deposit is chemical, this treatment should remove it. If the ring is actually caused by etching of the glass, it cannot be removed unless the bottle is polished.**

---❖---

Soup, Cream,
5 In. . . . . . . . .20.00 to 24.00

Sugar . . . . . . . . . . . . . .11.00

Sugar, Cover . . . .34.00 to 43.00

Sugar &
Creamer . . . . .20.00 to 21.00

Sugar & Creamer,
Cover . . . . . . . . . . . . .40.00

Tray, Condiment . . . . . . .95.00

Tumbler, Iced Tea, 12 Oz.,
5 In. . . . . . . . .47.00 to 52.00

Tumbler, Juice, 5 Oz.,
3 1/4 In. . . . . . .13.00 to 18.00

Tumbler, Juice, Footed, 5 Oz.,
4 In. . . . . . . . .17.00 to 18.00

Tumbler, Water, 9 Oz.,
4 In. . . . . . . . .20.00 to 21.00

Tumbler, Water, Footed, 9 Oz.,
4 1/2 In. . . . . . .30.00 to 38.00

Vase, 6 In. . . . . . . . . . . .60.00

**CRYSTAL**

Berry Bowl,
4 1/2 In. . . . . . .10.00 to 16.00

Bowl, 6 In. . . . . . . . . . . .23.00

Candlestick, 2 3/4 In. . . . .25.00

Coaster,
3 1/4 In. . . . . . .12.00 to 13.00

Compote, Ruffled,
3 1/2 In. . . . . . . . . . . . .20.00

Creamer . . . . . . . . .6.00 to 8.00

Cup & Saucer . . .7.00 to 11.00

Nut Cup, Ruffled, 5 In. . . .18.00

Pitcher, Juice, Footed,
28 Oz., 7 1/2 In. . . . . . .25.00

Pitcher, Milk, Cone,
24 Oz., 6 1/4 In. . . . . . .30.00

Pitcher, Water, 48 Oz.,
7 1/2 In. . . . . .50.00 to 55.00

Plate, Dinner, 10 In. . . . . .10.00

Plate, Salad, 8 In. . .4.00 to 8.00

Plate, Sherbet,
6 In. . . . . . . . . . .4.00 to 5.00

Platter, Oval, 11 In. . . . . . .11.00

Salt & Pepper . . .40.00 to 42.50

Saucer . . . . . . . . . . . . . .3.00

Sherbet, Footed . . . . . . . .10.00

Soup, Cream . . . . .8.00 to 14.00

Sugar . . . . . . . . . .7.00 to 8.00

Sugar, Cover . . . . . . . . . .24.00

Tumbler, Iced Tea,
12 Oz., 5 In. . . . . . . . .25.00

Tumbler, Water, Footed, 9 Oz.,
4 1/2 In. . . . . . .13.00 to 26.00

Vase, 6 In. . . . . . . . . . . .25.00

**GREEN**

Berry Bowl,
4 1/2 In. . . . . . .13.00 to 15.00

Berry Bowl, Master,
8 In. . . . . . . . .23.00 to 26.00

Bowl, 5 1/2 In. . . . . . . . .15.00

Butter, Cover . . . . . . . . .100.00

Candlestick, Pair . . . . . . .50.00

Candy Dish,
Cover . . . . . . . . . . . . .95.00

Coaster,
3 1/4 In. . . . . . .15.00 to 20.00

Coaster,
5 1/2 In. . . . . . .14.00 to 17.50

Cup . . . . . . . . . . .7.50 to 9.00

Cup & Saucer . .11.00 to 12.00

Grill Plate . . . . . . . . . . .12.00

Pitcher, Juice, Cone,
Footed, 28 Oz.,
7 1/2 In. . . . . . .32.00 to 35.00

Plate, Dinner,
10 In. . . . . . . . .15.00 to 17.00

Plate, Salad,
8 1/2 In. . . . . . .8.50 to 10.00

Plate, Sherbet, 6 In. . . . . .4.00

Platter, Oval, 11 In. . . . . .16.00

Salt & Pepper,
Footed . . . . . .40.00 to 55.00

Saucer . . . . . . . . .3.00 to 5.00

Sherbet, Footed . . .9.00 to 10.00

Soup, Cream,
4 3/4 In. . . . . . .14.00 to 16.00

Sugar & Creamer . . . . . . .18.00

Tumbler, Iced Tea,
12 Oz., 5 In. . . . . . . . .45.00

Tumbler, Juice, Footed, 5 Oz.,
3 1/4 In. . . . . . .14.00 to 16.00

Tumbler, Juice, Footed,
6 Oz., 3 1/2 In. . . . . . .50.00

Tumbler, Water, 9 Oz.,
4 In. . . . . . . . .12.00 to 15.00

Tumbler, Water, Footed, 9 Oz.,
4 1/2 In. . . . . . .26.00 to 32.00

**PINK**

Berry Bowl, 4 1/2 In. . . . .17.00

Candy Dish,
Cover . . . . . .110.00 to 152.00

Compote, Ruffled,
3 1/2 In. . . . . . . . . . . . .25.00

Nut Cup, Ruffled,
  5 In. . . . . . . . .18.00 to 22.00
Pitcher, Water, 48 Oz.,
  7 1/2 In. . . . . . . . . . . .140.00
Tumbler, Juice, Footed, 5 Oz.,
  3 1/4 In. . . . . . .14.00 to 20.00
Tumbler, Water, 9 Oz.,
  4 In. . . . . . . . . . . . . . . .19.00

**FLOWER & LEAF BAND,** see
  Indiana Custard

**FLOWER BASKET,** see No. 615

---

## FLOWER GARDEN WITH BUTTERFLIES

There really is a butterfly hiding in the flower on this U.S. Glass Company pattern called Flower Garden with Butterflies, Butterflies and Roses, Flower Garden, or Wildrose with Apple Blossom. It was made in the late 1920s in a variety of colors, including Amber, Black, Blue, Canary Yellow, Crystal, Green, and Pink.

**BLUE**
Powder Jar, Cover,
  6 1/4 In. . . . . . . . . . . .220.00
**CANARY YELLOW**
Plate, Salad, Sterling
  Trim, 8 In. . . . . . . . . . .30.00
**CRYSTAL**
Powder Jar, 7 1/2 In. . . . . .80.00
**GREEN**
Compote . . . . . . . . . . . .25.00
Plate, Dinner, 10 In. . . . . .46.00

**PINK**
Bottle, Cologne,
  No Stopper . . . . . . . . .100.00
Powder Jar, Cover, Footed,
  7 1/2 In. . . . . . . . . . . .155.00

**FLOWER RIM,** see Vitrock

---

## FOREST GREEN

There is no need to picture Forest Green in a black-and-white drawing because it is the color that identifies the pattern. Anchor Hocking Glass Corporation, Lancaster, Ohio, made this very plain pattern from 1950 to 1957. Other patterns were also made in this same deep green color, but these are known by the pattern name.

Batter Bowl,
  Spout . . . . . . . .18.00 to 25.00
Bowl, 7 3/8 In. . .13.00 to 20.00
Bowl, Deep,
  5 1/4 In. . . . . . . . .8.00 to 9.00
Bowl, Popcorn . . . . . . . . .9.00
Bowl, Popcorn, 7 Piece . . .75.00
Bowl, Square,
  4 5/8 In. . . . . . . .4.50 to 5.50
Bowl, Vegetable, Square,
  7 3/8 In. . . . . . .15.00 to 22.00
Creamer . . . . . . . . . . . . .6.00
Cup . . . . . . . . . . . . . . . .5.00
Cup, For Snack Plate . . . . .9.00
Cup & Saucer,
  Square . . . . . . . .6.00 to 7.00
Mixing Bowl,
  6 In. . . . . . . . . .6.00 to 17.00
Pitcher, Milk, 22 Oz.,
  5 3/4 In. . . . . .22.00 to 22.50
Pitcher, Water, Round,
  86 Oz. . . . . . . . . . . . . .45.00
Plate, Bread & Butter, Square,
  6 5/8 In. . . . . . . .6.50 to 7.00
Plate, Dinner, Square,
  9 1/2 In. . . . . . . . . . . .12.00
Plate, Luncheon, Square,
  8 3/8 In. . . . . . . . . . . . .8.00
Platter, Rectangular,
  11 In. . . . . . .20.00 to 24.00

---

---

Punch Bowl Set,
  14 Piece . . . . .74.00 to 95.00
Punch Cup . . . . . . .1.50 to 2.50
Saucer . . . . . . . . . . . . . .1.50
Soup, Dish, Square,
  6 In. . . . . . . . . . . . . . .16.00
Sugar . . . . . . . . . . . . . . .6.00
Sugar & Creamer . . . . . . .10.00
Tumbler, Iced Tea,
  13 Oz. . . . . . . . . . . . . .6.00
Tumbler, Iced Tea, 15 Oz.,
  6 1/2 In. . . . . . . .6.00 to 10.00
Tumbler, Juice, 5 Oz.,
  3 1/2 In. . . . . . . . .3.00 to 4.00
Tumbler, Long Boy,
  15 Oz. . . . . . . . . . . . . .6.00
Tumbler, Water, 9 Oz.,
  4 3/4 In. . . . . . . . . . . . .4.00
Tumbler, Water, 11 Oz. . . .4.00
Vase, 6 3/8 In. . . . .3.50 to 9.00
Vase, 9 In. . . . . . . . . . . . .8.00

---

## FORTUNE

Anchor Hocking Glass Corporation made Fortune pattern in 1937 and 1938. The simple design was made in Crystal or Pink.

**CRYSTAL**
Candy Dish, Cover . . . . .22.00
**PINK**
Berry Bowl, 4 In. . .4.00 to 6.00
Bowl, Handle, 4 1/2 In. . . .4.00
Candy Dish, Cover . . . . . .25.00

Tumbler, Juice, 5 Oz.,
3 1/2 In. . . . . . . . . . . . .11.00
Tumbler, Water, 9 Oz.,
4 In. . . . . . . . .10.00 to 14.00

**FOSTORIA,** see American

## FRUITS

Pears, grapes, apples, and other fruits are displayed in small bunches on the pieces of Fruits pattern. Hazel Atlas Glass Company and several other companies made this pattern about 1931 to 1933. Pieces are known in Crystal, Green, Pink, and Iridescent finish.

### CRYSTAL
Berry Bowl, 5 In. . . . . . . .12.50
Cup . . . . . . . . . . . . . . . .7.50
Cup & Saucer . . . . . . . .13.50
Plate, Luncheon, 8 In. . . . . .7.00
Saucer . . . . . . . . . . . . . .4.50

### GREEN
Cup . . . . . . . . . . . . . . . .8.00
Cup & Saucer . .10.00 to 13.50
Pitcher, Water, 7 In. . . . . .70.00
Plate, Luncheon, 8 In. . . . . .6.50
Saucer . . . . . . . . . . . . . .5.00
Tumbler, Water, Cherry,
4 In. . . . . . . . . . . . . . .25.00

---

**Spray the inside
of a glass flower vase
with a nonstick cooking
spray. This will keep
the vase from staining
if water is left in it
too long.**

---

## ·G·

## GAME BIRD

Game Bird, sometimes called Wild Bird, was made by Anchor Hocking Glass Corporation from about 1959 to 1962. The opaque white glass was decorated with a decal of a bird.

### CANADA GOOSE
Mug, 8 Oz. . . . . .5.50 to 10.00
Tumbler . . . . . . . . . . . . .12.50

### MALLARD DUCK
Mug, 8 Oz. . . . . .5.50 to 10.00
Tumbler . . . . . . . . . . . . .12.50

### RING-NECKED PHEASANT
Tumbler . . . . . . . . . . . . .12.50

### RUFFLED GROUSE
Mug, 8 Oz. . . . . .5.50 to 10.00
Mug Set, 4 Piece . . . . . .25.00
Tumbler . . . . . . . . . . . . .12.50

---

## GEORGIAN

Georgian, also known as Lovebirds, was made by the Federal Glass Company, Columbus, Ohio, from 1931 to 1936. The pattern shows alternating sections with birds in one and a basket of flowers in the next, or may have no lovebirds. Dinner sets were made mostly in Crystal, although Green pieces were also manufactured. Notice that it is mold-etched and in no way resembles the Fenton glass pattern called Georgian, listed in this book as Georgian Fenton. Reproduc-

tions have been made. They are listed at the end of the Depression Glass section.

### CRYSTAL
Berry Bowl, Master,
7 1/2 In. . . . . . . . . . . . .60.00
Bowl, Cereal, 5 3/4 In. . . .22.50
Bowl, Vegetable, Oval,
9 In. . . . . . . . . . . . . . .60.00
Butter, Cover . . . . . . . . .70.00
Platter, Closed Handles,
11 1/2 In. . . . . . . . . . . .65.00
Sherbet, Footed . . . . . . . .12.00
Sugar & Creamer, Footed,
4 In. . . . . . . . . . . . . . .25.00

### GREEN
Berry Bowl,
4 1/2 In. . . . . . . .5.00 to 10.00
Bowl, Cereal,
5 3/4 In. . . . . . .16.00 to 26.00
Bowl, Deep,
6 1/2 In. . . . . . .60.00 to 75.00
Bowl, Oval, Salad,
9 In. . . . . . . . .60.00 to 75.00
Butter, Cover . . .70.00 to 85.00
Coaster, Hot Plate, 5 In. . .30.00
Creamer, Footed,
3 In. . . . . . . . . .4.00 to 11.00
Creamer, Footed, 4 In. . . .15.00
Cup . . . . . . . . . . . . . . .10.00
Cup & Saucer . .12.00 to 14.00
Plate, Dinner, 9 1/4 In. . . .32.00
Plate, Luncheon,
8 In. . . . . . . . . .8.00 to 11.00
Plate, Sherbet,
6 In. . . . . . . . . . .5.00 to 8.00
Platter, Closed Handles,
11 1/2 In. . . . . .49.00 to 75.00
Saucer . . . . . . . . . . . . . .3.00
Sherbet . . . . . . .9.00 to 15.00
Sugar, Cover, Footed,
3 In. . . . . . . . . .35.00 to 53.00

Sugar, Footed,
4 In. . . . . . . . .10.00 to 22.00
Sugar & Creamer, Cover,
Footed, 4 In. . . .25.00 to 63.00
Tumbler, Iced Tea,
12 Oz. . . . . .135.00 to 165.00
Tumbler, Juice, 4 In. . . . . .57.00
Tumbler, Water, 9 Oz.,
4 In. . . . . . . . .55.00 to 70.00

**GLADIOLA,** see Royal Lace

## GLORIA

Gloria is an etched glass pattern made by Cambridge Glass Company about 1930. It is similar to the Tiffin pattern called Flanders. Gloria was made in Amber, Crystal, Emerald Green, Green, Heatherbloom (pink-purple), Pink, and Yellow. Full dinner sets were made as well as serving pieces, vases, and candlesticks.

**CRYSTAL**
Bowl, Salad, Tab Handle,
9 In. . . . . . . . . . . . . . .25.00
Cup, Square, Footed . . . .25.00
Plate, Bread & Butter,
6 In. . . . . . . . . . . . . . . .5.00

**Dental wax (ask your dentist about it) is a good adhesive to keep figurines on shelves or lids on teapots.**

**GREEN**
Bowl, Salad, Square,
6 In. . . . . . . . . . . . . . .12.00
Plate, Dinner,
9 1/2 In. . . . . . .70.00 to 75.00
**YELLOW**
Bowl, 2 Handles, 10 In. . .70.00
Bowl, Gold Trim, 13 In. . .75.00
Plate, Dinner, 9 1/2 In. . . .75.00
Plate, Salad, 7 1/2 In. . . . .20.00
Platter, 11 1/2 In. . . . . . .120.00

**GRAPE,** see also Woolworth

## GRAY LAUREL

Gray Laurel is a Fire-King dinnerware made by Anchor Hocking Glass Corporation in 1953. The pattern has a laurel leaf design around the edge of the plates and bowls and the side of the cups. The pieces are Gray. The same pattern of laurel leaves was made in a lustrous orange-yellow color from 1952 to 1963 and was known as Peach Lustre. Bubble and Boopie pattern crystal stemware was made with a similar design to go with the dinnerware.

Bowl, Dessert, 4 7/8 In. . . .3.00
Creamer, Footed . . . . . . . .4.00
Cup . . . . . . . . . . . . . . . .3.00

Custard Cup, 6 Oz. . . . . . . .3.00
Plate, Dinner, 9 1/8 In. . . . .5.00
Saucer . . . . . . . . . . . . . .2.00
Sugar, Footed . . . . . . . . . .4.00
Sugar & Creamer, Footed . .4.00

**·H·**

**HAIRPIN,** see Newport
**HANGING BASKET,** see No. 615

## HARP

The pattern name Harp describes the small lyre-shaped instruments that are included on the borders of these pieces of glass. This Jeannette Glass Company pattern was made from 1954 to 1957. Pieces are found in Crystal, Crystal with gold trim, Light Blue, and Pink.

**CRYSTAL**
Cake Stand,
9 In. . . . . . . . .18.00 to 25.00
Cake Stand, Gold Trim,
9 In. . . . . . . . . . . . . . .15.00
Coaster, Gold
Trim . . . . . . . . .3.00 to 4.00
Cup . . . . . . . . . . . . . . . .25.00
Cup & Saucer . . . . . . . .35.00
Cup & Saucer,
Gold Trim . . . .18.00 to 35.00
Plate, Bread & Butter,
7 In. . . . . . . . . . . . . . .10.50
Plate, Bread & Butter, Gold
Trim, 7 In. . . . .10.00 to 14.00
Tray, Rectangular . . . . . .30.00
Vase, 6 In. . . . . . .18.00 to 30.00
Vase, Gold Trim,
6 In. . . . . . . . .17.00 to 18.00
**PINK**
Cake Stand, 9 In. . . . . . .35.00
Cake Stand, Gold Trim,
9 In. . . . . . . . . . . . . . .22.00

## HERITAGE

Federal Glass Company, Columbus, Ohio, made Heritage in the 1930s through the 1960s. Evidently the serving pieces were made in Blue, Light Green, and Pink, but the plates and dinnerware pieces were made only in Crystal. Amber and Crystal reproduction bowls were made in 1987.

### CRYSTAL
Berry Bowl, 5 In. . .5.00 to 8.00
Berry Bowl, Master,
  8 1/2 In. . . . . . .35.00 to 40.00
Bowl,
  10 1/2 In. . . . . .10.00 to 17.00
Cup . . . . . . . . . . .4.00 to 8.00
Cup & Saucer . . .7.00 to 13.00
Plate, Dinner, 9 1/4 In. . . .12.00
Plate, Luncheon,
  8 In. . . . . . . . . . .8.00 to 9.00
Sandwich Server,
  12 In. . . . . . . . . . . . . . .13.00
Saucer . . . . . . . . . . . . . . .3.00
Sugar . . . . . . . . .20.00 to 22.50
Sugar & Creamer,
  Cover . . . . . . . . . . . . .33.00

**HEX OPTIC,** see Hexagon Optic

## HEXAGON OPTIC

Hexagon Optic, also called Honeycomb or Hex Optic, really does have an accurate, descriptive name. Pink or Green sets of kitchenware were made in this pattern by Jeannette Glass Company, Jeannette, Pennsylvania, from 1928 to 1932. In the years near

1960 some Iridescent sets and some Ultramarine (blue-green) pieces were made.

### GREEN
Cup . . . . . . . . . . . . . . . . .4.00
Cup & Saucer . . . . . . . . . .6.00
Pitcher, Water, Footed,
  48 Oz., 9 In. . . . . . . . .44.00
Plate, Breakfast,
  8 In. . . . . . . . . . .5.00 to 6.00
Tumbler, Water, 9 Oz.,
  3 3/4 In. . . . . . . . . . . . . .2.00

### PINK
Tumbler, Iced Tea, Footed,
  7 In. . . . . . . . . . . . . . . .5.50

**HEXAGON TRIPLE BAND,** see Colony

**HINGE,** see Patrician

## HOBNAIL

Hobnail is the name of this pattern, although many similar patterns have been made with the hobbed decorations. Hocking Glass Company, Lancaster, Ohio, made this pattern from 1934 to 1936, and it can be distinguished from other hobbed patterns by a honeycomb design with long sides and pointed ends. Mostly Crystal or Pink beverage sets were made. Some pieces were made with red rims or black feet.

### CRYSTAL
Bowl, Cereal,
  5 1/2 In. . . . . . . . .4.00 to 7.00
Cup . . . . . . . . . . . . . . . . .4.00

Pitcher, Water, 67 Oz. . . .22.00
Plate, Luncheon, 8 In. . . . . .4.00
Plate, Sherbet, 6 In. . . . . . .2.50
Salt & Pepper . . . . . . . . .55.00
Sherbet . . . . . . . . . . . . . .3.00
Tumbler, Juice, 5 Oz. . . . . .4.00
Tumbler, Water, 9 Oz. . . . .5.50
Tumbler, Wine, Footed,
  3 Oz. . . . . . . . . . . . . . . .8.00
Tumbler, Wine, Red
  Trim, 3 Oz. . . . . . . . . . .5.00
Whiskey,
  1 1/2 Oz. . . . . . .3.50 to 6.00

### PINK
Basket . . . . . . . . . . . . . .85.00
Cup . . . . . . . . . . . . . . . . .8.00
Goblet, Cocktail,
  3 Oz. . . . . . . . . . . . . . .45.00
Goblet, Water, 9 Oz. . . . . .45.00
Plate, Luncheon,
  8 1/2 In. . . . . . . . . . . . .30.00
Plate, Sherbet, 6 In. . . . . . .3.50
Saucer . . . . . . . . . . . . . . .2.50
Sherbet . . . . . . . . . . . . . .7.00
Tumbler, Water,
  10 Oz. . . . . . . . . . . . . .40.00

**HOBNAIL,** see also Moonstone

## HOLIDAY

Holiday is one of the later Depression glass patterns. It was made from 1947 through 1949 by Jeannette Glass Company. The pattern is found in dinnerware sets of Crystal, Iridescent, and Shell Pink (opaque). A few pieces of Opaque Shell Pink were made. The pattern is sometimes also called Buttons & Bows or Russian.

### CRYSTAL
Berry Bowl, 5 1/8 In. . . . .12.00
Bowl, Vegetable, Oval,
9 1/2 In. . . . . . . . . . . . .28.00
Butter  . . . . . . . . . . . . . .38.00
Creamer  . . . . . . . . . . . . .8.00
Cup  . . . . . . . . . . . . . . . . .7.00
Pitcher, Milk, 16 Oz.,
4 3/4 In. . . . . . . . . . . . . .65.00
Plate, Dinner, 9 In. . . . . . .16.00
Plate, Sherbet, 6 In. . . . . .5.00
Platter, Oval, 11 3/8 In. . .22.00
Saucer  . . . . . . . . . . . . . . .4.00
Sherbet  . . . . . . . . . . . . . .6.00
Soup, Dish, 7 3/4 In. . . . . .60.00
Sugar, Cover . . . . . . . . . .25.00
Tumbler, Juice, Footed,
4 In. . . . . . . . . . . . . . . .50.00
Tumbler, Water, 10 Oz.,
4 In. . . . . . . . . . . . . . . .20.00

### IRIDESCENT
Berry Bowl, 5 1/8 In. . . . . .9.00
Platter, Oval, 11 3/8 In. . . .9.00
Tumbler, Juice, Footed,
4 In. . . . . . . . . . . . . . . . .8.00

### PINK
Berry Bowl,
5 1/8 In. . . . . . .5.00 to 14.00
Bowl, Vegetable, Oval,
9 1/2 In. . . . . . .25.00 to 27.50
Butter, Cover  . . .38.00 to 40.00
Cake Plate, Footed,
10 1/2 In. . . .100.00 to 125.00
Candlestick,
3 In. . . . . . . . .42.00 to 55.00
Candlestick, 3 In.,
Pair  . . . . . . .110.00 to 115.00
Creamer, Footed  . .6.00 to 12.50
Cup  . . . . . . . . . .4.00 to 12.00
Cup & Saucer  . .12.00 to 13.00
Pitcher, Milk, 16 Oz.,
4 3/4 In. . . . . .48.00 to 65.00
Pitcher, Water, 52 Oz.,
6 3/4 In. . . . . .35.00 to 38.00
Plate, Bread & Butter,
6 In. . . . . . . . . . . . . . . . .6.00

Plate, Dinner,
9 In. . . . . . . . .12.00 to 22.00
Plate, Sherbet,
6 In. . . . . . . . . . .5.00 to 6.50
Platter, Oval,
11 3/8 In. . . . .16.00 to 22.50
Sandwich Tray,
10 1/2 In. . . . . . . . . . . .25.00
Saucer  . . . . . . . . .4.00 to 5.00
Saucer, Ring . . . . . . . . . . .4.50
Sherbet  . . . . . . . .6.00 to 7.00
Soup, Dish,
7 3/4 In. . . . . .40.00 to 59.00
Sugar &
Creamer  . . . .18.00 to 19.00
Sugar & Creamer,
Cover . . . . . . .33.00 to 35.00
Tumbler, Iced Tea, Footed,
6 In. . . . . . .150.00 to 195.00
Tumbler, Juice, Footed,
4 In. . . . . . . . 40.00 to 55.00
Tumbler, Water, 10 Oz.,
4 In. . . . . . . . .20.00 to 25.00

## HOMESPUN

Homespun, often called Fine
Rib, is a cause of confusion.
Jeannette Glass Company
made Crystal, Light Blue, and
Pink pieces in this pattern in
1939 and 1940. Hazel Atlas
Glass Company made other
pieces in Crystal and Cobalt
Blue. Homespun made by
Jeannette Glass Company is
listed here.

### BLUE
Pitcher, Juice, 96 Oz. . . . .65.00
Tumbler, Iced Tea, Footed,
13 Oz., 5 1/4 In. . . . . . .27.00
Tumbler, Juice, Footed,
5 Oz., 4 In. . . . .12.00 to 14.50

### PINK
Berry Bowl, Master,
8 1/4 In. . . . . . . . . . . . . .80.00
Bowl, Closed Handles,
4 1/2 In. . . . . . .10.00 to 12.00
Butter  . . . . . . . . . . . . . .15.00
Cup  . . . . . . . . .10.00 to 12.00
Cup & Saucer  . .14.00 to 18.00
Plate, Dinner,
9 1/4 In. . . . . . .15.00 to 17.00
Plate, Sherbet,
6 In. . . . . . . . . . .6.00 to 7.00
Platter, Closed Handles,
Oval, 13 In. . . . . . . . . .25.00
Saucer  . . . . . . . . . . . . . . .5.50
Sherbet  . . . . . . . . . . . . .16.00
Sugar  . . . . . . . . . . . . . .12.00
Sugar & Creamer  . . . . . .32.00
Tumbler, Iced Tea, Footed,
15 Oz., 6 1/2 In.  . . . . .30.00
Tumbler, Juice, Footed,
5 Oz., 4 In. . . . .6.00 to 11.00
Tumbler, Water, 9 Oz.,
4 In. . . . . . . . . . . . . . . .20.00
Tumbler, Water, Footed,
9 Oz., 6 1/4 In.  . . . . . .30.00

**HONEYCOMB,** see Hexagon
Optic

**HORIZONTAL ROUNDED BIG RIB,**
see Manhattan

**HORIZONTAL FINE RIB,** see
Manhattan

**HORIZONTAL RIBBED,** see
Manhattan

**HORIZONTAL SHARP BIG RIB,** see
Manhattan

**HORSESHOE,** see No. 612

❖

**Don't turn on the porch
light if you will be gone
for a long time. It tells
everyone that you are
away. Install a photo-
electric cell light that
automatically turns on
at dusk and off at
daylight, or install a
gaslight.**

❖

# INDIANA CUSTARD

The design makes the old name Flower & Leaf Band clear, but collectors prefer to call this pattern Indiana Custard. It is an opaque glassware of Custard color and Ivory made by the Indiana Glass Company. Primarily luncheon sets were made from the 1930s to the 1950s. Some pieces have bands that are decorated with pastel colors or decal designs. The same pattern was made of Milk Glass in 1957. It was called Orange Blossom.

**IVORY**

Berry Bowl,
  5 1/2 In. . . . . . .10.00 to 14.00

Berry Bowl, Master,
  9 In. . . . . . . . . . . . . . .32.00

Bowl, Vegetable, Oval,
  9 1/2 In. . . . . . .32.50 to 35.00

Butter, Cover . . .45.00 to 72.00

Creamer . . . . . . . . . . . . .6.00

Cup & Saucer . . . . . . . . .7.00

Plate, Dinner, 9 3/4 In. . . .28.00

Platter, Oval, 11 1/2 In. . .36.00

---

**Don't put glass with an iridescent finish in the dishwasher. The hot water and soap will remove the finish.**

---

Saucer . . . . . . . .8.00 to 12.00
Sugar . . . . . . . . . . . . . . .15.00
Sugar, Cover . . . .25.00 to 34.00

---

# IRIS

The design of Iris is unusually bold for Depression glass. Molded representations of stalks of iris fill the center of a ribbed plate. Other pieces in the pattern show fewer irises, but the flower is predominant. Edges of pieces may be ruffled or beaded. It was made by Jeannette Glass Company, Jeannette, Pennsylvania, from 1928 to 1932 and then again in the 1950s and 1970s. Early pieces were made in Crystal, Green, Iridescent, and Pink; later pieces were made in Blue-Green, Green, Red-Yellow, or White. The pattern is also called Iris & Herringbone. Reproduction candy vases have been made in a variety of colors since 1977.

**CRYSTAL**

Berry Bowl, Beaded Edge,
  4 1/2 In. . . . . . .38.00 to 42.00

Berry Bowl, Beaded Edge,
  Master, 8 In. . .80.00 to 125.00

Bowl, Cereal,
  5 In. . . . . . . .115.00 to 125.00

Bowl, Fruit, Ruffled,
  11 In. . . . . . . . .20.00 to 58.00

Bowl, Fruit, Straight Edge,
  11 In. . . . . . . . .57.50 to 60.00

Bowl, Salad, Ruffled,
  9 1/2 In. . . . . . . . . . . . .13.00

Butter, Cover . . .47.50 to 55.00

Candlestick,
  Pair . . . . . . . . .38.00 to 40.00

Candy Jar,
  Cover . . . . . .145.00 to 165.00

Coaster . . . . . .110.00 to 112.00

Creamer . . . . . . . . . . . . .12.00

Cup . . . . . . . . . .15.00 to 18.00

Cup, After
  Dinner . . . . . . .28.00 to 50.00

Cup & Saucer . . .25.00 to 30.00

Cup & Saucer, After
  Dinner . . . . . . . . . . . .225.00

Goblet, Cocktail, 3 Oz.,
  4 1/4 In. . . . . . .14.00 to 24.50

Goblet, Cocktail, 4 Oz.,
  5 3/4 In. . . . . . .22.00 to 25.00

Goblet, Water, 8 Oz.,
  5 3/4 In. . . . . . .23.00 to 29.50

Goblet, Wine,
  4 In. . . . . . . . .15.00 to 16.00

Nut Set . . . . . . . . . . . . .98.00

Pitcher, Water, Footed,
  9 1/2 In. . . . . . .35.00 to 40.00

Plate, Dinner,
  9 In. . . . . . . . .50.00 to 58.00

Plate, Luncheon,
  8 In. . . . . . . . . . . . . .125.00

Plate, Sherbet,
  5 1/2 In. . . . . . .14.00 to 15.00

Sandwich Server,
  11 3/4 In. . . . . .25.00 to 32.00

Sauce Bowl, Ruffled,
  5 In. . . . . . . . . . .6.00 to 9.00

Saucer . . . . . . .12.00 to 18.00

Saucer, After Dinner . . . .160.00

Sherbet, Footed,
  2 1/2 In. . . . . . .25.00 to 32.00

Sherbet, Footed,
  4 In. . . . . . . . .21.00 to 23.00

Soup, Dish,
  7 1/2 In. . . . .155.00 to 175.00

Sugar &
  Creamer . . . . .25.00 to 35.00

Sugar & Creamer,
  Cover . . . . . . . .35.00 to 45.00

Tumbler, 4 In. . . . . . . . .130.00

Tumbler, 4 Oz.,
   5 1/2 In. . . . . . . . . . . . .25.00

Tumbler, Iced Tea, Footed,
   6 In. . . . . . . . .16.00 to 32.00

Vase, 9 In. . . . . .28.00 to 32.50

### IRIDESCENT

Berry Bowl, Beaded Edge,
   4 1/2 In. . . . . . . .9.00 to 12.00

Berry Bowl, Master,
   Beaded Edge, 8 In. . . . .22.50

Bowl, Fruit, Ruffled,
   11 In. . . . . . . . .11.00 to 24.00

Bowl, Salad, Ruffled,
   9 1/2 In. . . . . . .13.00 to 18.00

Butter, Cover . . .40.00 to 42.00

Candlestick . . . . . . . . . .20.00

Candlestick, Pair . . . . . . .42.50

Creamer, Footed . .8.00 to 13.00

Cup . . . . . . . . . . . . . . . .14.00

Cup & Saucer . .20.00 to 25.00

Goblet, Wine,
   4 In. . . . . . . . .22.00 to 35.00

Pitcher, Water, Footed,
   9 1/2 In. . . . . . .36.00 to 40.00

Plate, Dinner,
   9 In. . . . . . . . .33.00 to 42.00

Plate, Sherbet,
   5 1/2 In. . . . . . . .7.50 to 13.00

Plate, Sherbet, Footed,
   4 In. . . . . . . . .13.00 to 15.00

Sandwich Server,
   11 3/4 In. . . . . .27.00 to 30.00

Sauce Bowl, Ruffled,
   5 In. . . . . . . . .21.00 to 25.00

Sauce Bowl Set, Ruffled,
   6 Piece . . . . . . . . . . . .115.00

Sherbet, Footed,
   2 1/2 In. . . . . . .11.00 to 14.00

Soup, Dish,
   7 1/2 In. . . . . . .58.00 to 60.00

Sugar, Cover . . . . . . . . . .20.00

Sugar & Creamer,
   Cover . . . . . . . . . . . . . .35.00

Tumbler, Iced Tea, Footed,
   6 In. . . . . . . . .14.00 to 22.00

Vase, Footed,
   9 In. . . . . . . . .20.00 to 27.00

**IRIS & HERRINGBONE,** see Iris

**IVEX,** see Chinex Classic;
   Cremax

# ·J·

## JADITE

Jadite is a color as well as a pattern. Kitchenware was made in Jadite from 1936 to 1938 by Jeannette Glass Company. A matching set of dinnerware in the same green glass was called Jane-Ray. These pieces are listed in their own section. All of the pieces of kitchenware made of Jadite were also made of a blue glass called Delphite, but it is incorrect to call any but the green dishes by the name Jadite. For more information about related patterns and colors, see Alice, Charm, Fire-King, Gray Laurel, Jane-Ray, Peach Lustre, Philbe, Swirl Fire-King, Turquoise Blue, and Wheat in this book.

Ashtray . . . . . . . . . . . . .20.00

Batter Bowl, Handle,
   7 1/2 In. . . . . . . . . . . . .24.00

Batter Jug, Cover . . . . . .395.00

Berry Bowl, 4 3/4 In. . . . . .4.00

Bowl, Cereal, 5 7/8 In. . . .16.00

Bowl, Dessert, 4 3/4 In. . . .6.00

Bowl, Leaf, Handle . . . . . .8.00

Bowl, Rolled Lip, Deep,
   15 Oz. . . . . . . . . . . . . . .9.00

Canister, Coffee, Square,
   5 1/2 In. . . . . . . . . . . . .55.00

Canister, Spice, No Cover,
   2 x 3 In. . . . . . . . . . . . .25.00

Cup . . . . . . . . . . . . . . . . .5.00

Cup & Saucer . . . .3.00 to 6.00

Cup & Saucer, After
   Dinner . . . . . . . . . . . . .88.00

Eggcup . . . . . . . . . . . . .18.00

Jar, Grease, Round . . . . .32.00

Jug, Ball, Tilt . . . . . . . . .175.00

Leftover, Cover,
   8 1/2 x 4 1/2 In. . . . . . . .32.00

Leftover, Embossed Cover,
   5 x 9 In. . . . . . . . . . . . .40.00

Leftover, No Cover,
   4 1/2 x 5 1/2 In. . . . . . . .16.00

Measuring Cup,
   1/3 Cup Size . . . . . . . .32.00

Measuring Cup,
   1/4 Cup Size . . . . . . . .40.00

Mug, Chocolate,
   Flared Top . . . . . . . . . . .5.00

Mug, Coffee,
   7 Oz. . . . . . . . . .5.00 to 8.00

Plate, Bread & Butter,
   5 1/2 In. . . . . . . . . . . . . .4.25

Plate, Dinner,
   9 In. . . . . . . . . .6.00 to 11.00

Plate, Salad,
   6 3/4 In. . . . . . . .4.00 to 5.00

Plate, Salad, 6 In. . .4.50 to 9.00

Platter, 12 In. . . . . . . . . .15.00

Reamer, Lemon . . . . . . .35.00

Salt & Pepper . . . . . . . . .45.00

Salt & Pepper, Square . . . .27.00

Saucer . . . . . . . . . . . . . . .4.00

Saucer, After Dinner . . . . .40.00

Shaving Mug . . . . . . . . . . .8.00

Soup, Dish, Flanged,
   9 In. . . . . . . . . . . . . . . .50.00

Tom & Jerry Set,
   11 Piece . . . . . . . . . . .295.00

Water Dispenser,
   Refrigerator . . . . . . . . .325.00

## JAMESTOWN

Jamestown was made by the Fostoria Glass Company from 1958 to 1982. It was made in Amber, Amethyst, Blue, Crystal, Green, Pink, and Red.

**AMBER**

Bowl, Dessert, 6 In. . . . . .15.00

Goblet, 10 Oz. . . . .8.00 to 12.00

Nappy, 6 In. . . . . . . . . . . .8.00
Pitcher, Water, 48 Oz.,
7 In. . . . . . . . .50.00 to 90.00
Plate, Luncheon, 7 In. . . . . .5.00
Tumbler, Iced Tea,
12 Oz. . . . . . .10.00 to 15.00
Tumbler, Juice, 5 Oz. . . . . .9.00

### AMETHYST
Creamer . . . . . . . . . . . . .22.00
Goblet, 10 Oz.,
5 7/8 In. . . . . . .15.00 to 18.00
Tumbler, Iced Tea,
12 Oz., 6 In. . . . . . . . .18.00

### BLUE
Creamer . . . . . . . . . . . . .27.00
Goblet, 10 Oz.,
5 7/8 In. . . . . . .15.00 to 24.00
Sherbet . . . . . . . . . . . . .18.00
Tumbler, Ice Tea,
12 Oz., 6 In. . . . . . . . .22.00
Tumbler, Juice, 5 Oz.,
4 In. . . . . . . . . . . . . .15.00

### CRYSTAL
Plate, Salad, 8 In. . . . . . .15.00
Platter, 14 In. . . . . . . . .31.00

### GREEN
Goblet, Water, 10 Oz.,
5 7/8 In. . . . . . . . . . . . .9.50
Sherbet . . . . . . . . . . . . .12.00
Tumbler, Juice, 5 Oz.,
4 In. . . . . . . . . . . . . .20.00

### PINK
Plate, Luncheon, 7 In. . . . .24.00
Sherbet . . . . . . . . . . . . .22.00

### RED
Goblet, Water, 10 Oz.,
5 7/8 In. . . . . . . . . . . .20.00
Sherbet . . . . . . . . . . . . .16.00
Tumbler, Iced Tea,
12 Oz., 6 In. . . . . . . . .27.00

## JANE-RAY
Jane-Ray is a plain dinnerware with ribbed edge made of Jadite from 1945 to 1963 by Anchor Hocking Glass Corporation, Lancaster, Ohio. The matching kitchenware sets of the same green glass are called Jadite. Other related sections in this book are Alice, Charm, Fire-King, Gray Laurel, Jadite, Peach Lustre, Philbe, Swirl Fire-King, Turquoise Blue, and Wheat.

### JADITE
Bowl, Cereal,
5 7/8 In. . . . . . .8.00 to 12.00
Bowl, Dessert,
4 7/8 In. . . . . . . .5.00 to 6.00
Creamer . . . . . . . .5.00 to 6.00
Cup . . . . . . . . . . . . . . .3.00
Cup & Saucer . . . .3.00 to 6.00
Plate, Dinner,
9 1/8 In. . . . . . .5.00 to 11.00
Plate, Salad,
7 3/4 In. . . . . . . .5.00 to 9.00
Platter . . . . . . . .9.00 to 22.00
Saucer . . . . . . . . .1.50 to 4.00
Soup, Dish,
7 5/8 In. . . . . . .8.00 to 17.00
Sugar & Creamer, Cover .14.00

## JUBILEE
In the early 1930s the Lancaster Glass Company, Lancaster, Ohio, made this luncheon set decorated with etched flowers. It was made in a yellow shade, called Topaz, and in Pink. Collectors will find many similar patterns. The original Lancaster Jubilee had twelve petals and an open center on each flower.

### PINK
Bowl, Fruit, 9 In. . . . . . .50.00
Candlestick, Pair . . . . . . .50.00

### TOPAZ
Bowl, 3-Footed, Curved,
11 1/2 In. . . . . . . . . . .185.00
Creamer . . . . . . . . . . . . .20.00
Cup . . . . . . . . . . . . . . .14.00
Cup & Saucer . .20.00 to 25.00
Goblet, Water, 10 Oz.,
6 In. . . . . . . . .33.00 to 42.00
Mayonnaise, 16 Petals . .140.00
Pitcher, Water . . . . . . . .100.00
Plate, Luncheon,
8 3/4 In. . . . . . .12.00 to 17.00
Plate, Salad,
7 In. . . . . . . .10.00 to 14.00
Saucer . . . . . . . . .5.00 to 6.00
Sugar . . . . . . . . . . . . . .20.00
Sugar &
Creamer . . . . .35.00 to 40.00
Tray, 2 Handles,
11 In. . . . . . . .40.00 to 85.00
Tray, Center Handle,
11 In. . . . . . . . . . . . . .225.00

## JUNE
June is one of very few patterns that can be dated with some accuracy from the color. Fostoria Glass Company, Fostoria, Ohio, made full dinnerware sets but changed the color. From 1928 to 1944 the glass was Azure, Green, or Rose. Crystal was made from 1928 to 1952. If your set is Topaz, it dates from 1929 to 1938. Gold-tinted glass was made from 1938 to 1944. Pieces made of color with Crystal stems or bases were made only from 1931 to 1944. Reproductions have been made in Azure (blue), Crystal, Rose (pink), and Topaz (yellow). A liner is a plate that goes under a bowl or gravy boat.

## AZURE

| | |
|---|---|
| Ashtray | .75.00 |
| Bouillon, Footed | .75.00 |
| Bowl, 5 In. | .55.00 |
| Candy, 3 Sections | .185.00 |
| Compote | .145.00 |
| Cup & Saucer | .42.50 |
| Finger Bowl | .95.00 |
| Finger Bowl Liner, 6 In. | .25.00 |
| Goblet, Champagne, 6 Oz., 6 In. | .50.00 to 55.00 |
| Goblet, Water, 8 1/4 In. | .80.00 |
| Ice Bucket | .225.00 |
| Nut Dish | .95.00 |
| Plate, Lemon | .45.00 |
| Plate, Luncheon, 8 1/4 In. | .24.00 |
| Plate, Salad, 7 1/2 In. | .18.50 |
| Salt & Pepper | .175.00 to 250.00 |
| Sherbet, High | .50.00 |
| Sherbet, Low, 6 Oz., 4 1/4 In. | .37.50 |
| Tumbler, Iced Tea, Footed, 6 In. | .72.50 |

## CRYSTAL

| | |
|---|---|
| Berry Bowl, 5 In. | .20.00 |
| Compote, 4 In. | .45.00 |
| Cup & Saucer | .20.00 to 45.00 |
| Finger Bowl, Liner, 6 In. | .35.00 |
| Grapefruit, Liner | .125.00 |
| Ice Bucket, Tongs | .85.00 |
| Pitcher | .495.00 |
| Plate, Salad, 7 1/2 In. | .7.00 |
| Platter, 12 In. | .75.00 |
| Sherbet, Low, 6 Oz., 4 1/4 In. | .20.00 |
| Tumbler, Water, Footed, 5 1/4 In. | .20.00 |

## ROSE

| | |
|---|---|
| Baker, Oval, 9 1/2 In. | .175.00 |
| Bowl, 5 In. | .50.00 to 60.00 |
| Goblet, Champagne | .47.50 |
| Goblet, Wine, 3 Oz. | .95.00 |
| Plate, Bread & Butter, 6 In. | .12.00 |
| Relish, Divided | .65.00 |
| Salt & Pepper, Footed, Glass Cover | .245.00 |

| | |
|---|---|
| Sauceboat | .275.00 |
| Sherbet, High, 6 Oz., 6 In. | .48.00 |
| Sherbet, Low, 6 Oz., 4 1/4 In. | .25.00 |
| Torte Plate, 14 In. | .95.00 |
| Tumbler, Iced Tea, Footed, 6 In. | .70.00 |
| Tumbler, Water, Footed, 5 1/4 In. | .52.50 |

## TOPAZ

| | |
|---|---|
| Ashtray | .55.00 |
| Berry Bowl, 5 In. | .35.00 |
| Candlestick, 3 In. | .37.50 |
| Compote, 6 In. | .85.00 |
| Creamer, Footed | .30.00 |
| Cup, After Dinner | .30.00 |
| Cup & Saucer | .35.00 to 40.00 |
| Finger Bowl | .42.50 |
| Finger Bowl Liner | .12.00 |
| Goblet, Champagne, 6 Oz., 6 In. | .32.50 |
| Goblet, Claret, 4 Oz., 6 In. | .125.00 |
| Goblet, Cordial, 3/4 Oz., 4 In. | .150.00 |
| Ice Dish Liner | .20.00 to 32.50 |
| Mayonnaise, Footed, Liner | .100.00 to 120.00 |
| Parfait | .65.00 |
| Pitcher | .495.00 |
| Plate, Dinner, 9 1/2 In. | .45.00 |
| Plate, Dinner, 10 1/4 In. | .32.50 |
| Plate, Luncheon, 8 3/4 In. | .18.50 |
| Plate, Salad, 7 1/2 In. | .15.00 |
| Salt & Pepper | .155.00 |
| Saucer | .8.00 |
| Sherbet, High, 6 Oz., 6 In. | .28.00 |
| Sugar, Cover | .225.00 |
| Sugar & Creamer, Individual | .150.00 |
| Tray, Center Handle | .75.00 |
| Tumbler, Iced Tea, Footed, 6 In. | .47.50 to 50.00 |
| Tumbler, Water, Footed, 9 Oz., 5 1/4 In. | .22.00 to 32.00 |
| Whipped Cream Bowl | .45.00 |
| Whiskey, Footed | .75.00 |

**KNIFE & FORK**, see Colonial

## •L•

## LACE EDGE

To add to the confusion in the marketplace, this pattern, which is most often called Lace Edge, has been called Loop, Old Colony, Open Lace, or Open Scallop. The pieces themselves are often confused with other similar patterns, such as Imperial's Laced Edge, and cups or tumblers may also be mixed up with Queen Mary or Coronation. The Hocking pattern, made by Hocking Glass Company in Lancaster, Ohio, from 1935 to 1938, can usually be identified by the familiar sunburst base common to many of that company's designs. Most of the pieces of Lace Edge were made in Pink, although Crystal is also found.

## CRYSTAL

| | |
|---|---|
| Bowl, 9 1/2 In. | .27.00 |
| Bowl, Fruit, 8 1/4 In. | .40.00 |
| Bowl, Vegetable, 2 Sections | .135.00 |
| Butter, Cover | .72.00 |
| Candlestick, Pair | .550.00 |
| Creamer | .50.00 |
| Cup & Saucer | .60.00 |
| Grill Plate | .22.00 |
| Mayonnaise, 2 Piece | .140.00 |
| Plate, Bread & Butter, 6 1/2 In. | .25.00 |
| Plate, Dinner, 10 1/2 In. | .32.00 to 100.00 |

Plate, Salad, 8 1/4 In. . . . .40.00
Platter, 12 In. . . . . . . . .170.00
Relish, 3 Sections . . . . . .28.00
Soup, Dish . . . . . . . . . .100.00
Sugar . . . . . . . . . . . . . .50.00
Tumbler, Water,
   4 1/2 In. . . . . . . . . . . . .70.00

### PINK
Bowl, 9 1/2 In. . .22.00 to 25.00
Bowl, Cereal,
   6 3/8 In. . . . . .22.00 to 24.00
Bowl, Footed,
   10 1/2 In. . . . . . . . . . .100.00
Bowl, Ribbed, 9 1/2 In. . .29.00
Bowl, Salad,
   7 3/4 In. . . . . .22.00 to 24.00
Butter, Cover . . . . . . . . .65.00
Compote, Cover, Footed,
   7 In. . . . . . . . . . . . . .47.50
Compote, Footed, 7 In. . . .25.00
Cookie Jar . . . .65.00 to 72.00
Creamer . . . . . . . . . . . .33.00
Cup . . . . . . . . .24.00 to 30.00
Cup & Saucer . . . . . . . .37.00
Grill Plate, 10 1/2 In. . . . .24.00
Plate, Dinner,
   10 1/2 In. . . . .20.00 to 35.00
Plate, Luncheon,
   8 1/4 In. . . . . . . . . . . .20.00
Platter, 12 3/4 In. . . . . . .26.00
Platter, 5 Sections,
   12 3/4 In. . . . .32.00 to 35.00
Relish, 3 Sections,
   7 1/2 In. . . . . . . . . . . .65.00
Relish, 3 Sections,
   10 1/2 In. . . . .22.00 to 28.00
Saucer . . . . . . . . . . . . .10.00
Sherbet . . . . . .97.50 to 125.00
Tumbler, Juice, 5 Oz.,
   3 1/2 In. . . . . . . . . . . .90.00
Tumbler, Water,
   4 1/2 In. . . . . .22.00 to 23.00

LACY DAISY, see No. 618

---

**Store glasses right side up to protect the rims. Do not stack glasses.**

---

## LAKE COMO
At first glance, Lake Como looks more like a piece of ceramic than a piece of glass . It is Opaque White with blue decal decorations picturing a lake and part of an ancient ruin. It was made by Hocking Glass Company from 1934 to 1937.

Salt & Pepper . . .35.00 to 40.00

---

## LAUREL
Opaque glass was used by McKee Glass Company, Jeannette, Pennsylvania, to make Laurel dinnerware in the 1930s. The pattern, with a raised band of flowers and leaves as the only decoration, is sometimes called Raspberry Band. A few pieces have decals of a dog in the center, and that group is called Scottie Dog. The dinnerware was made in French Ivory, Jade Green, Powder Blue, or White Opal. A child's set was made with a colored rim.

### FRENCH IVORY
Berry Bowl, 4 3/4 In. . . . . .6.00
Bowl, Cereal, 6 In. . . . . . .9.50
Candlestick, Single . . . . . .25.00
Grill Plate, 9 In. . .9.00 to 12.50
Plate, Dinner,
   9 In. . . . . . . . . .9.00 to 14.00
Plate, Salad, 7 In. . .7.00 to 9.00
Plate, Sherbet,
   6 In. . . . . . . . . . .5.00 to 7.00

Platter, Oval, 11 In. . . . . .25.00
Sherbet . . . . . . . . . . . . .11.00

### JADE GREEN
Berry Bowl, Master,
   9 In. . . . . . . . . . . . . .18.00
Bowl, Cereal, 3-Footed,
   6 In. . . . . . . . . . . . . . .15.00
Bowl, Cereal, 6 In. . . . . . .7.00
Bowl, Vegetable, Oval,
   9 3/4 In. . . . . . . . . . . .16.00
Cheese Dish, Cover . . . . .42.00
Grill Plate, 9 In. . . . . . . .10.00
Plate, Dinner, 9 In. . . . . .10.00
Plate, Salad, 7 In. . . . . . . .7.00
Platter, Oval, 11 In. . . . . .19.00
Soup, Dish . . . . . . . . . . .40.00
Tumbler, Water, 9 Oz.,
   4 1/2 In. . . . . . . . . . . .50.00

### WHITE OPAL
Bowl, Vegetable, Oval,
   9 3/4 In. . . . . . . . . . . .14.00
Cup . . . . . . . . . . . . . . . .4.00
Salt & Pepper . . . . . . . .55.00
Saucer . . . . . . . . . . . . . .3.00

LILY MEDALLION, see American Sweetheart

LINCOLN DRAPE, see Princess

## LINCOLN INN
Lincoln Inn was made by the Fenton Glass Company, Williamstown, West Virginia, from 1928 until c.1936. The ridged dinnerware sets were made of Amber, Amethyst, Black, Cobalt Blue, Crystal, Green, Jadite (opaque green), Light Blue, Pink, and Red. A recent copy of the Lincoln Inn pitcher was made by Fenton Glass Company in Iridescent carnival glass.

### COBALT BLUE
Goblet, Champagne . . . . .25.00
Goblet, Water . . . . . . . . . .35.00

### CRYSTAL
Sherbet . . . . . . . . . . . . . .10.00
Tumbler, Iced Tea, 12 Oz. 75.00

### JADITE
Plate, Dinner, 12 In. . . . . .50.00

**LINE 300,** see Peacock & Wild Rose

**LITTLE HOSTESS,** see Moderntone Little Hostess Party Set

**LOOP,** see Lace Edge

**LORAIN,** see No. 615

**LOUISA,** see Floragold

**LOVEBIRDS,** see Georgian

**LYDIA RAY,** see New Century

## MADRID

Madrid has probably had more publicity than any other Depression glass pattern. It was originally made by the Federal Glass Company, Columbus, Ohio, from 1932 to 1939, using the molds developed for Sylvan. It was made first in Green, then in Amber; Madonna Blue and Pink pieces were made for a limited time. In 1976 Federal Glass reworked the molds and made full sets of amber glass called Recollection. These can be identified by a small "76" worked into the pattern. In 1982 Crystal pieces of Recollection were made. In more recent years Blue, Pink, and Crystal pieces have been reproduced by the Indiana Glass Company. It is sometimes called Paneled Aster, Primus, and Winged Medallion.

### AMBER
Berry Bowl, Master,
  9 3/4 In. . . . . . . . . . . . .18.00
Bowl, Salad, 9 1/2 In. . . . .30.00
Bowl, Vegetable, Oval,
  10 In. . . . . . . . . . . . . . .18.00
Butter . . . . . . . . . . . . . .29.00
Butter, Cover . . .62.00 to 70.00
Cake Plate,
  11 1/4 In. . . . . .13.00 to 24.00
Candlestick, 2 1/4 In.,
  Pair . . . . . . . . . . . . . . .22.00
Console, 11 In. . . . . . . . .15.00
Cookie Jar . . . . .35.00 to 50.00
Creamer . . . . . . . . .6.00 to 9.00
Cup . . . . . . . . . . . .3.00 to 5.00
Cup & Saucer . .10.00 to 12.00
Mold, Jell-O . . . .13.00 to 14.00
Pitcher, 8 1/2 In. . . . . . . .65.00
Pitcher, Juice,
  5 1/2 In. . . . . . .50.00 to 55.00
Plate, Luncheon,
  8 7/8 In. . . . . . . .6.00 to 9.50
Plate, Salad, 7 1/2 In. . . . .12.00

Plate, Sherbet,
  6 In. . . . . . . . . . .4.00 to 5.50
Platter, Oval,
  11 1/2 In. . . . . .15.00 to 22.00
Relish, 2 Sections,
  10 1/4 In. . . . . . . . . . . .15.00
Salt & Pepper,
  Flat . . . . . . . . .45.00 to 48.00
Salt & Pepper, Footed . . .105.00
Sauce Bowl, 5 In. . .4.50 to 9.00
Sherbet . . . . . . . .5.25 to 9.00
Soup, Cream, 4 3/4 In. . . .15.00
Soup, Dish,
  7 In. . . . . . . . . .11.00 to 16.00
Sugar, Cover . . . .45.00 to 49.50
Sugar &
  Creamer . . . . .15.00 to 16.00
Trivet . . . . . . . . . . . . . .35.00
Tumbler, 5 Oz.,
  3 7/8 In. . . . . . . . . . . . .14.00
Tumbler, 9 Oz.,
  4 1/4 In. . . . . . .11.00 to 19.50
Tumbler, 12 Oz.,
  5 1/2 In. . . . . . .14.00 to 22.50
Tumbler, Footed, 5 Oz.,
  4 In. . . . . . . . . . . . . . .14.00
Tumbler, Footed, 10 Oz.,
  5 1/2 In. . . . . . .20.00 to 33.50
Tumbler, Juice, 5 Oz.,
  3 7/8 In. . . . . . . . . . . . .55.00

### CRYSTAL
Creamer . . . . . . . . . . . . . .8.50
Cup . . . . . . . . . . . . . . . . .3.00
Grill Plate, 10 1/2 In. . . . . .9.00

### GREEN
Bowl, Salad, 8 In. . . . . . . .17.00
Bowl, Vegetable, Oval,
  10 In. . . . . . . . . . . . . . .17.00
Creamer . . . . . . . . . . . . .11.00
Cup . . . . . . . . . . . . . . . .10.00
Cup & Saucer . . . . . . . . .13.00
Plate, Dinner, 10 1/2 In. . . .35.00
Plate, Luncheon, 8 7/8 In. . .8.50
Plate, Sherbet, 6 In. . . . . . .4.00
Platter, Oval,
  11 1/2 In. . . . . .16.00 to 18.00
Salt & Pepper . . . . . . . .70.00
Sauce Bowl, 5 In. . . . . . . .6.00
Sherbet . . . . . . .5.00 to 13.00
Sugar . . . . . . . . . . . . . . .7.50
Sugar & Creamer . . . . . . .12.50

Tumbler, 9 Oz.,
4 1/4 In. . . . . . . . . . . . .30.00

### MADONNA BLUE
Plate, Dinner, 10 1/2 In. . .75.00
Salt & Pepper, Footed . . .160.00

**MAGNOLIA,** see Dogwood

---

## MANHATTAN
Manhattan is another modern-looking pattern with a design made of molded circles. It was made by Anchor Hocking Glass Corporation from 1938 to 1941, primarily in Crystal. A few Green, Iridescent, Pink, and Red pieces also are known. The pattern has been called many names, such as Horizontal Fine Rib, Horizontal Ribbed, Horizontal Rounded Big Rib, Horizontal Sharp Big Rib, and Ribbed.

### CRYSTAL
Ashtray, Round, 4 In. . . . .11.00
Ashtray, Square,
4 1/2 In. . . . . . . . . . . . .25.00
Berry Bowl, Handles,
5 3/8 In. . . . . . . . . . . . .18.00
Bowl, Fruit, Footed, Handle,
9 1/2 In. . . . . . .35.00 to 40.00
Candlestick, Double . . . . .32.00
Candlestick,
Pair . . . . . . . . .12.00 to 15.00
Coaster, 3 1/2 In. . . . . . . .15.00
Compote,
5 3/4 In. . . . . . .15.00 to 30.00
Cookie Jar, Cover . . . . . .35.00
Creamer . . . . . . . . . . . . .10.00
Cup . . . . . . . . .19.00 to 20.00

---

---

Cup & Saucer . . . . . . . . .24.50
Goblet, Wine,
4 In. . . . . . . . . . .2.50 to 5.00
Pitcher, Juice,
24 Oz. . . . . . .25.00 to 35.00
Plate, Dinner,
10 1/4 In. . . . . .17.00 to 20.00
Plate, Salad, 8 1/2 In. . . . .15.00
Plate, Sherbet,
6 In. . . . . . . . . . .4.00 to 7.00
Relish, 5 Sections,
14 In. . . . . . . . . . . . . . .20.00
Relish, Ruby
Inserts . . . . . .50.00 to 65.00
Relish Insert . . . . . . . . . .3.50
Salt & Pepper . . .18.00 to 33.00
Sandwich Tray,
14 In. . . . . . . .18.00 to 20.00
Sauce Bowl, Handles,
4 1/2 In. . . . . . . .6.00 to 9.00
Sherbet, Footed . . . . . . . .9.00
Soup, Cream, 4 1/2 In. . . .34.00
Sugar . . . . . . . . .9.00 to 10.00
Sugar & Creamer . . . . . .20.00
Tumbler . . . . . .15.00 to 18.00
Vase, 8 In. . . . . . .13.00 to 20.00

### PINK
Berry Bowl, Handles,
5 3/8 In. . . . . . . . . . . . .18.00
Bowl, Fruit, Footed,
Handle, 9 1/2 In. . . . . . .37.00
Candy Dish, Footed . . . . .12.00
Compote . . . . . . . . . . . .38.00
Salt & Pepper . . .50.00 to 55.00
Sherbet . . . . . . . . . . . . .15.00
Sugar . . . . . . . . .10.00 to 11.00
Sugar &
Creamer . . . . .18.50 to 25.00

---

Tumbler, Footed,
10 Oz. . . . . . . .19.00 to 22.00

### RUBY
Relish Tray Insert . . . . . .6.00

**MANY WINDOWS,** see Roulette

---

## MARTHA WASHINGTON
The Cambridge Glass Company of Cambridge, Ohio, started manufacturing Martha Washington pattern in 1932. The glass was made in Amber, Crystal, Forest Green, Gold Krystol, Heatherbloom, Royal Blue, and Ruby.

### CRYSTAL
Berry Bowl . . . . . . . . . . .16.00
Bowl, 9 In. . . . . . . . . . . .65.00
Goblet, Water, 10 Oz. . . . .28.00
Plate, Dinner, 12 In. . . . . .40.00
Plate, Salad, 8 3/8 In. . . . .18.00

**MAYFAIR,** see Rosemary

---

## MAYFAIR FEDERAL
The Mayfair patterns can easily be recognized, but if you are buying by mail, the names are sometimes confusing. Mayfair Federal is the pattern sometimes called Rosemary Arches. It was made in Amber, Crystal, or Green by Federal Glass Company in 1934, but was discontinued because of a patent conflict with Hocking's Mayfair pattern, referred to as Mayfair Open Rose.

### AMBER
Bowl, Vegetable, Oval,
    10 In. . . . . . . . . . . . . . .30.00
Platter, Oval, 12 In. . . . . .27.50
Saucer, 5 In. . . . . . . . . . . .6.50
Soup, Cream . . . . . . . . . .15.00

### GREEN
Creamer . . . . . . . . . . . . .14.00
Plate, Dinner, 10 In. . . . . .9.00
Platter . . . . . . . . . . . . . .38.00
Tumbler, 9 Oz.,
    4 1/2 In. . . . . . . . . . . . .26.00

## MAYFAIR OPEN ROSE
Mayfair Open Rose was made
by Hocking Glass Company
from 1931 to 1937. It was made
primarily in Light Blue and
Pink, with a few Green and
Yellow pieces. Crystal examples are rare. The cookie jar
and the whiskey glass have
been reproduced since 1982.

### BLUE
Bowl, 11 3/4 In. . . . . . . . .75.00
Bowl, Fruit, Deep,
    12 In. . . . . . . . . . . . . . .95.00
Bowl, Oval, Divided,
    11 1/4 In. . . . . . . . . . . .65.00
Bowl, Vegetable, 7 In. . . .50.00
Bowl, Vegetable,
    10 In. . . . . . . . .65.00 to 75.00
Bowl, Vegetable, Cover,
    10 In. . . . . . . . . . . . . .100.00
Bowl, Vegetable, Oval,
    9 1/2 In. . . . . . . . . . . . .70.00

Cake Plate, Footed,
    10 In. . . . . . . . . . . . . . .79.00
Cake Plate, Handles,
    12 In. . . . . . . . .66.00 to 70.00
Candy Dish, Cover . . . . .286.00
Celery Dish, Divided,
    9 In. . . . . . . . . .55.00 to 65.00
Celery Dish, Divided,
    10 In. . . . . . . . . . . . . . .75.00
Creamer . . . . . . .75.00 to 80.00
Cup & Saucer . .75.00 to 82.00
Grill Plate, 9 1/2 In. . . . .56.00
Pitcher, 6 In. . . . . . . . . .185.00
Plate, 5 3/4 In. . . . . . . . .25.00
Plate, Dinner,
    9 1/2 In. . . . . .50.00 to 75.00
Plate, Luncheon,
    8 1/2 In. . . . . . . . . . . . .55.00
Plate, Sherbet,
    Off-Center Indent,
    6 1/2 In. . . . . . .26.00 to 30.00
Platter, Oval,
    12 In. . . . . . . . .60.00 to 75.00
Sandwich Server, Center
    Handle . . . . . . .75.00 to 85.00
Sherbet,
    4 3/4 In. . . . . .70.00 to 110.00
Sugar . . . . . . . . . . . . . . .80.00
Vase, Sweet
    Pea . . . . . . .110.00 to 135.00

### CRYSTAL
Pitcher, 37 Oz., 6 In. . . . .14.00
Platter, Handles, 5 Sections,
    Oval, 12 In. . . .11.00 to 20.00

### GREEN
Bowl, 11 3/4 In. .33.00 to 40.00
Bowl, Fruit, Deep,
    12 In. . . . . . . .40.00 to 45.00
Sandwich Server, Center
    Handle . . . . . .30.00 to 45.00

### PINK
Bowl, 11 3/4 In. . . . . . . .55.00
Bowl, Cereal,
    5 1/2 In. . . . . . .20.00 to 27.00
Bowl, Fruit, Deep,
    12 In. . . . . . . . . . . . . . .61.00
Bowl, Vegetable, 7 In. . . .28.00
Bowl, Vegetable, Handles,
    10 In. . . . . . . . .18.00 to 31.00
Bowl, Vegetable, Oval,
    9 1/2 In. . . . . . .25.00 to 40.00
Butter, Cover . . .65.00 to 70.00

Cake Plate, Footed,
    10 In. . . . . . . .28.00 to 35.00
Candy Dish, Footed,
    Cover . . . . . . .50.00 to 53.00
Celery Dish, Divided,
    10 In. . . . . . . . . . . . . .210.00
Cookie Jar, Cover . . . . . .50.00
Creamer . . . . . .27.00 to 32.00
Cup . . . . . . . . .15.00 to 19.50
Cup & Saucer . . . . . . . .30.00
Decanter,
    Stopper . . . . .165.00 to 175.00
Goblet, Cocktail, 4 In. . .115.00
Goblet, Water, 9 Oz.,
    5 3/4 In. . . . . . . . . . . . .70.00
Grill Plate,
    9 1/2 In. . . . . . .28.00 to 40.00
Pitcher, 37 Oz., 6 In. . . . .50.00
Pitcher, 60 Oz.,
    8 In. . . . . . . . . .50.00 to 60.00
Pitcher, 80 Oz.,
    8 1/2 In. . . . . .95.00 to 130.00
Plate, 5 3/4 In. . . .11.00 to 12.00
Plate, Dinner,
    9 1/2 In. . . . . . .50.00 to 65.00
Plate, Luncheon,
    8 1/2 In. . . . . . .26.00 to 31.00
Plate, Sherbet,
    6 1/2 In. . . . . . .10.00 to 14.00
Platter, Handle, Oval,
    12 In. . . . . . . . .24.00 to 26.00
Relish, 4 Sections,
    8 3/4 In. . . . . . .25.00 to 27.00
Salt & Pepper, Flat . . . . . .65.00
Sandwich Server, Center
    Handle . . . . . . .42.00 to 50.00
Saucer . . . . . . .32.00 to 34.00
Sherbet, Footed,
    3 In. . . . . . . . .15.00 to 17.00
Sherbet, Footed,
    4 3/4 In. . . . . . . . . . . . .34.00
Soup, Cream, 5 In. . . . . .42.50
Sugar . . . . . . . . . . . . . . .30.00
Sugar &
    Creamer . . . . .50.00 to 62.00
Tumbler, Footed, 10 Oz.,
    5 1/4 In. . . . . . . . . . . . .36.00
Tumbler, Footed,
    Iced Tea, 15 Oz.,
    6 1/2 In. . . . . . .39.00 to 42.00
Tumbler, Iced Tea,
    13 1/2 Oz., 5 1/4 In. . . . .38.00
Tumbler, Juice, Footed,
    5 Oz., 3 1/2 In. . . . . . .125.00

Tumbler, Water, 9 Oz.,
4 1/4 In. . . . . . .24.00 to 34.00
Vase, Sweet Pea . . . . . . .135.00

**MEADOW FLOWER,** see No. 618

**MEANDERING VINE,** see Madrid

## MISS AMERICA

Miss America, or Diamond Pattern, was made by Hocking Glass Company from 1933 to 1936 in many colors, including Crystal, Green, Ice Blue, Jadite, Pink, Red, and Ritz Blue. It is similar to English Hobnail but can be distinguished by the typical Hocking sunburst base and hobs that are more pointed than those of the Westmoreland pattern. In 1977 some reproduction butter dishes were made of Amberina, Crystal, Green, Ice Blue, Pink, or Red. Saltshakers, pitchers, and tumblers are also being reproduced.

### CRYSTAL
Berry Bowl, 4 1/2 In. . . . .12.00
Bowl, Cereal,
6 1/4 In. . . . . . . .6.00 to 18.00
Bowl, Curved In, 8 In. . . .20.00
Candy Jar, Cover,
11 1/2 In. . . . . .55.00 to 60.00
Celery Dish, 10 1/2 In. . . .17.00
Coaster, 5 3/4 In. . . . . . .15.00

Compote, 5 In. . .10.00 to 14.00
Creamer . . . . . . . . . . . . .5.00
Cup & Saucer . .10.00 to 15.50
Goblet, Water, 5 1/2 In. . .17.00
Goblet, Wine, 3 3/4 In. . . .24.00
Grill Plate, 10 1/4 In. . . . .11.00
Pitcher, 65 Oz.,
8 In. . . . . . . . .35.00 to 42.00
Plate, Dinner,
10 1/4 In. . . . . .11.00 to 18.00
Plate, Sherbet . . . . . . . . . .3.00
Platter, Oval, 12 1/4 In. . .14.00
Relish, 4 Sections,
8 3/4 In. . . . . . .9.75 to 12.00
Relish, 5 Sections,
11 3/4 In. . . . . .17.00 to 25.00
Salt & Pepper . . . . . . . .30.00
Saucer . . . . . . . . . . . . . .4.00
Sherbet . . . . . . . .6.00 to 8.00
Sugar &
Creamer . . . . .16.00 to 18.00

### GREEN
Berry Bowl, 4 1/2 In. . . . .10.00
Bowl, Cereal, 6 In. . . . . .22.00
Plate, 6 3/4 In. . . . . . . . .10.00
Salt &
Pepper . . . .275.00 to 320.00

### PINK
Bowl, Cereal,
6 1/4 In. . . . . .22.00 to 25.00
Bowl, Curved In, 8 In. . . .97.50
Bowl, Vegetable, Oval,
10 In. . . . . . . .25.00 to 35.00
Candy Jar, Cover,
11 1/2 In. . . .140.00 to 170.00
Celery Dish,
10 1/2 In. . . . . .25.00 to 35.00
Coaster,
5 3/4 In. . . . . .32.00 to 34.00
Compote, 5 In. . .19.00 to 37.50
Creamer . . . . . .18.00 to 22.00
Cup . . . . . . . . .20.00 to 26.00
Cup & Saucer . .27.00 to 35.00
Goblet, Water,
5 1/2 In. . . . . .42.00 to 54.00
Goblet, Wine,
3 3/4 In. . . . . .73.00 to 85.00
Grill Plate,
10 1/4 In. . . . .24.00 to 28.00
Pitcher, 8 In. . . . . . . . .149.00

Plate, Dinner,
10 1/4 In. . . . .27.50 to 35.00
Plate, Salad,
8 1/2 In. . . . . . . . . . . .25.00
Plate, Sherbet,
5 3/4 In. . . . . . .10.00 to 17.00
Platter, Oval,
12 1/4 In. . . . .26.00 to 46.00
Relish, 4 Sections,
8 3/4 In. . . . . .20.00 to 30.00
Salt & Pepper . . .55.00 to 70.00
Saucer . . . . . . . . .5.00 to 8.00
Sherbet . . . . . . .12.00 to 16.50
Sugar . . . . . . . . . . . . . .18.50
Sugar &
Creamer . . . . .32.00 to 39.00
Tumbler, Iced Tea,
5 3/4 In. . . . . . . . . . . .65.00
Tumbler, Juice, 4 In. . . . .50.00
Tumbler, Water,
4 1/2 In. . . . . . .30.00 to 38.00

### RED
Sherbet . . . . . . . . . . . .220.00

**MISS AMERICA,** see also English Hobnail

**MODERNE ART,** see Tea Room

## MODERNTONE

Moderntone, or Wedding Band, was made by Hazel Atlas Glass Company from 1935 to 1942. The simple pattern is popular today with Art Deco enthusiasts. It was made of Amethyst, Cobalt Blue, Crystal, and Pink glass. It was also made of an opaque, almost white glass called Platonite, which is listed here under Moderntone Platonite.

**AMETHYST**
Berry Bowl, 5 In. . . . . . . .25.00
Berry Bowl, Master,
8 3/4 In. . . . . . . . . . . . .50.00
Cup . . . . . . . . . .9.00 to 12.00
Cup & Saucer . . . . . . . .15.00
Plate, Dinner, 8 7/8 In. . . .15.00
Plate, Luncheon,
7 3/4 In. . . . . . .7.00 to 14.00
Plate, Sherbet,
5 7/8 In. . . . . . . .3.00 to 6.00
Platter, Oval,
12 In. . . . . . . .47.00 to 60.00
Saucer . . . . . . . . . . . . . . .5.00
Sherbet . . . . . . . . . . . . .12.50
Soup, Cream . . . .15.00 to 24.50
Sugar . . . . . . . . . .6.00 to 14.00
Sugar &
Creamer . . . . .16.00 to 22.00
Tumbler, Water, 9 Oz. . . .30.00

**COBALT BLUE**
Berry Bowl,
5 In. . . . . . . . .21.00 to 27.00
Berry Bowl, Master,
8 3/4 In. . . . . . .35.00 to 75.00
Butter, Cover . .100.00 to 115.00
Cheese Dish, Cover . . . .400.00
Creamer . . . . . . .10.00 to 12.00
Cup . . . . . . . . . .6.25 to 11.00
Cup & Saucer . .15.00 to 18.00
Custard Cup . . . .15.00 to 22.00
Plate, Dinner,
8 7/8 In. . . . . . .13.00 to 22.50
Plate, Luncheon,
7 3/4 In. . . . . . .9.50 to 14.00
Plate, Salad,
6 3/4 In. . . . . . .10.00 to 13.00
Plate, Sherbet,
5 7/8 In. . . . . . . .5.00 to 6.50
Platter, Oval,
11 In. . . . . . . .39.00 to 65.00
Platter, Oval, 12 In. . . . . .80.00
Salt & Pepper . . .30.00 to 48.00
Sandwich Tray,
10 1/2 In. . . . . .54.00 to 60.00

---

Check the metal strips holding any heavy wall-hung shelves. After a few years, the shelf holder may develop "creep" and gradually bend away from the wall.

---

Saucer . . . . . . . . . .2.00 to 8.00
Sherbet . . . . . . .10.00 to 20.00
Soup, Cream,
4 3/4 In. . . . . . .17.50 to 24.00
Soup, Cream,
Ruffled, 5 In. . . . . . . . .60.00
Sugar . . . . . . . . . .8.75 to 10.00
Sugar &
Creamer . . . . .18.00 to 25.00
Tumbler, Juice, 5 Oz. . . .50.00
Tumbler, Water,
9 Oz. . . . . . . .36.00 to 45.00
Whiskey . . . . . . .40.00 to 50.00

**CRYSTAL**
Creamer . . . . . . . . .4.00 to 7.00
Plate, Salad, 6 3/4 In. . . . . .5.00
Soup, Dish, 7 1/2 In. . . . . . .8.00

**PINK**
Whiskey . . . . . . . . . . . . .10.00

## MODERNTONE LITTLE HOSTESS PARTY SET

The Moderntone Little Hostess Party Set was also made by Hazel Atlas Glass Company in the late 1940s. This was a child's set of dishes made in Platonite with fired-on colors. We have seen Beige, Blue, Chartreuse, Gray, Green, Maroon, Orange (rust), Pink, Turquoise, Yellow, and pastels, but other colors were probably made.

**BEIGE**
Cup & Saucer . . . . . . . .20.00

---

Plate . . . . . . . . . . . . . .10.00
**BLUE**
Plate . . . . . . . . . .9.00 to 10.00
Saucer . . . . . . . . . . . . . . .7.00
**GRAY**
Cup . . . . . . . . . .10.00 to 13.00
Cup & Saucer . .19.00 to 20.00
Plate . . . . . . . . . .7.00 to 10.00
**GREEN**
Cup . . . . . . . . . . . . . . . . .9.00
Cup & Saucer . .16.00 to 19.00
Plate . . . . . . . . . .8.00 to 12.00
Saucer . . . . . . . . .2.75 to 8.00
Sugar . . . . . . . . . . . . . . .14.00
**MAROON**
Cup . . . . . . . . . .13.00 to 14.00
Plate . . . . . . . . . .11.00 to 12.50
Teapot . . . . . . . . . . . . . .125.00
**ORANGE**
Creamer . . . . . . . . . . . . .12.50
Cup . . . . . . . . .12.00 to 13.00
Cup & Saucer . . . . . . . .23.00
Plate . . . . . . . . . .8.50 to 10.00
Saucer . . . . . . . . . . . . . . .8.00
Sugar . . . . . . . .10.50 to 16.00
Sugar &
Creamer . . . . .24.00 to 25.00
**PASTELS**
Tea Set,
14 Piece . . . . .93.00 to 100.00
Tea Set, 16 Piece . . . . . .245.00
**PINK**
Creamer . . . . . . .12.00 to 15.00
Cup . . . . . . . . . .9.00 to 10.00
Plate . . . . . . . . . .6.00 to 10.00
Saucer . . . . . . . . . . . . . . .7.00
Sugar . . . . . . . . . . . . . . .15.00
**TURQUOISE**
Cup . . . . . . . . . . . . . . . . .7.00
Cup & Saucer . .16.00 to 23.00
Plate . . . . . . . . . .6.25 to 12.50
Saucer . . . . . . . . . . . . . . .7.00
Teapot,
Cover . . . . . .120.00 to 130.00
**YELLOW**
Cup . . . . . . . . . . . . . . . . .3.85
Cup & Saucer . .16.00 to 22.00
Plate . . . . . . . . . .8.50 to 10.00
Saucer . . . . . . . . .7.00 to 8.00

## MODERNTONE PLATONITE

Moderntone Platonite was made by Hazel Atlas Glass Company from 1940 to the early 1950s. Platonite, an almost white glass, was covered with a variety of bright fired-on colors, including Black, Light or Dark Blue, Light or Dark Green, Red, Orange, Yellow, and White trimmed with a small colored rim. Clear glass pieces are listed in this book under Moderntone.

### GREEN
Berry Bowl, 5 In. . . . . . . . .3.00
Bowl, 8 In. . . . . . . . . . . .14.00
Bowl, Cereal, 6 1/2 In. . . . .9.00
Cup . . . . . . . . . . .2.00 to 4.00
Plate, Dinner, 8 7/8 In. . . . .3.00
Plate, Salad, 6 3/4 In. . . . . .2.00
Plate, Sherbet, 6 3/4 In. . . .4.75
Sandwich Tray,
   10 1/2 In. . . . . . . . . . . . .7.00
Saucer . . . . . . . . . .50 to 1.00
Sherbet . . . . . . . .3.50 to 5.50
Sugar . . . . . . . . . .3.00 to 5.00
Tumbler, Juice . . . . . . . . .3.00
Tumbler, Water,
   9 Oz. . . . . . . . .9.00 to 11.00

### LIGHT BLUE
Berry Bowl, No Rim,
   5 In. . . . . . . . . . . . . . . .7.50
Berry Bowl, Rim, 5 In. . . .25.00
Cup & Saucer . .15.00 to 16.50
Plate, Dinner,
   8 7/8 In. . . . . . .5.50 to 17.50
Plate, Sherbet,
   6 3/4 In. . . . . . .5.00 to 12.50
Saltshaker . . . . . . . . . . . .8.50
Saucer . . . . . . . . . . . . . .15.00

Sherbet . . . . . . . . . . . . .2.50
Soup, Cream . . . . . . . . . .10.00

### ORANGE
Saucer . . . . . . . . . . . . . .5.00

### TURQUOISE
Soup, Cream . . . . . . . . . .10.00

### WHITE
Cup . . . . . . . . . . . . . . . .2.00
Cup & Saucer,
   Blue Ring . . . . . . . . . . .7.00
Cup & Saucer,
   Green Ring . . . . . . . . . .7.00
Cup & Saucer,
   Yellow Ring . . . . . . . . .7.00
Salt & Pepper, Pair . . . . .20.00
Sherbet . . . . . . . . . . . . .2.00

### YELLOW
Berry Bowl, No Rim,
   5 In. . . . . . . . . . . . . . . .6.00
Bowl, Cereal, 6 1/2 In. . . . .9.00
Creamer . . . . . . . .3.00 to 5.00
Cup . . . . . . . . . . . . . . . .2.00
Cup & Saucer . . . . . . . .19.00
Gravy Boat, Underplate . .70.00
Plate, Dinner, 8 7/8 In. . . .5.50
Plate, Sherbet, 6 3/4 In. . . .2.00
Platter, 12 In. . . . . . . . . . .6.00
Saucer . . . . . . . . . .50 to 2.00
Sherbet . . . . . . . .4.50 to 5.50
Soup, Cream, 5 In. . . . . . .9.00

## MOONDROPS

The New Martinsville Glass Manufacturing Company, New Martinsville, West Virginia, made Moondrops from 1932 to the late 1940s. Collectors like the pieces with the fan-shaped knobs or stoppers. The pattern was made in Amber, Amethyst, Black, Cobalt Blue, Crystal, Evergreen, Ice Blue, Jadite, Light Green, Medium Blue, Pink, Rose, Ruby, and Smoke.

### AMBER
Bowl, Soup, 6 1/4 In. . . . .35.00
Cup & Saucer . . . . . . . . .14.00
Goblet, Cordial,
   2 7/8 In. . . . . . . . . . . . .23.90
Pitcher, 8 1/8 In. . . . . . .200.00
Plate, Bread & Butter,
   5 7/8 In. . . . . . . . . . . . . .6.00
Plate, Luncheon,
   8 1/2 In. . . . . . . . . . . . .10.00
Relish, 3 Sections, 8 In. . .18.00
Saucer . . . . . . . . . . . . . .3.00
Sugar, 4 In. . . . . . . . . . . .8.00
Sugar & Creamer, 4 In. . . .19.90
Tumbler, 8 Oz.,
   4 3/8 In. . . . . . . . . . . . .10.00
Tumbler, 9 Oz.,
   4 7/8 In. . . . . . . . . . . . .10.00
Whiskey,
   2 3/4 In. . . . . . .7.50 to 10.00
Whiskey, Handle,
   2 3/4 In. . . . . .11.00 to 16.00

### AMETHYST
Cup . . . . . . . . . . . . . . . .8.00
Plate, Bread & Butter,
   5 7/8 In. . . . . . . . . . . . . .6.00

### COBALT BLUE
Cup . . . . . . . . . . . . . . . .15.00
Goblet, Cordial,
   2 7/8 In. . . . . .34.00 to 45.00
Sugar, 4 In. . . . . . . . . . . .15.00
Tumbler, 8 Oz.,
   4 3/8 In. . . . . . . . . . . . .23.50
Whiskey, 2 3/4 In. . . . . . .16.00

### CRYSTAL
Goblet, Wine, 4 In. . . . . . .20.00

### LIGHT GREEN
Cup & Saucer . . . . . . . . .14.00

### RUBY
Bowl, 3-Footed, Ruffled,
   9 1/2 In. . . . . . . . . . . . .65.00
Compote, 4 In. . .25.00 to 35.00

Creamer,
2 3/4 In. . . . . . .18.00 to 20.00

Cup . . . . . . . . .12.00 to 18.00

Cup & Saucer . .18.00 to 21.00

Decanter Set, Juice,
5 Piece . . . . . . . . . . . .120.00

Goblet, Wine,
4 In. . . . . . . . .19.00 to 22.00

Goblet, Wine, Metal
Stem, 5 1/8 In. . . . . . . .15.00

Sherbet, 2 5/8 In. . . . . . .14.00

Sugar, 3 1/2 In. . . . . . . . .13.50

Sugar & Creamer,
2 3/4 In. . . . . . . . . . . . .40.00

Sugar & Creamer,
3 3/4 In. . . . . . . . . . . . .30.00

Tumbler, 4 7/8 In. . . . . . .16.50

Tumbler, 8 Oz.,
4 3/8 In. . . . . . . . . . . . .21.00

Tumbler, Handle,
4 7/8 In. . . . . . . . . . . . .13.00

Whiskey, Handle,
2 3/4 In. . . . . . .15.00 to 16.00

Wine, 4 Oz. . . . . . . . . . .20.00

## MOONSTONE

The opalescent hobnails on this pattern give it the name Moonstone. It was made by Anchor Hocking Glass Corporation, Lancaster, Ohio, from 1941 to 1946. A few pieces are seen in Green. Reproductions have been made. They are listed at the end of the Depression Glass section.

### CRYSTAL

Bonbon, Heart
Shape . . . . . . . .8.00 to 13.00

Bowl, 7 3/4 In. . . . . . . . .14.00

Bowl,
Cloverleaf . . . .10.00 to 12.00

Bowl, Crimped,
9 1/2 In. . . . . . .17.00 to 25.00

Bowl, Crimped, Handle,
6 1/2 In. . . . . . . . . . . . .18.00

Bowl, Dessert, Crimped,
5 1/2 In. . . . . . . . . . . . . .8.00

Candleholder,
Pair . . . . . . . . .14.00 to 15.00

Candy, Cover,
2 Handles . . . . .26.00 to 28.00

Cigarette Box, Cover,
6 In. . . . . . . . . .24.00 to 25.00

Creamer . . . . . . . . . . . . .8.00

Cup . . . . . . . . . . . .5.00 to 6.00

Cup & Saucer . .12.00 to 13.00

Goblet, 10 Oz. . .15.00 to 20.00

Plate, Luncheon,
8 3/8 In. . . . . . . . . . . . .15.00

Plate, Sherbet, 6 1/4 In. . . .5.00

Puff Box, Cover,
4 3/4 In. . . . . . . . . . . . .25.00

Relish, Divided,
7 3/4 In. . . . . . .9.00 to 15.00

Sandwich Tray,
10 3/4 In. . . . . . . . . . . .25.00

Sherbet . . . . . . . .3.00 to 7.00

Sugar . . . . . . . . . . . . . . .9.00

Sugar & Creamer . . . . . .18.00

Vase, 5 1/2 In. . . . . . . . .12.00

### GREEN

Bowl, Crimped, Handle,
6 1/2 In. . . . . . . . . . . . .15.00

## MT. PLEASANT

Mt. Pleasant, sometimes called Double Shield, was made by L. E. Smith Company, Mt. Pleasant, Pennsylvania, from the mid-1920s to 1934. The pattern was made in Amber; Black Amethyst, a very deep purple that appears black unless held in front of a strong light; Cobalt Blue; Crystal; Green; Pink; and White. Some pieces have gold or silver trim.

### BLACK AMETHYST

Bowl, Flared, Footed,
9 In. . . . . . . . . . . . . . . .28.00

Mayonnaise, 3-Footed,
5 1/2 In. . . . . . .16.00 to 24.00

Mint Dish, Center Handle,
6 In. . . . . . . . . . . . . . . .19.00

Plate, 2 Handles, 8 In. . . . .18.00

Plate, 2 Hexagon Handles,
7 In. . . . . . . . . . . . . . . .12.00

Plate, Scalloped, 8 In. . . . .15.00

Sandwich Server, Center
Handle, 9 In. . .19.00 to 35.00

Sugar . . . . . . . . .17.00 to 19.00

Sugar & Creamer . . . . . . .37.00

### COBALT BLUE

Bowl, 2 Handles, Square,
8 In. . . . . . . . . . . . . . . .38.00

Bowl, Fruit, Footed, Square,
4 In. . . . . . . . . . . . . . . .16.00

Bowl, Fruit, Scalloped,
10 In. . . . . . . . . . . . . . .34.00

Bowl, Roll Handle, Footed,
7 In. . . . . . . . . . . . . . . .18.00

Cake Plate, 2 Handles,
10 1/2 In. . . . . .23.00 to 26.00

Creamer . . . . . . .12.00 to 22.50

Cup . . . . . . . . . . . . . . . .14.00

Cup & Saucer . .13.00 to 18.00

Grill Plate, 9 In. . .8.00 to 20.00

Mayonnaise, Footed,
5 1/2 In. . . . . . .15.00 to 32.50

Plate, 2 Handles, 8 In. . . . .13.00

Plate, Leaf Shape,
8 In. . . . . . . . . .10.00 to 18.50

Plate, Scalloped,
8 In. . . . . . . . . .14.00 to 16.00

Plate, Square, 8 In. . . . . . .20.00

Salt & Pepper . . . . . . . . .36.00

Sherbet . . . . . . .12.00 to 16.50

Tumbler,
Footed . . . . . . .15.00 to 25.00

### GREEN

Creamer . . . . . . . . . . . . .18.00

Grill Plate, 9 In. . . . . . . . .10.00

## MT. VERNON

Mt. Vernon was made in the late 1920s through the 1940s by the Cambridge Glass Company, Cambridge, Ohio. It was made in Amber, Carmen (red), Crystal, Emerald Green, Heatherbloom, Royal Blue, and Violet.

### AMBER
Relish, 5 Sections . . . . . .35.00
### CARMEN
Decanter, 40 Oz. . . . . . .140.00
Whiskey . . . . . . . . . . .20.00
### CRYSTAL
Goblet, Wine . . . . . . . . . .9.00
Plate, Bread & Butter,
  6 In. . . . . . . . . . . . . . .7.00
Plate, Dinner, 10 1/2 In. . .35.00
### HEATHERBLOOM
Compote, 6 1/2 In. . . . . . .85.00

## NAVARRE

Fostoria Glass Company, Fostoria, Ohio, made Navarre pattern glass from 1937 to 1980. It is an etched pattern. Some of the pieces were made on the Baroque glass blank, others on more modern shapes. It was originally made only in Crystal. A few later pieces were made in the 1970s in Pink, Blue, or Green.

### BLUE
Goblet, Champagne, 6 Oz.,
  5 5/8 In. . . . . . .25.00 to 42.00
Goblet, Claret, 4 1/2 Oz.,
  6 1/2 In. . . . . . .55.00 to 65.00
Goblet, Water, 10 Oz.,
  7 5/8 In. . . . . . .28.00 to 52.00
Tumbler, Iced Tea, Footed,
  13 Oz., 5 7/8 In. . . . . . .52.00

### CRYSTAL
Bonbon, Footed,
  7 3/8 In. . . . . . . . . . . . .30.00
Bowl, Flared, 12 In. . . . .60.00
Cake Plate, Handle, 10 In. 50.00
Candlestick, 3-Light,
  6 3/4 In. . . . . . . . . . . . .75.00
Candlestick, Double, 5 In.,
  Pair . . . . . . . . . . . . . . .75.00
Celery Dish, 9 In. . . . . . .47.50
Compote,
  5 1/2 In. . . . . . .45.00 to 65.00
Creamer, Footed,
  4 1/4 In. . . . . . . . . . . . .20.00
Cruet, Salad Dressing, Stopper,
  6 1/2 In. . . . .125.00 to 396.00
Cup & Saucer . .24.00 to 30.00
Dish, Mayonnaise, Footed,
  3 Piece . . . . . . .35.00 to 62.00
Finger Bowl, 4 1/2 In. . . .65.00
Goblet, Claret, 4 1/2 Oz.,
  6 1/2 In. . . . . . . . . . . . .60.00
Goblet, Cocktail, 3 1/2 Oz.,
  6 In. . . . . . . . . . . . . . .28.00
Goblet, Cordial, 1 Oz.,
  3 7/8 In. . . . . . . . . . . . .50.00
Goblet, Water, 10 Oz.,
  7 5/8 In. . . . . . . . . . . . .35.00
Goblet, Wine, 3 1/4 Oz.,
  5 1/2 In. . . . . . . . . . . . .35.00
Ice Bucket, 4 3/8 In. . . . .155.00

Pitcher, Water, Footed,
  48 Oz. . . . . . . . . . . . .495.00
Plate, Breakfast,
  9 1/2 In. . . . . . . . . . . . .45.00
Plate, Luncheon,
  8 1/2 In. . . . . . . . . . . . .22.00
Plate, Salad,
  7 1/2 In. . . . . . .14.00 to 18.00
Relish, 2 Sections, Square,
  6 In. . . . . . . . . . . . . . .32.50
Relish, 3 Sections,
  7 1/2 In. . . . . . . . . . . . .45.00
Sherbet,
  4 3/8 In. . . . . . .20.00 to 35.00
Sugar & Creamer . . . . . . .45.00
Tidbit, Footed,
  8 1/4 In. . . . . . . . . . . . .27.50
Tumbler, Juice, Footed,
  5 Oz., 4 3/8 In. . . . . . . . .25.00
Tumbler, Water, Footed,
  10 Oz., 5 3/8 In. . . . . . . .28.00

## NEW CENTURY

New Century used to be incorrectly called Lydia Ray by some collectors. It was made by Hazel Atlas Glass Company, a firm with factories in Ohio, Pennsylvania, and West Virginia, from 1930 to 1935. It has a series of ribs in the glass design. It is found in Amethyst, Cobalt Blue, Crystal, Green, and Pink. Ovide is sometimes incorrectly called New Century.

### AMETHYST
Cup & Saucer . . .8.00 to 10.00
Tumbler, 5 Oz.,
  3 1/2 In. . . . . . . . . . . . .12.00
Tumbler, Juice, 5 Oz.,
  3 1/2 In. . . . . . . . . . . . .12.00

### COBALT BLUE
Cup & Saucer  . . . . . . . .10.00

Tumbler, Iced Tea,
12 Oz., 5 1/4 In.  . . . . .25.00

Tumbler, Juice, 5 Oz.,
3 1/2 In.  . . . . . .15.00 to 18.00

Tumbler, Water, 9 Oz.,
4 1/8 In. . . . . . . . . . . . .18.00

### CRYSTAL
Pitcher, Water, 80 Oz.,
8 In. . . . . . . . . . . . . . .45.00

Plate, Dinner, 10 Oz.  . . . .12.00

Plate, Luncheon, 8 1/2 In. . .9.50

Sherbet, 3 In.  . . . . . . . . .10.00

### GREEN
Bowl, 8 In.  . . . . .22.00 to 26.00

Cup & Saucer  . . . . . . . . .16.00

Decanter, Stopper . . . . . .40.00

Plate, Luncheon,
8 1/2 In.  . . . . . . . . . . .15.00

Salt & Pepper  . . . . . . . .15.00

Soup, Cream, 4 3/4 In.  . . .25.00

Tumbler, Water, 9 Oz.,
4 1/8 In. . . . . . .12.00 to 15.00

### PINK
Cup & Saucer  . . . . . . . .10.00

Saucer  . . . . . . . . . . . . . .4.50

Tumbler, Water, 9 Oz.,
4 1/8 In. . . . . . .11.00 to 14.00

---

## NEWPORT

Newport, or Hairpin, was made by Hazel Atlas Glass Company from 1936 to 1940. It is known in Amethyst, Cobalt Blue, Pink, Platonite (white), and a variety of fired-on colors. Reproductions have been made. They are listed at the end of the Depression Glass section.

### AMETHYST
Bowl, Cereal, 5 1/4 In.  . . .30.00

Cup & Saucer  . . . . . . . .15.00

Plate, Dessert, 6 In. . . . . . .6.00

Plate, Dinner,
8 13/16 In. . . . . . . . . . .30.00

Plate, Luncheon,
8 1/2 In.  . . . . . .10.00 to 15.00

Salt & Pepper  . . . . . . . .45.00

Saltshaker  . . . . . . . . . . .20.00

Sherbet, Footed  . .12.00 to 13.00

Soup, Cream,
4 3/4 In.  . . . . . .16.00 to 18.00

Sugar . . . . . . . . . . . . . .13.00

Sugar &
Creamer  . . . . .15.00 to 35.00

Tumbler, Water, 9 Oz.,
4 1/2 In. . . . . . . . . . . . .30.00

### COBALT BLUE
Bowl, Cereal,
5 1/4 In.  . . . . . .31.00 to 35.00

Creamer  . . . . . .13.00 to 15.00

Cup  . . . . . . . . . . . . . . .10.00

Cup & Saucer  . .14.00 to 17.00

Plate, Dessert,
5 7/8 In.  . . . . . . . .7.50 to 9.00

Plate, Luncheon,
8 1/2 In.  . . . . . .15.00 to 16.50

Plate, Sherbet  . . . . . . . . .9.00

Sandwich Server,
11 1/2 In. . . . . . . . . . . .48.00

Saucer  . . . . . . . . . . . . . .7.00

Sherbet  . . . . . . . .13.50 to 18.50

Soup, Cream,
4 3/4 In.  . . . . . .16.00 to 18.00

Sugar & Creamer  . . . . . .39.50

Tumbler, Water, 9 Oz.,
4 1/2 In. . . . . . . . . . . . .39.00

### PINK
Berry Set, 7 Piece . . . . . .75.00

Cup & Saucer  . . . . . . . .15.00

Plate, Dessert, 5 7/8 In. . . . .6.00

Platter, Oval, 11 3/4 In.  . .47.00

### PLATONITE
Creamer, Fired-On
Yellow  . . . . . . . . . . . .8.76

Saucer  . . . . . . . . . . . . . ..50

Sugar . . . . . . . . . . . . . . .1.50

Sugar, Fired-On Spruce
Green  . . . . . . . . . . . . .7.00

**NO. 601,** see Avocado

## NO. 610

Many patterns are listed both by the original pattern number and by a name. No. 610 is often called Pyramid or Rex. It was made from 1926 to 1932 by the Indiana Glass Company. Green and Pink were used more than Crystal, White, and Yellow. In 1974 and 1975 reproductions were made in Black and Blue by Tiara.

### CRYSTAL
Berry Bowl,
4 3/4 In. . . . . . .60.00 to 75.00

Pitcher, 1/2 Gal. . . . . . .500.00

Sugar & Creamer, Tray,
3 Piece  . . . . . . . . . . . .90.00

Tumbler, Iced Tea, Footed,
11 Oz. . . . . . . . . . . . .150.00

### GREEN
Berry Bowl, 4 3/4 In.  . . . .65.00

Bowl, Oval, 9 1/2 In.  . . . .70.00

Ice Bucket  . . .150.00 to 165.00

Pickle, 9 1/2 In.  . . . . . . .50.00

Pitcher, 1/2 Gal. . . . . . .835.00

Relish, 4 Sections,
9 1/2 In. . . . . . .75.00 to 80.00

Tumbler, Water, Footed,
8 Oz. . . . . . . . . . . . . . .55.00

### PINK
Berry Bowl, 4 3/4 In.  . . . .69.00

Berry Bowl, Master,
8 1/2 In. . . . . . . . . . . . .30.00
Bowl, Oval, 9 1/2 In. . . . .28.00

### YELLOW
Berry Bowl,
4 3/4 In. . . . . . .55.00 to 85.00
Berry Bowl, Master,
8 1/2 In. . . . . .70.00 to 110.00
Bowl, Oval,
9 1/2 In. . . . . . .50.00 to 80.00
Pickle Dish,
9 1/2 In. . . . . . .52.00 to 55.00
Pitcher,
1/2 Gal. . . . .785.00 to 850.00
Tray, For Sugar &
Creamer . . . . . . . . . . . .50.00
Tumbler, Iced Tea,
Footed, 11 Oz. . . . . . . .475.00

## NO. 612

Indiana Glass Company, Dunkirk, Indiana, called this pattern No. 612, but collectors call it Horseshoe. It was made from 1930 to 1933 primarily in Green and Yellow, with a smaller number of Pink pieces. Sugar and creamer sets were also made in Crystal. Plates came in two styles, one with the center pattern, one plain.

### GREEN
Berry Bowl, Master,
9 1/2 In. . . . . . .37.50 to 45.00
Bowl, Oval,
10 1/2 In. . . . . .24.00 to 70.00
Bowl, Salad, 7 1/2 In. . . . .22.50
Creamer, Footed . . . . . . . .17.00
Cup . . . . . . . . .10.00 to 12.00
Cup & Saucer . .11.00 to 19.00
Plate, Breakfast,
9 3/8 In. . . . . . .13.50 to 15.00
Plate, Dessert,
6 In. . . . . . . . . . .5.00 to 6.00
Plate, Luncheon,
8 3/8 In. . . . . . .9.50 to 11.00
Relish, 3 Sections,
Footed . . . . . . . . . . . . .25.00
Sandwich Server,
11 1/2 In. . . . . . . . . . . .20.00
Saucer . . . . . . . . . . . . . . .5.00
Sherbet, Footed . .10.00 to 15.00
Sugar . . . . . . . . .12.00 to 17.00
Sugar & Creamer . . . . . . .31.50
Tumbler, Footed, Water,
9 Oz., 4 1/2 In. . . . . . . .22.00

### YELLOW
Berry Bowl, 4 1/2 In. . . . .70.00
Bowl, Cereal,
6 1/2 In. . . . . . .15.00 to 24.00
Bowl, Salad,
7 1/2 In. . . . . . .25.00 to 32.00
Bowl, Vegetable, Oval,
10 1/2 In. . . . . . . . . . . .27.50
Creamer . . . . . . . . . . . . .18.00
Cup & Saucer . . . . . . . .17.00
Pitcher, Water, 64 Oz.,
8 1/2 In. . . . .375.00 to 850.00
Plate, Dessert, 6 In. . . . . . .5.50
Plate, Luncheon,
8 3/8 In. . . . . . .7.00 to 11.00
Platter, Oval,
10 3/4 In. . . . . .15.00 to 35.00
Relish, 3 Sections,
Footed . . . . . .31.00 to 40.00
Sandwich Server,
11 1/2 In. . . . . .15.00 to 32.00
Saucer . . . . . . . . . . . . . . .4.50
Sherbet, Footed . .15.00 to 17.00
Sugar, Footed . . . . . . . . . .16.00
Sugar & Creamer,
Footed . . . . . .32.00 to 36.00
Tumbler, Water, Footed,
9 Oz. . . . . . . . .20.00 to 25.00

## NO. 615

No. 615 is often called Lorain or sometimes Basket, Bridal Bouquet, Flower Basket, or Hanging Basket. It was made by the Indiana Glass Company from 1929 to 1932 of Crystal, Green, and Yellow. Sometimes Crystal pieces have blue, green, red, or yellow borders. Reproduction pieces were made of Milk Glass or Olive Green.

### CRYSTAL
Cup . . . . . . . . . . . . . . . .9.50
Plate, Salad, 7 3/4 In. . . . .10.00

### GREEN
Bowl, Oval, 9 3/4 In. . . . .40.00
Cup . . . . . . . . . . . . . . .11.00
Plate, Dinner, Square,
10 In. . . . . . . . . . . . . . .40.00
Plate, Luncheon,
8 3/8 In. . . . . . .20.00 to 21.00
Plate, Salad,
7 3/4 In. . . . . . .10.00 to 11.00
Sherbet, Footed . .20.00 to 28.00
Tumbler, Water, Footed,
9 Oz., 4 3/4 In. . . . . . . .20.00

### YELLOW
Bowl, Cereal, 6 In. . . . . . .71.00
Bowl, Salad,
7 1/4 In. . . . . . .50.00 to 69.00
Bowl, Vegetable, Oval,
9 1/4 In. . . . . . .46.00 to 50.00
Creamer . . . . . . . . . . . . .20.00
Cup . . . . . . . . .12.00 to 20.00
Cup & Saucer . .20.00 to 30.00
Plate, Dinner,
10 1/4 In. . . . . .60.00 to 75.00
Plate, Luncheon,
8 3/8 In. . . . . . .16.50 to 30.00
Plate, Salad,
7 3/4 In. . . . . . .10.00 to 16.00
Plate, Sherbet, 5 1/2 In. . .11.00
Platter,
11 1/2 In. . . . . .35.00 to 50.00

Relish, 4 Sections,
8 In. . . . . . . . . .32.00 to 35.00
Saucer . . . . . . . . . .4.00 to 7.00
Sherbet, Footed . .25.00 to 35.00
Sugar, Footed . . .20.00 to 22.00
Tumbler, Water, Footed, 9 Oz.,
4 3/4 In. . . . . . .28.00 to 30.00

## NO. 618

Another Indiana Glass Company pattern made from 1932 to 1937 was No. 618, or Pineapple & Floral. It is also called Meadow Flower, Lacy Daisy, or Wildflower. The pattern was made of Amber, Crystal, and fired-on Green and Red. Reproductions were made in Olive Green in the late 1960s.

### AMBER
Cup & Saucer . .12.50 to 14.00
Plate, Dinner, 9 3/8 In. . . .18.00
Soup, Cream, Handle . . . .20.00

### CRYSTAL
Ashtray,
4 1/2 In. . . . . . .9.75 to 16.00
Bowl, Cereal, 6 In. . . . . .25.00
Bowl, Salad, 7 In. . .2.00 to 3.00
Bowl, Vegetable, Oval,
10 In. . . . . . . . . . . . . .12.00
Cup & Saucer . .13.50 to 15.00
Plate, Dessert, 6 In. . . . . . .5.00
Plate, Dinner, 9 1/2 In. . . .17.00
Plate, Indentation,
11 1/2 In. . . . . . . . . . . .12.00
Plate, Luncheon, 8 1/2 In. . .8.00
Platter, Closed Handle,
11 In. . . . . . . . . . . . . .18.00
Platter, Relish, Sections,
11 1/2 In. . . . . .15.00 to 18.00
Sandwich Server,
11 1/2 In. . . . . .18.00 to 25.00
Sherbet, Diamond-Shape . . 6.00

Sherbet, Footed . .16.00 to 18.00
Sugar &
Creamer . . . . .13.00 to 15.00
Tumbler, Water, 8 Oz.,
4 1/4 In. . . . . . . . . . . . .35.00

## NO. 620

No. 620, also known as Daisy, was made by Indiana Glass Company. In 1933 the pattern was made in Crystal, and in 1940 in Amber; in the 1960s and 1970s reproductions were made in Dark Green and Milk Glass. Some pieces have a fired-on Red color.

### AMBER
Berry Bowl, 4 1/2 In. . . . . .8.00
Bowl, Oval, 10 In. . . . . . .16.00
Cake Plate,
11 1/2 In. . . . . . .9.00 to 13.00
Creamer, Footed . . . . . . . .8.00
Cup . . . . . . . . . . . . . . . .6.00
Cup & Saucer . . . .5.50 to 8.00
Plate, Dessert,
6 In. . . . . . . . . . .4.00 to 9.00
Plate, Dinner,
9 3/8 In. . . . . . . .8.00 to 9.00
Platter, 10 3/4 In. . . . . . .14.00
Relish, 3 Sections,
8 3/8 In. . . . . . .30.00 to 35.00
Saucer . . . . . . . . . . . . . .3.00
Soup, Cream,
4 1/2 In. . . . . . .6.00 to 12.00
Sugar . . . . . . . . . .6.00 to 9.00
Sugar &
Creamer . . . . .12.50 to 14.50
Tumbler, Water, Footed,
9 Oz. . . . . . . . .18.00 to 20.00

### DARK GREEN
Bowl, Vegetable, Oval,
10 In. . . . . . . . . . . . . . .11.00
Cup & Saucer . . . . . . . . .5.50

Plate, Dinner, 9 3/8 In. . . . .6.50
Plate, Salad,
7 3/8 In. . . . . . . . .3.50 to 6.50
Tumbler, Iced Tea, Footed,
12 Oz. . . . . . . . . . . . . .22.50

**NO. 622,** see Pretzel

**NO. 624,** see Christmas Candy

## NORMANDIE

A few Depression glass patterns were made in Iridescent Marigold color, which has been collected as carnival glass. Normandie products made in this iridescence, called Sunburst, appear in the carnival glass listings as Bouquet and Lattice; when the pattern is in the other known colors, it is called Normandie. Look for it in Amber, Crystal, Pink, and Spring Green, as well as in the Iridescent color. Normandie was made by the Federal Glass Company from 1933 to 1940.

### AMBER
Berry Bowl, 5 In. . .4.00 to 6.00
Bowl, Cereal, 6 1/2 In. . . . .6.00
Creamer, Footed . . . . . . . .16.00
Cup . . . . . . . . . . . . . . . .7.50
Cup & Saucer . . .8.00 to 11.00
Pitcher, Water,
8 In. . . . . . . . 75.00 to 89.00

Plate, Dessert, 6 In. . . . . . .4.50
Plate, Dinner, 11 In. . . . . .27.75
Plate, Luncheon,
 9 1/4 In. . . . . .12.50 to 15.00
Plate, Salad, 7 3/4 In. . . . .10.00
Salt & Pepper . . . . . . . .55.00
Saucer . . . . . . . . . . . . . .4.00
Sugar & Creamer . . . . . . .16.50
Tumbler, Iced Tea, 12 Oz.,
 5 In. . . . . . . . . . . . . . .50.00
Tumbler, Juice, 5 Oz.,
 4 In. . . . . . . . . . . . . . .38.00
Tumbler, Water, 9 Oz.,
 4 1/4 In. . . . . . .20.00 to 25.00

### IRIDESCENT
Berry Bowl, Master,
 8 1/2 In. . . . . . . . . . . . .10.50
Bowl, 5 In. . . . . . .3.00 to 5.00
Bowl, Cereal,
 6 1/2 In. . . . . . . .6.00 to 9.00
Bowl, Vegetable, Oval,
 10 In. . . . . . . . . . . . . . .17.00
Creamer . . . . . . . . .6.00 to 8.00
Cup & Saucer . . . .5.75 to 9.00
Grill Plate, 11 In. . .5.50 to 9.00
Plate, Luncheon,
 9 1/4 In. . . . . . .15.00 to 16.50
Plate, Sherbet,
 6 In. . . . . . . . . . .2.00 to 3.00
Sherbet, Footed . . . .5.00 to 7.00
Sugar &
 Creamer . . . . .12.00 to 14.00

### PINK
Berry Bowl, Master,
 8 1/2 In. . . . . . . . . . . . .42.00
Bowl, Vegetable, Oval,
 10 In. . . . . . . . . . . . . . .70.00
Cup . . . . . . . . . .6.00 to 12.00
Cup & Saucer . .10.00 to 14.50
Plate, Luncheon,
 9 1/4 In. . . . . . . . . . . . .28.00

---

**To clean wax from glass candlesticks, scrape with a wooden stick, then wash off the remaining wax with rubbing alcohol.**

---

Plate, Salad,
 7 3/4 In. . . . . . .10.00 to 14.00
Plate, Sherbet,
 6 In. . . . . . . . . . .7.00 to 8.00
Sherbet, Footed . . . . . . . .8.50
Tumbler, Iced Tea, 12 Oz.,
 5 In. . . . . . . . . . . . . . .100.00
Tumbler, Water, 9 Oz.,
 4 1/4 In. . . . . . . . . . . . .50.00

---

## OLD CAFE

Old Cafe is one of the few patterns with only one name. It was made by the Anchor Hocking Glass Corporation, Lancaster, Ohio, from 1936 to 1938. Pieces are found in Crystal, Pink, and Royal Ruby.

### CRYSTAL
Bowl, 9 In. . . . . . . . . . . . .9.00
Bowl, Cereal, Tab Handle,
 5 1/2 In. . . . . . . . . . . . . .8.00
Candy Dish, Low, 8 In. . . .5.00
Candy Dish, Ruby
 Cover . . . . . . . . . . . .15.00
Dish, Olive, 6 In. . . . . . . .6.00
Tumbler, Juice, 3 In. . . . . .10.00

### PINK
Bowl, 5 In. . . . . . . . . . . .12.00
Bowl, Closed Handles,
 9 In. . . . . . . . . . . . . . .10.00
Candy Dish, Low,
 8 In. . . . . . . . . .9.50 to 15.00
Cup . . . . . . . . . . .5.00 to 6.00
Cup & Saucer . . . . . . . .15.50
Pitcher, Water, 80 Oz. . . .80.00
Tumbler, Juice, 3 In. . . . . .16.00
Tumbler, Water, 4 In. . . . .16.00

### ROYAL RUBY
Bowl, Cereal, 5 1/2 In. . . .19.00
Candy Dish, Low,
 8 In. . . . . . . . . .10.00 to 15.00
Cup . . . . . . . . . . . . . . . .7.00

---

Plate, Closed Handle,
 9 In. . . . . . . . . . . . . . .15.00

## OLD ENGLISH

Old English, or Threading, was made by the Indiana Glass Company, Dunkirk, Indiana, in the late 1920s and early 1930s. It was first made in Amber, Crystal, and Forest Green. Pink was a later color.

### FOREST GREEN
Bowl, Footed, 9 In. . . . . .35.00
Creamer, Footed . . . . . . .15.00
Cup . . . . . . . . . . . . . . .10.00
Pitcher, Footed . . . . . . . .77.00
Plate, Breakfast, 9 In. . . . .15.00
Plate, Salad, 7 1/2 In. . . . .17.00
Platter, Oval, 11 1/2 In. . .26.00
Sherbet, Footed . . . . . . . .15.00
Tumbler, Juice, Footed,
 4 1/2 In. . . . . . . . . . . . .30.00
Tumbler, Water, Footed,
 5 1/2 In. . . . . . . . . . . . .42.00

**OLD FLORENTINE,** see Florentine No. 1

**OPALESCENT HOBNAIL,** see Moonstone

**OPEN LACE,** see Lace Edge

**OPEN ROSE,** see Mayfair Open Rose

**OPEN SCALLOP,** see Lace Edge

**OPTIC DESIGN,** see Raindrops

**ORIENTAL POPPY,** see Florentine No. 2

## OVIDE

Hazel Atlas Glass Company made Ovide pattern from 1929 to the 1950s. It was made in Green at first. By 1932 it was Black and by 1935 Platonite or Opaque White glass was used with fired-on colors. Pieces were made with colored rims; overall fired-on colors; or decorations, which included things like birds, windmills, or Art Deco geometrics. Ovide is sometimes incorrectly called New Century.

### BLACK
Creamer, Footed . . . . . . . . .6.50

### GREEN
Plate, Breakfast, 9 In. . . . . .6.00
Sugar . . . . . . . . . . . . . . . .4.00

### PLATONITE
Bowl, Cereal, Black
    Flowers, 5 In. . . . . . . . .10.00
Creamer, Blue Flowers . . . .9.00
Cup & Saucer, Green
    Stripe . . . . . . . . . . . . . .5.00
Eggcup, Flying Geese . . . .22.00
Plate, Breakfast, Wide Red
    Scroll, 9 In. . . . . . . . . . .6.75
Plate, Flying Geese,
    9 In. . . . . . . . . . . . . . . .25.00
Saucer, Green Stripe . . . . . . .50
Sherbet, Flying Geese,
    6 In. . . . . . . . . . . . . . . .15.00
Sherbet, Red & Black
    Windmill, 6 In. . . . . . . .14.00
Sherbet, Red Stripe, 6 In. . .4.50
Tumbler, Black Flowers . .15.00

**OVIDE,** see also New Century

**OXFORD,** see Chinex Classic

## OYSTER & PEARL

Anchor Hocking Glass Corporation, Lancaster, Ohio, made only accessory pieces in the Oyster & Pearl pattern from 1938 to 1940. The first pieces were Crystal or Pink. Those with a white outside and fired-on pink or green interiors were made later, as were Royal Ruby pieces.

### CRYSTAL
Bowl, Fruit, 10 1/2 In. . . .20.00
Relish, 2 Sections,
    10 1/4 In. . . . . . . . . . . .10.00
Sandwich Tray, 13 In. . . .20.00

### PINK
Bowl, Fruit, 10 1/2 In. . . .14.00
Bowl, 2 Handles,
    6 1/2 In. . . . . . . . . . . . .18.00
Bowl, Heart Shape,
    5 1/4 In. . . . . . .8.00 to 15.00
Relish, 2 Sections,
    10 1/4 In. . . . . .10.00 to 15.00
Sandwich Tray,
    13 1/2 In. . . . . . . . . . . .34.00

### ROYAL RUBY
Bowl, Fruit,
    10 1/2 In. . . . . .55.00 to 75.00
Bowl, Fruit, Handle,
    5 1/2 In. . . . . . .13.00 to 19.75
Bowl, Handle,
    6 1/2 In. . . . . . .20.00 to 23.00
Bowl, Heart Shape,
    5 1/4 In. . . . . . . . . . . . .15.00
Candleholder, 3 1/2 In.,
    Pair . . . . . . . .25.00 to 50.00

**PANELED ASTER,** see Madrid

**PANELED CHERRY BLOSSOM,** see
    Cherry Blossom

**PANSY & DORIC,** see Doric &
    Pansy

**PARROT,** see Sylvan

## PATRICIAN

Federal Glass Company, Columbus, Ohio, made Patrician, sometimes called Hinge or Spoke, from 1933 to 1937. Full dinner sets were made in Golden Glo and Green, and smaller quantities in Crystal and Pink. Yellow pieces were produced later.

### CRYSTAL
Berry Bowl, 5 In. . . . . . . . .9.50
Berry Bowl, Master,
    8 1/2 In. . . . . . . . . . . . .24.00
Cookie Jar,
    Cover . . . . . . .50.00 to 65.00
Cup . . . . . . . . . . .8.00 to 8.50
Grill Plate, 10 1/2 In. . . . .13.50
Pitcher, 75 Oz., 8 In. . . .100.00
Pitcher, Applied Handle,
    75 Oz., 8 1/2 In. . . . . . .150.00
Plate, Dinner, 10 1/2 In. . .13.50
Plate, Salad, 7 1/2 In. . . . .15.00
Platter, Oval, 11 1/2 In. . .30.00
Salt & Pepper . . .57.00 to 65.00
Sherbet . . . . . . .10.00 to 13.00
Sugar . . . . . . . . . . . . . . . .9.00
Sugar, Cover . . . . . . . . . .64.00

---

**Put a silver spoon in a
glass before pouring in
hot water. It will absorb
heat and keep the glass
from cracking.**

---

❖

**Watch burning candles in glass candlesticks. If the candle burns too low, the hot wax and flame may break the glass.**

❖

Tumbler, Iced Tea, 14 Oz.,
  5 1/2 In. . . . . . .38.00 to 45.00
Tumbler, Juice, 5 Oz.,
  4 In. . . . . . . . . . . . . . . .21.00
Tumbler, Water, 9 Oz.,
  4 1/2 In. . . . . . . . . . . . .25.00

### GOLDEN GLO
Berry Bowl,
  5 In. . . . . . . . . .10.50 to 12.00
Berry Bowl, Master,
  8 1/2 In. . . . . . .43.00 to 52.50
Bowl, Cereal,
  6 In. . . . . . . . .22.50 to 31.00
Bowl, Vegetable, Oval,
  10 In. . . . . . . .30.00 to 35.00
Butter, Cover . . .90.00 to 92.00
Cookie Jar,
  Cover . . . . . . .75.00 to 89.50
Creamer, Footed . .6.75 to 15.00
Cup . . . . . . . . . .8.00 to 10.00
Cup & Saucer . .15.00 to 20.00
Grill Plate,
  10 1/2 In. . . . . .12.50 to 13.50
Jam Jar . . . . . . .30.00 to 31.00
Pitcher, 75 Oz.,
  8 In. . . . . . . .110.00 to 120.00
Pitcher, Applied Handle,
  75 Oz., 8 1/4 In. . . . . . .125.00
Plate, Dinner,
  10 1/2 In. . . . . . . . . . . .10.00
Plate, Luncheon,
  9 In. . . . . . . . . .8.75 to 15.00
Plate, Salad,
  7 1/2 In. . . . . . .14.00 to 18.00
Plate, Sherbet,
  6 In. . . . . . . . . .9.00 to 10.00
Platter, Oval,
  11 1/2 In. . . . . .15.00 to 30.00
Salt & Pepper . . .38.00 to 65.00
Saucer . . . . . . . . . . . . . .12.00
Sherbet . . . . . . .10.00 to 13.00

Soup, Cream,
  4 3/4 In. . . . . . .12.00 to 18.00
Sugar . . . . . . . . . .6.00 to 9.00
Sugar, Cover . . . .45.00 to 65.00
Sugar & Creamer . . . . . . .19.00
Tumbler, Footed, 8 Oz.,
  5 1/4 In. . . . . . .37.00 to 50.00
Tumbler, Iced Tea, 14 Oz.,
  5 1/2 In. . . . . . .40.00 to 42.00
Tumbler, Juice, 5 Oz.,
  4 In. . . . . . . . . .28.00 to 30.00
Tumbler, Water, 9 Oz.,
  4 1/2 In. . . . . . .24.00 to 27.50

### GREEN
Berry Bowl, Master,
  8 1/2 In. . . . . . .34.00 to 37.00
Bowl, Cereal, 6 In. . . . .25.00 to 27.00
Bowl, Vegetable, Oval,
  10 In. . . . . . . . . . . . . . .37.00
Butter, Cover . .100.00 to 115.00
Cookie Jar, Cover . . . . .200.00
Creamer,
  Footed . . . . . .10.00 to 12.00
Cup . . . . . . . . . .8.50 to 12.00
Cup & Saucer . .19.00 to 20.00
Grill Plate, 10 1/2 In. . . . .15.00
Plate, Luncheon,
  9 In. . . . . . . . . .9.00 to 12.00
Plate, Salad,
  7 1/2 In. . . . . . .16.00 to 18.00
Platter, Oval, 11 1/2 In. . . .23.50
Salt & Pepper . . .60.00 to 70.00
Sherbet . . . . . . .12.00 to 14.00
Soup, Cream, 4 3/4 In. . . .10.00
Sugar . . . . . . . . .8.00 to 10.00
Sugar &
  Creamer . . . . .19.00 to 21.00
Tumbler, Juice, 5 Oz.,
  4 In. . . . . . . . . .30.00 to 36.00
Tumbler, Water, 9 Oz.,
  4 1/2 In. . . . . . . . . . . . .30.00

### PINK
Berry Bowl,
  5 In. . . . . . . . .11.00 to 17.00
Berry Bowl, Master,
  8 1/2 In. . . . . . . . . . . . .35.00
Bowl, Vegetable, Oval,
  10 In. . . . . . . . . . . . . . .20.00
Butter, Cover . . . . . . . .225.00
Creamer . . . . . . . . . . . .12.00
Grill Plate, 10 1/2 In. . . . .36.00
Salt & Pepper . . . . . . . .85.00

Tumbler, Iced Tea,
  14 Oz., 5 1/2 In. . . . . . .46.00
Tumbler, Water, 9 Oz.,
  4 1/2 In. . . . . . . . . . . . .30.00

## PEACH LUSTRE

Peach Lustre is both a pattern and a color name used for Fire-King dinnerware made by Anchor Hocking Glass Corporation from 1952 to 1963. The pattern has a laurel leaf design around the edge of the plates and bowls and the side of the cups. The pieces are a lustrous orange-yellow color. The same pattern of laurel leaves was made in 1953 in gray and was known as Gray Laurel pattern. Bubble and Boopie pattern crystal stemware were made with a similar design to go with the dinnerware.

Bowl, Cereal,
  7 5/8 In. . . . . . . . .3.00 to 5.00
Bowl, Fruit, 4 7/8 In. . . . . .1.50
Bowl, Vegetable,
  8 1/2 In. . . . . . . . . . . . . .7.00
Casserole, French,
  Table Lid . . . . . . . . . . . .5.00
Casserole, Tab Handle,
  5 x 9 In. . . . . . . . . . . . .10.00
Creamer, Footed . . .2.50 to 5.00
Cup & Saucer . . . . . . . . .3.00
Cup & Saucer, After
  Dinner . . . . . . . . . . . . .40.00
Pie Plate, 9 In. . . . . . . . . .5.00
Plate, Dinner, 9 1/8 In. . . . .6.50
Saucer . . . . . . . . . . . . . . .1.00
Sugar . . . . . . . . . . . . . . .2.50
Sugar, Footed . . . . . . . . . .6.00
Sugar & Creamer,
  Footed . . . . . . . . .7.00 to 8.00
Tom & Jerry Set,
  9 Piece . . . . . . . . . . . .95.00
Vase, Ribbed . . . . .6.00 to 7.50

**PEACOCK & ROSE,** see Peacock & Wild Rose

## PEACOCK & WILD ROSE

Line 300 was the name used by Paden City Glass Company, Paden City, West Virginia, for the pattern now called Peacock & Wild Rose. It was made in the 1930s of Amber, Black, Cobalt Blue, Crystal, Green, Light Blue, Pink, and Red. A few of the lists call this pattern Peacock & Rose.

#### BLACK
Vase, 10 In. . . . . . . . . .350.00
Vase, Elliptical, 10 In. . .600.00

#### CRYSTAL
Bowl, Footed, 10 1/2 In. . .95.00

#### GREEN
Console, Rolled Edge,
   14 In. . . . . . . . . . . . . .225.00
Vase, 10 In. . . . . . . . . .135.00
Vase, Elliptical, 10 In. . .375.00

#### PINK
Bowl, Footed, 10 1/2 In. . .70.00
Cake Plate, Footed,
   11 In. . . . . . .115.00 to 125.00
Vase, 10 In. . . . . . . . . .155.00

**PEBBLE OPTIC,** see Raindrops

**PETAL SWIRL,** see Swirl

## PETALWARE

Macbeth-Evans Glass Company made Petalware from 1930 to 1940. It was first made in Crystal and Pink. In 1932 the dinnerware was made in Monax, in 1933 in Cremax. The pattern remained popular, and in 1936 Cobalt Blue and several other variations were made. Some pieces were hand-painted with pastel bands of ivory, green, and pink. Some pieces were decorated with a gold or red rim. Flower or fruit designs in bright colors were used on others. Bright bands of fired-on blue, green, red, and yellow were used to decorate some wares. All of these patterns have their own names. These include Banded Petalware, Daisy Petals, Diamond Point, Petal, Shell, and Vivid Bands.

#### COBALT BLUE
Mustard,
   Underplate . . . .12.00 to 15.00

#### CREMAX
Berry Bowl, Master,
   9 In. . . . . . . . . .7.00 to 30.00
Cup . . . . . . . . . . . . . . . .10.00
Cup & Saucer . . .7.00 to 14.00
Cup & Saucer, Pastel
   Bands . . . . . . . . . . . . .10.00
Plate, Dinner, 9 In. . . . . . .5.50
Plate, Dinner, Gold
   Trim, 9 In. . . . . . . . . . .14.00
Plate, Salad, 8 In. . . . . . . .3.00
Plate, Salad, Gold
   Trim, 8 In. . . . . . . . . . .10.00
Plate, Salad, Pastel Bands,
   8 In. . . . . . . . . . .8.00 to 9.00
Salver, 11 In. . . . . . . . . . .9.00
Salver, Pastel Bands,
   11 In. . . . . . . . . . . . . .13.00
Saucer . . . . . . . . . . . . . . .3.50
Saucer, Pastel Bands . . . . .3.00
Sherbet, Gold Trim . . . . .12.00
Soup, Cream, 4 1/2 In. . . .16.00
Soup, Cream, Gold Trim,
   4 1/2 In. . . . . . . . . . . . .12.00

Sugar . . . . . . . . .7.00 to 10.00

#### CRYSTAL
Bowl, Cereal, Gold Trim,
   5 3/4 In. . . . . . . . . . . . . .8.00
Cup & Saucer . . .4.00 to 14.00
Plate, Salad, 8 In. . . . . . .10.00
Sugar & Creamer . . . . . . .23.50
Tumbler, Water, Red Band,
   12 Oz., 4 5/8 In. . . . . .88.50

#### MONAX
Berry Bowl, Master,
   9 In. . . . . . . . . .18.00 to 23.00
Bowl, Cereal,
   5 3/4 In. . . . . . . .8.00 to 11.00
Bowl, Cereal, Gold Trim,
   5 3/4 In. . . . . . . . . . . . . .8.00
Casserole, Cover, 1/2 Qt. . .5.00
Cup & Saucer . . .6.00 to 12.00
Lamp Shade . . . . .9.00 to 15.00
Plate, Dinner,
   9 In. . . . . . . . . .4.00 to 13.00
Plate, Salad,
   8 In. . . . . . . . . .4.00 to 15.00
Plate, Sherbet,
   6 In. . . . . . . . . . .2.00 to 6.00
Platter, Oval, 13 In. . . . . .17.00
Salver, 11 In. . . . . . . . . .10.00
Sherbet, Footed,
   4 In. . . . . . . . . . .7.00 to 8.00
Soup, Cream, 4 1/2 In. . . .10.00
Soup, Dish, 7 In. . . . . . . .57.00
Sugar, Footed . . . . .5.00 to 9.50
Sugar, Gold Trim,
   Footed . . . . . . . . . . . . .12.00
Sugar &
   Creamer . . . . . .9.75 to 10.00

#### PINK
Berry Bowl, Master,
   9 In. . . . . . . . . . . . . . .25.00
Bowl, Cereal,
   5 3/4 In. . . . . . . .8.50 to 13.00
Cake Stand, Harp . . . . . . .25.00
Compote, 6 In. . . . . . . . .15.00
Creamer,
   Footed . . . . . . .13.00 to 15.00
Goblet, Water, 6 1/4 In. . .12.00
Plate, Dinner,
   9 In. . . . . . . . . .11.00 to 15.00
Plate, Salad, 8 In. . . . . . . .5.00
Platter, Oval,
   13 In. . . . . . . . .15.00 to 19.00
Punch Cup . . . . . . . . . . . .6.00

Salver, 11 In. . . . . . . . . .17.00
Saucer . . . . . . . . . . . . . .2.00
Snack Set, 4 . . . . . . . . . .45.00
Soup, Cream,
  4 1/2 In. . . . . . .10.00 to 18.00
Sugar . . . . . . . . . . . . . .11.00
Sugar, Cover, Footed . . . .25.00
Sugar, Footed . . . . . . . . .11.00
Tidbit, 6 Sections . . . . . .30.00
Vase, 7 In. . . . . . .29.00 to 35.00

## PHILBE

Philbe is a Fire-King dinnerware made by the Anchor
Hocking Glass Corporation
from 1937 to the 1940s. It was
made in Blue, Crystal, Green,
and Pink. The Blue sometimes
has platinum trim. Philbe is the
dinnerware pattern; the matching kitchenware is called Fire-
King Oven Glass.

**BLUE**
Creamer . . . . . . . . . . . .135.00
Cup . . . . . . .135.00 to 160.00
Plate, Grill, 10 1/2 In. . . .80.00
Plate, Luncheon, 8 In. . . .50.00

**CRYSTAL**
Bowl, Cereal,
  5 1/2 In. . . . . . .15.00 to 18.00
Cup . . . . . . . . . . . . . . .55.00
Bowl, Salad,
  7 In. . . . . . . . .20.00 to 25.00
Creamer, Footed . . . . . .36.00
Mug, Child's . . . . . . . . .12.00
Sugar, Cover . . . . . . . . . .10.00
Tumbler, Footed,
  10 Oz., 5 In. . . . . . . . .25.00

**GREEN**
Creamer, Footed,
  3 1/4 In. . . . . . . . . . . .110.00
Pitcher, Juice,
  6 In. . . . . . .595.00 to 695.00
Plate, 10 1/2 In. . . . . . . .60.00

**PINK**
Bowl, Salad, 7 In. . . . . . .50.00
Cup . . . . . . . . . . . . . .100.00
Plate, Luncheon,
  8 In. . . . . . . . .35.00 to 40.00
Tumbler, Iced Tea,
  6 1/2 In. . . . . . . . . . . . .75.00

**PHILBE,** see also Fire-King

**PIE CRUST,** see Cremax

**PINEAPPLE & FLORAL,** see No. 618

**PINWHEEL,** see Sierra

**POINSETTIA,** see Floral

**POPPY NO. 1,** see Florentine No. 1

**POPPY NO. 2,** see Florentine No. 2

## PORTIA

Portia was made by Cambridge
Glass Company from 1932 to
the early 1950s. It was made in
Amber, Crystal, Green, Heatherbloom, and Yellow.

**CRYSTAL**
Ashtray, 5 1/2 In. . . . . . . .45.00
Cup . . . . . . . . . . . . . . .35.00
Cup & Saucer . . . . . . . .42.50
Decanter, Footed,
  28 Oz. . . . . . . . . . . . .295.00
Dish, Mayonnaise,
  2 Piece . . . . . . . . . . . .72.50
Goblet, Cocktail, 3 Oz. . . .32.50
Goblet,
  Cordial . . . . .65.00 to 125.00
Goblet, Parfait, 5 Oz. . . . .95.00
Goblet, Water, 10 Oz. . . . .35.00
Goblet, Wine, 2 1/2 Oz. . .50.00
Jam Jar, Cover . . . . . . . .75.00

Oyster Cocktail,
  4 1/2 Oz. . . . . . . . . . . .37.50
Oyster Cocktail, Icer,
  4 1/2 Oz., 2 Piece . . . . .72.50
Pitcher, Tankard . . . . . . .47.50
Plate, Bread & Butter,
  6 1/2 In. . . . . . . . . . . . .14.50
Plate, Salad, 8 In. . . . . . .17.50
Relish, 3 Sections, 9 In. . .55.00
Relish, 3 Sections,
  12 In. . . . . . . . . . . . . . .68.00
Relish, 5 Sections,
  12 In. . . . . . . . .55.00 to 75.00
Relish, Handle, 14 In. . . . .95.00
Sherbet, Tall, 6 Oz. . . . . . .25.00
Soup, Cream, Liner . . . . .30.00
Tumbler, Iced Tea, Footed,
  12 Oz. . . . . . . . . . . . . .45.00

**PRETTY POLLY PARTY DISHES,**
  see Doric & Pansy

## PRETZEL

Pretzel, also called No. 622 or
Ribbon Candy, was made by
Indiana Glass Company, Dunkirk, Indiana, in the 1930s.
Avocado, Crystal, and Teal
pieces were made. Some reproductions appeared in the 1970s
in Amber and Blue.

**CRYSTAL**
Berry Bowl, Stippled,
  Master, 9 3/8 In. . . . . . .13.00
Bowl, Fruit, 4 1/2 In. . . . . .3.00
Celery Dish, 10 1/4 In. . . . .1.50

Creamer . . . . . . . . .3.00 to 6.00
Cup . . . . . . . . . . .4.50 to 6.00
Cup & Saucer . . . .5.50 to 7.00
Plate, Bread & Butter,
    6 In. . . . . . . . . . . .1.75 to 3.00
Plate, Cheese, Handle,
    6 In. . . . . . . . . . . . . . . .7.00
Plate, Dinner,
    9 3/8 In. . . . . . .7.00 to 15.00
Plate, Indentation, Square,
    7 In. . . . . . . . . . . . . . . .9.00
Plate, Salad, 8 3/8 In. . . . . .6.00
Relish, 3 Sections, 7 In. . . .9.00
Sandwich Server,
    11 1/2 In. . . . . . . . . . . . .8.00
Saucer . . . . . . . . . . . . . . .1.00
Soup, Coupe,
    7 1/2 In. . . . . . .7.00 to 10.00
Sugar . . . . . . . . . .4.00 to 6.00
Sugar & Creamer . .6.50 to 9.00
Tumbler, Iced Tea,
    12 Oz., 5 1/2 In. . . . . .77.50
Tumbler, Water, 9 Oz.,
    4 1/2 In. . . . . . . . . . . .55.00

## PRIMO

Green and Mandarin Yellow
are the two colors of Primo
advertised in the 1932 U.S.
Glass Company catalog.

**GREEN**
Ashtray . . . . . . . . . . . . . .8.75
Cake Plate, Footed,
    10 In. . . . . . . . . . . . . .23.50
Cup . . . . . . . . . .9.00 to 14.50
Cup & Saucer . . . . . . . . .15.00
Grill Plate, 10 In. . . . . . .12.00
Plate, Dinner, 10 In. . . . .25.50
Plate, Salad,
    7 1/2 In. . . . . .10.25 to 14.00
Saucer . . . . . . . . . . . . . 3.25

Sherbet . . . . . . . . . . . . .14.25
Sugar . . . . . . . . . . . . . . .12.00
Tumbler, Water, 9 Oz.,
    5 3/4 In. . . . . .18.50 to 23.50

**MANDARIN YELLOW**
Creamer . . . . . . . . . . . . . .8.50
Cup . . . . . . . . . . . . . . . .14.50
Grill Plate, 10 In. . . . . . .11.25
Sherbet . . . . . . . . . . . . .14.50
Tumbler, Water, Footed, 9 Oz.,
    5 3/4 In. . . . . .16.00 to 20.00

## PRIMROSE

Primrose was a pattern made by
Anchor Hocking Glass Corporation from 1960 to 1962. The
white opaque glass was decorated with a red primrose.

**WHITE**
Baking Pan, Utility,
    6 1/2 x 10 1/2 In. . . . . . .5.00
Bowl, Dessert, 6 Oz. . . . . .3.00
Cake Pan, Round, 8 In. . . .5.00
Cup, 8 Oz. . . . . . . . . . . . .2.00
Plate, Salad, 7 3/8 In. . . . .2.50
Saucer . . . . . . . . . . . . . . .1.50
Snack Set, 2 Piece . . . . . .2.50
Snack Set, 8 Piece . . . . .20.00
Sugar . . . . . . . . . . . . . . . .2.50
Sugar, Cover . . . . . . . . . .5.00
Sugar & Creamer . . . . . . .6.00

**PRIMUS,** see Madrid

## PRINCESS

Hocking Glass Company, Lancaster, Ohio, made the popular
Princess pattern from 1931 to
1935. The first sets were made
in Green or Yellow, shaded
from Apricot to Topaz, so if
you are assembling a set, be
careful of the color variations.

Pink was added last. There are
Blue pieces found in the West.
Some pieces have a frosted finish, some are decorated with
hand-painted flowers. Green is
sometimes trimmed with gold;
other colors are trimmed with
platinum. This pattern is sometimes called Drape & Tassel,
Lincoln Drape, or Tassel. Reproductions have been made.
They are listed at the end of the
Depression Glass section.

**GREEN**
Ashtray, 4 1/2 In. . . . . . .70.00
Berry Bowl,
    4 1/2 In. . . . . . .25.00 to 29.00
Bowl, Cereal,
    5 In. . . . . . . . . .25.00 to 35.00
Bowl, Hat Shape,
    9 1/2 In. . . . . . . . . . . .42.50
Bowl, Salad, Octagonal,
    9 In. . . . . . . . . .30.00 to 50.00
Bowl, Vegetable, Oval,
    10 In. . . . . . . . .28.00 to 32.00
Butter, Cover . . .50.00 to 95.00
Cake Stand, Footed,
    10 In. . . . . . . . .25.00 to 45.00
Candy Jar,
    Cover . . . . . . .52.00 to 60.00
Coaster . . . . . . . . . . . . .35.00
Cookie Jar,
    Cover . . . . . . .35.00 to 60.00
Creamer, Oval . . . . . . . .15.00

Cup . . . . . . . . . . .8.00 to 20.00

Cup & Saucer . .18.00 to 25.00

Grill Plate,
9 1/2 In. . . . . . .25.00 to 38.00

Grill Plate, Tab Handles,
10 1/2 In. . . . . . . . . . . . .12.00

Pitcher, 60 Oz.,
8 In. . . . . . . . .55.00 to 58.00

Pitcher, Juice, 37 Oz.,
6 In. . . . . . . . .26.00 to 66.00

Plate, Dinner, 9 1/2 In. . . .26.00

Plate, Salad,
8 1/4 In. . . . . . .14.00 to 18.00

Plate, Sherbet, 5 1/2 In. . .10.00

Platter, Closed Handles,
12 In. . . . . . . . .15.00 to 24.00

Relish, 2 Sections,
7 1/2 In. . . . . . . . . . . . .33.00

Salt & Pepper,
4 1/2 In., Pair . . . . . . . .69.00

Salt & Pepper, 5 1/2 In.,
Pair . . . . . . . . . . . . . .40.00

Sandwich Server, Handle,
11 1/2 In. . . . . . . . . . . .18.50

Shaker, Spice, 5 1/2 In.,
Pair . . . . . . . . . . . . . .40.00

Sherbet, Footed . .10.00 to 25.00

Sugar . . . . . . . . . . . . . . .10.00

Sugar, Cover . . . .30.00 to 42.00

Tumbler, Cocktail, Cone
Footed, 3 Oz., 3 In. . . . .24.00

Tumbler, Footed, 12 1/2 Oz.,
6 1/2 In. . . . . .66.50 to 135.00

Tumbler, Iced Tea, 13 Oz.,
5 1/4 In. . . . . .32.00 to 33.00

Tumbler, Water, Cone
Footed, 9 Oz., 4 In. . . . .35.00

Tumbler, Water, Footed,
10 Oz., 5 1/4 In. . . . . . .30.00

Tumbler, Water, Square Footed,
9 Oz., 4 In. . . . .28.00 to 32.00

Vase, 8 In. . . . . . .36.00 to 45.00

### PINK

Berry Bowl,
4 1/2 In. . . . . . .25.00 to 35.00

Bowl, Cereal, 5 In. . . . . . .25.00

Bowl, Hat Shape,
9 1/2 In. . . . . . . . . . . . .65.00

Bowl, Salad, Octagonal,
Handles,
9 In. . . . . . . . .25.00 to 65.00

Bowl, Vegetable, Oval,
10 In. . . . . . . .30.00 to 32.00

---

❖

**Wipe glass dry with
newspapers for a
special shine.**

❖

---

Cake Stand,
10 In. . . . . . . .30.00 to 32.00

Candy Dish, Cover . . . . . .65.00

Cup . . . . . . . . . .9.00 to 14.00

Cup & Saucer . .18.00 to 24.00

Grill Plate, 9 1/2 In. . . . . .16.00

Grill Plate, 10 1/2 In. . . . .20.00

Grill Plate, Closed
Handles, 10 1/4 In. . . . .35.00

Pitcher, Juice, 37 Oz.,
6 In. . . . . . . . .50.00 to 75.00

Pitcher, Water, 60 Oz.,
8 In. . . . . . . . .55.00 to 70.00

Plate, Dinner, 9 1/2 In. . . .25.00

Plate, Salad,
8 In. . . . . . . . .14.00 to 25.00

Plate, Sherbet,
5 1/2 In. . . . . . .10.00 to 12.00

Platter, Closed Handles,
12 In. . . . . . . . . . . . . .24.00

Sherbet . . . . . . . . . . . . .22.00

Tumbler, Footed,
5 1/2 In. . . . . . . . . . . . .34.00

Tumbler, Iced Tea, 13 Oz.,
5 1/4 In. . . . . . .42.00 to 99.00

Tumbler, Iced Tea, Footed,
12 1/2 Oz., 6 1/2 In. . . .105.00

Tumbler, Water, 9 Oz.,
4 In. . . . . . . . . . . . . . .30.00

Tumbler, Water, Footed, 10 Oz.,
5 1/4 In. . . . . . .26.00 to 30.00

Vase, 8 In. . . . . . . . . . . .50.00

### TOPAZ

Bowl, Cereal, 5 In. . . . . . .24.00

Bowl, Vegetable, Oval,
10 In. . . . . . . . . . . . . .60.00

Cup . . . . . . . . . . .5.00 to 8.00

Cup & Saucer . .10.00 to 12.50

Grill Plate, 9 1/2 In. . . . . .5.50

Grill Plate, Closed
Handles, 10 1/2 In. . . . .12.00

Pitcher, Water, 60 Oz.,
8 In. . . . . . . . .70.00 to 99.50

Plate, Dinner,
9 1/2 In. . . . . . .11.00 to 16.00

---

Plate, Sherbet,
5 1/2 In. . . . . . . . .2.00 to 3.00

Salt & Pepper, 4 1/2 In. . .80.00

Sherbet, Footed . .35.00 to 40.00

Sugar & Creamer . . . . . . .22.50

Tumbler, Iced Tea,
13 Oz., 5 1/4 In. . . . . . .26.00

Tumbler, Iced Tea, Footed,
12 1/2 Oz.,
6 1/2 In. . . . . . .10.00 to 28.00

Tumbler, Juice, 5 Oz.,
3 In. . . . . . . . . .18.00 to 28.00

Tumbler, Water, Footed,
10 Oz., 5 1/4 In. . . . . . .20.00

Tumbler, Water, Square Footed,
9 Oz., 4 3/4 In. . . . . . . .16.00

**PRISMATIC LINE,** see Queen
Mary

**PROVINCIAL,** see Bubble

**PYRAMID,** see No. 610

## QUEEN MARY

Queen Mary, sometimes called
Prismatic Line or Vertical
Ribbed, was made by Anchor
Hocking Glass Corporation
from 1936 to 1943. It was made
first in Pink, later in Crystal
and Royal Ruby.

### CRYSTAL

Ashtray, Oval,
2 x 3 1/4 In. . . . . . . . . . . .3.00

Berry Bowl, 4 In. . .3.00 to 4.00

Bowl, Cereal, 6 In. .6.50 to 8.00

Butter, Cover . . . . . . . .100.00

Candlestick, 2-Light,
4 1/2 In. . . . . . . . . . . . .12.50

Candy Dish,
Cover . . . . . . .20.00 to 30.00
Cigarette Jar, Oval,
2 x 3 In. . . . . . . . . . . . . .5.50
Coaster, Square, 4 1/4 In. . .5.00
Compote, 5 3/4 In. . . . . . .8.00
Creamer . . . . . . . . . . . . . .6.00
Cup, Large . . . . . . . . . . . .5.50
Cup & Saucer . . . . . . . . .6.50
Plate, 6 5/8 In. . . . . . . . . .4.00
Plate, 12 In. . . . . . . . . . . .9.00
Plate, Salad, 8 3/4 In. . . . .5.00
Salt & Pepper . . . . . . . .20.00
Sandwich Server, 12 In. . . .9.00
Saucer, Cup Ring . . . . . . .3.00
Sherbet, Footed . . . . . . . .5.00

### PINK
Berry Bowl,
4 1/2 In. . . . . . . .4.75 to 6.00
Berry Bowl, 5 In. . . . . . . .8.50
Bowl, Cereal, 6 In. . . . . .23.00
Bowl, Handle, 4 In. . . . . .5.00
Butter, Cover . . . . . . . . .135.00
Creamer, Oval . . . .6.00 to 18.00
Cup . . . . . . . . . .6.50 to 10.00
Cup, Large . . . . . .6.00 to 7.00
Cup & Saucer . . . . . . . .10.00
Plate, 6 In. . . . . . . . . . . .5.50
Plate, 7 In. . . . . . . . . . . .8.00
Plate, Dinner,
9 3/4 In. . . . . . .50.00 to 55.00
Saucer . . . . . . . . .5.00 to 6.00
Sherbet, Footed . . . . . . . . .9.00
Sugar, Dual . . . . . . . . . .10.00
Tumbler, 5 Oz.,
3 1/2 In. . . . . . . . . . . . . .9.00
Tumbler, 9 Oz.,
4 In. . . . . . . . . .9.00 to 17.50
Tumbler, Footed, 10 Oz.,
5 In. . . . . . . . .66.00 to 75.00

## RADIANCE
New Martinsville Glass Company, New Martinsville, West Virginia, made Radiance pattern from 1936 to 1939. It was made in Amber, Crystal, Emerald Green, Ice Blue, Pink, and

Red. A few rare pieces were made in Cobalt Blue. A pattern by the same name was made by Cambridge.

### AMBER
Bowl, Crimped, 12 In. . . .45.00
Bowl, Flared, 12 In. . . . .27.00
Butter, Chrome Cover . . . .45.00
Cup & Saucer . . . . . . . .18.00
Pitcher,
64 Oz. . . . . .160.00 to 169.00
Salt & Pepper . . . . . . . .50.00
Tumbler, 9 Oz. . . . . . . . .20.00

### CRYSTAL
Butter, Cover . . . . . . . .140.00
Creamer . . . . . . . . . . . . .7.00
Cup, Footed . . . . . . . . . .8.00
Plate, Luncheon, 8 In. . . . .7.00
Punch Cup . . . . . . . . . . .5.00
Saucer . . . . . . . . . . . . . .3.00

### ICE BLUE
Bonbon, 6 In. . . . . . . . . .35.00
Candlestick, 2-Light,
Pair . . . . . . . . . . . . . .150.00
Candy Dish, Cover,
3 Sections . . . . . . . . . .125.00
Creamer . . . . . .22.00 to 25.00
Cup . . . . . . . . . . . . . . .18.00
Cup & Saucer . . . . . . . .26.00
Pitcher, 64 Oz. . . . . . . . .225.00
Plate, Luncheon, 8 In. . . . .16.00
Punch Cup . . . . .10.00 to 17.00
Saucer . . . . . . . . . . . . . .9.00
Sugar . . . . . . . . . . . . . .22.00
Vase, 12 In. . . . . . . . . . .50.00

### RED
Bowl, Crimped, 12 In. . . .75.00
Cup & Saucer . . . . . . . .24.00
Plate, Luncheon, 8 In. . . . .13.00
Punch Cup . . . . . . . . . .15.00
Salt & Pepper . .75.00 to 125.00

## RAINDROPS
Watch out for confusion with Raindrops and another pattern called Pear Optic or Thumbprint. The rounded, fingernail-shaped impressions of the Raindrops pattern are on the inside of the pieces, the other pattern has hexagonal depressions on the outside. Federal Glass Company made Crystal and Green Raindrops luncheon sets from 1929 to 1933.

### CRYSTAL
Saucer . . . . . . . . . . . . . .2.00
Whiskey, 1 Oz., 1 7/8 In. . .5.00

### GREEN
Berry Bowl, 7 1/2 In. . . . .40.00
Creamer . . . . . . . . . . . . .8.00
Sugar & Creamer,
Cover . . . . . . . . . . . . . .47.00
Tumbler, 4 Oz., 3 In. . . . .4.25
Tumbler, 5 Oz.,
3 7/8 In. . . . . . . . .5.00 to 6.50
Tumbler, 10 Oz., 5 In. . . .12.00

---

**To remove an unwanted gummed price sticker, try heating it with a hair dryer. The glue will melt a bit and it will be easier to peel off the sticker.**

Tumbler, 14 Oz.,
5 3/8 In. . . . . . . . . . . .11.50

**RASPBERRY BAND,** see Laurel

**REX,** see No. 610

**RIBBED,** see Manhattan

## RIBBON

Black, Crystal, Green, and Pink pieces were made in Ribbon pattern in the 1930s. It was made by the Hazel Atlas Glass Company.

### GREEN
Berry Bowl, Master,
8 In. . . . . . . . .20.00 to 30.00
Bowl, 9 In. . . . . . . . . . . .27.00
Candy Dish, Cover,
Footed . . . . . .30.00 to 35.00
Creamer,
Footed . . . . . .14.00 to 15.00
Cup & Saucer . . . . . . . . .7.50
Plate, Luncheon,
8 In. . . . . . . . . .5.00 to 10.00
Plate, Sherbet,
6 1/4 In. . . . . . . .2.00 to 3.50
Sherbet . . . . . . . . . . . . . .6.00
Sugar . . . . . . . . . . . . . . .12.00
Sugar &
Creamer . . . .25.00 to 26.00
Tumbler, Footed, 10 Oz.,
6 In. . . . . . . . .27.50 to 29.00

**RIBBON CANDY,** see Pretzel

## RING

Hocking Glass Company made Ring from 1927 to 1933. The pattern, also known as Banded Ring, sometimes has colored rings added to the Crystal, Green, Mayfair Blue, Pink, or Red glass. The colored rings were made in various combinations of black, blue, orange, pink, platinum, red, and yellow. Platinum trim is on some pieces. Some solid red pieces also were made. The design is characterized by several sets of rings, each comprised of four rings. Circle, a similar Hocking pattern, has only one group of rings.

### CRYSTAL
Cocktail Shaker, 11 In. . . .12.00
Creamer, Platinum Rim . . .3.50
Cup, Platinum
Rim . . . . . . . . . .2.50 to 3.00
Cup & Saucer, Platinum
Rim . . . . . . . . . . . . . . . .3.00
Decanter, Stopper . . . . . . .18.75
Goblet, Champagne,
Platinum Rim,
3 1/2 Oz., 4 1/2 In. . . . . .3.50
Goblet, Water, 9 Oz.,
7 1/4 In. . . . . . .5.00 to 18.00
Ice Tub, Multicolored
Rings . . . . . . . . . . . . . .30.00
Pitcher, 60 Oz., 8 In. . . . . .12.00
Pitcher, Platinum Rim,
80 Oz., 8 1/2 In. . . . . . .18.00
Plate, Luncheon,
8 In. . . . . . . . . . . .2.00 to 7.00
Plate, Luncheon, Platinum
Rim, 8 In. . . . . .3.00 to 3.75
Plate, Off-Center Ring,
6 1/2 In. . . . . . . .3.00 to 5.00
Salt & Pepper, Platinum
Rim . . . . . . . . . . . . . . .40.00
Saltshaker . . . . . . . . . . .10.00

Sandwich Server, Center
Handle, Platinum
Rim . . . . . . . . .12.00 to 15.00
Sherbet, Footed,
4 3/4 In. . . . . . . .3.75 to 5.00
Sherbet, Underplate,
Low . . . . . . . . . . . . . . .20.00
Soup, Dish, Platinum
Rim, 7 In. . . . . . . . . . . .9.00
Sugar, Platinum Rim . . . . .3.50
Sugar & Creamer . . . . . . .6.50
Tumbler, 9 Oz., 4 1/4 In. . .3.50
Tumbler, 10 Oz.,
4 3/4 In. . . . . . . . . . . . . .5.00
Tumbler, Footed, 5 Oz.,
3 1/2 In. . . . . . . .3.00 to 3.75
Tumbler, Footed, Platinum
Rim, 12 Oz., 5 1/8 In. . . .6.00
Tumbler, Iced Tea, Footed,
6 1/2 In. . . . . . . . . . . . .6.50
Tumbler, Multicolored
Rings, 4 Oz., 3 In. . . . . .6.00
Tumbler, Platinum Rim,
8 Oz., 4 In. . . . . . . . . . .7.00
Vase, Multicolored Rings,
8 In. . . . . . . . . . . . . . . .25.00
Whiskey, Multicolored Rings,
1 1/2 Oz., 2 In. . .4.00 to 10.00

### GREEN
Berry Bowl, 5 In. . . . . . . .8.00
Berry Bowl, Master,
8 In. . . . . . . . .8.00 to 16.00
Cup . . . . . . . . . . . . . . . . .5.00
Goblet, 9 Oz.,
7 1/4 In. . . . . . .15.00 to 19.50
Pitcher, 80 Oz., 8 1/2 In. . .36.00
Plate, Luncheon, 8 In. . . . .9.00
Plate, Off-Center Ring,
6 1/2 In. . . . . . . . . . . . . .4.00
Plate, Sherbet, 6 1/4 In. . . .7.00
Sandwich Server, Center
Handle . . . . . . . . . . . . .36.00
Sherbet, Footed,
4 3/4 In. . . . . . .11.00 to 12.00
Sherbet, Off-Center Ring
Plate, 2 Piece . . . . . . . .19.00
Tumbler, 5 Oz., 3 1/2 In. . .6.00
Tumbler, 10 Oz.,
4 3/4 In. . . . . . . . . . . . . .9.50
Tumbler, 12 Oz.,
5 1/8 In. . . . . . . . . . . . . .9.00
Tumbler, Footed, 5 Oz.,
3 1/2 In. . . . . . . . . . . . .15.00

## ROCK CRYSTAL

Rock Crystal, sometimes called Early American Rock Crystal, was made in many solid colors by McKee Glass Company. Amber, Blue-Green, Cobalt Blue, Crystal, Green, Pink, Red, and Yellow pieces were made in the 1920s and 1930s.

**CRYSTAL**
Bowl, Plain Edge, 5 In. . . .16.00
Bowl, Salad, Scalloped
   Edge, 9 In. . . . . . . . . . .35.00
Candelabra, 2-Light, Pair  .40.00
Candelabra, 3-Light  . . . .30.00
Creamer, Footed, 9 Oz. . . .20.00
Cup  . . . . . . . . .16.00 to 17.00
Goblet, 8 Oz.,
   7 1/2 In. . . . . . .9.75 to 15.00
Goblet, Champagne,
   Footed, 6 Oz. . . . . . . . . .16.00
Goblet, Cocktail, Footed,
   3 1/2 Oz. . . . . . .9.00 to 16.50
Goblet, Whiskey,
   2 1/2 Oz. . . . . . . . . . . .18.00
Goblet, Wine,
   3 Oz. . . . . . . . .18.00 to 22.50
Parfait, Low Footed,
   3 1/2 Oz. . . . . . .6.00 to 10.00
Pitcher, Scalloped Edge,
   1 Qt. . . . . . . . . . . . . .125.00
Pitcher, Tankard,
   Fancy  . . . . . . . . . . . .299.00
Plate, 8 1/2 In.  . . . .7.50 to 9.00
Plate, Bread & Butter,
   6 In. . . . . . . . . . . . . . . . .5.00
Plate, Dinner, 10 1/2 In. . .47.50
Plate, Salad, 7 1/2 In. . . . . .6.00
Relish, 2 Sections,
   11 1/2 In. . . . . . . . . . . . .22.00
Relish, 5 Sections,
   12 1/2 In.    25.00 to 40.00

Relish, 6 Sections,
   14 In. . . . . . . . . . . . . .35.00
Sherbet, Footed,
   3 1/2 In. . . . . . .13.00 to 17.00
Vase, Footed, 11 In. . . . . .60.00

**GREEN**
Parfait, Low Footed,
   3 1/2 Oz. . . . . . . . . . . .20.00
Plate, 8 In. . . . . . . . . . . .15.00
Sandwich Server,
   Center Handle . . . . . . .50.00

**PINK**
Goblet, Champagne,
   Footed, 6 Oz. . . . . . . . .24.00
Goblet, Footed, 8 Oz. . . .25.00
Pitcher, Cover, 9 In. . . . .375.00
Tumbler, Juice, 5 Oz. . . .25.00

**RED**
Goblet, Champagne,
   Footed, 6 Oz. . . . . . . . .35.00
Goblet, Footed, 7 Oz. . . .50.00
Goblet, Footed, 8 Oz. . . .60.00
Plate, 7 1/2 In.  . . . . . . .18.00
Sherbet, Footed,
   3 1/2 Oz. . . . . . . . . . . .65.00
Sugar, Cover . . . . . . . . .110.00
Sundae, Low, 6 Oz.  . . . .35.00
Tumbler, Concave,
   12 Oz. . . . . . . . . . . . . .65.00
Tumbler, Straight, 9 Oz. . .50.00
Whiskey,
   2 1/2 Oz.  . . . .55.00 to 66.50

**YELLOW**
Cake Stand, Footed, 11 In. 30.00
Console, Footed, 12 In. . . .65.00
Goblet, Claret, 3 Oz. . . . . .65.00

**ROPE,** see Colonial Fluted

## ROSE CAMEO

Rose Cameo was made by the Belmont Tumbler Company, Bellaire, Ohio, in 1933. It has been found only in Green and only in six different pieces, three of which are bowls.

**GREEN**
Bowl, Cereal, 5 In. . . . . . .16.50
Plate, 7 In. . . . . . . . . . . .12.00
Sherbet  . . . . . . . . . . . .12.00
Tumbler, Straight, 5 In. . .17.00
Tumbler, Water, Footed,
   5 In. . . . . . . . .20.00 to 22.50

**ROSE LACE,** see Royal Lace

## ROSE POINT

Rose Point was made by the Cambridge Glass Company of Cambridge, Ohio, from 1936 to 1953. The elaborate pattern was made in Crystal and Crystal with gold trim. A few rare pieces were made in Red or Amber.

**CRYSTAL**
Ashtray Set, 5 Piece  . . . .325.00
Bowl, Footed, Oblong,
   12 In. . . . . . . . . . . . . .195.00
Bowl, Ruffled,
   10 In. . . . . . .165.00 to 295.00
Candlestick, 1-Light,
   5 In., Pair . . . . . . . . . .129.00
Candlestick, Prism,
   7 1/2 In. . . . . . . . . . . .125.00
Candy Box, Cover,
   3 Sections, 8 In. . . . . .135.00
Compote, 5 In. . . . . . . . .48.00
Console, Low, 7 In. . . . . .85.00
Cup & Saucer, Footed  . . .55.00
Decanter, Footed,
   14 Oz. . . . . . . . . . . . .950.00
Decanter, Sherry,
   28 Oz. . . . . . . . . . . . .650.00
Dish, Mayonnaise,
   3 Piece . . . . . . . . . . . .50.00
Finger Bowl  . . . . . . . . .95.00
Goblet, Champagne,
   7 Oz. . . . . . . . . . . . . . .33.00
Goblet, Cocktail,
   4 1/2 Oz.  . . . .35.00 to 49.00
Goblet, Cordial,
   1 Oz.  . . . . . . . .75.00 to 79.00

Goblet, Water,
10 Oz. . . . . . .45.00 to 55.00
Goblet, Wine,
2 1/2 Oz. . . . .50.00 to 75.00
Honey Dish, Cover . . . . .345.00
Ice Pail . . . . . . . . . . . .200.00
Ice Tub . . . . . . . . . . . .250.00
Jam Jar, Sterling Cover, Ladle,
7 Oz. . . . . . .195.00 to 295.00
Mustard, Cover, 3 Oz. . .160.00
Oyster Cocktail, 5 Oz. . . .42.50
Pickle, Footed, 7 In. . . . .65.00
Pitcher, Ice Lip, 76 Oz. . .450.00
Plate, Handles, 6 In. . . . .25.00
Relish, 2 Sections, 6 In. . .35.00
Relish, 3 Sections,
6 1/2 In. . . . . . . . . . . . .35.00
Sandwich Server, Footed,
12 In. . . . . . . . . . . . . .150.00
Sugar . . . . . . . . . . . . . .37.50
Sugar &
Creamer . . . . .32.00 to 65.00
Tumbler, Footed,
2 1/2 Oz. . . . . . . . . . .100.00
Tumbler, Iced Tea,
12 Oz. . . . . . . .47.50 to 50.00
Tumbler, Juice, Footed,
5 Oz. . . . . . . . . . . . . .42.50
Tumbler, Water, Low
Footed, 10 Oz. . . . . . . .50.00
Vase, Bud, 6 In. . . . . . . .85.00
Vase, Bud, Gold Encrusted,
6 In. . . . . . . . . . . . . . .125.00
Vase, Footed, 11 In. . . . .57.00

---

Be sure a copy of lists
of valuables, pho-
tographs, and other
information that will be
needed in case of an
insurance loss can be
found. Do not keep
them in your safe
deposit box because
your box key could be
lost in the fire. Give a
copy to a trusted friend.

---

Vase, Footed, 12 In. . . . .150.00
Vase, Globe, 5 In. . . . . . .145.00

---

## ROSEMARY

Rosemary, also called Cabbage
Rose with Single Arch or
Dutch Rose, was made by
Federal Glass Company from
1935 to 1937. It was made in
Amber, Green, Iridescent, and
Pink. Pieces with bases, like
creamers or cups, are sometimes confused with Mayfair
Federal because the molds used
were those originally designed
for the Mayfair pattern. The
lower half of the Rosemary
pieces are plain, the lower half
of Mayfair Federal has a band
of arches.

### AMBER
Berry Bowl, 5 In. . .4.50 to 6.00
Bowl, Cereal, 6 In. . . . . .30.00
Bowl, Vegetable, Oval,
10 In. . . . . . . .10.00 to 16.50
Creamer . . . . . . . . . . . .9.00
Cup . . . . . . . . . . . . . . .6.25
Plate, Dinner,
9 1/2 In. . . . . . .5.00 to 10.00
Plate, Salad,
6 3/4 In. . . . . . . .3.50 to 6.00
Platter, Oval,
12 In. . . . . . . .10.00 to 17.50
Saucer . . . . . . . . .2.50 to 5.00
Soup, Cream, 5 In. . . . . .15.00

---

Sugar . . . . . . . . . .6.00 to 8.25
Sugar & Creamer . . . . . . .19.00
Tumbler, Water, 9 Oz.,
4 1/2 In. . . . . .25.00 to 33.00

### GREEN
Bowl, Vegetable, Oval,
10 In. . . . . . . . . . . . . .37.00
Creamer . . . . . . . . . . . .13.00
Cup . . . . . . . . . . . . . . .10.25
Plate, Salad, 6 3/4 In. . . . .11.00
Platter, Oval, 12 In. . . . . .19.00
Saucer . . . . . . . . . . . . . .6.50
Soup, Cream, 5 In. . . . . .28.00
Sugar . . . . . . . . . . . . . .13.00
Tumbler, Water, Footed, 9 Oz.,
4 1/2 In. . . . . .30.00 to 38.00

### PINK
Berry Bowl, 5 In. . . . . . .15.00
Bowl, Cereal, 6 In. . . . . .40.00
Cup . . . . . . . . . . . . . . .11.00
Cup & Saucer . . . . . . . .17.00
Plate, Dinner, 9 1/2 In. . . .10.00
Saucer . . . . . . . . . . . . . .6.00
Soup, Cream, 5 In. . . . . .29.00

**ROSEMARY,** see also Mayfair
Federal

---

## ROULETTE

Anchor Hocking Glass Corporation made Roulette pattern
from 1935 to 1939. Primarily
Green luncheon and beverage
sets were manufactured, although some Crystal pieces
were made, as well as Pink
beverage sets. Collectors originally called the pattern Many
Windows.

### GREEN
Bowl, Fruit, 9 In. . . . . . .16.00
Cup . . . . . . . . . . .4.50 to 6.00
Cup & Saucer . .10.00 to 12.00

**Never bid at an auction
if you have not
previewed the items.**

Pitcher, 65 Oz., 8 In. . . . . .28.00
Plate, Luncheon,
  8 1/2 In. . . . . . . .4.50 to 7.25
Sandwich Server, 12 In. . .15.00
Saucer . . . . . . . . . . . . . . .5.00
Sherbet, Footed . . . . . . . .6.00
Tumbler, Footed,
  10 Oz., 5 1/2 In. . . . . .27.00
Tumbler, Iced Tea, 12 Oz.,
  5 1/8 In. . . . . . .31.00 to 45.00
Tumbler, Water, 9 Oz.,
  4 1/8 In. . . . . . .22.00 to 30.00
Whiskey, 1 1/2 Oz.,
  2 1/2 In. . . . . . . . . . . . .16.00

## ROUND ROBIN

Sometimes a pattern was advertised by the wholesaler, but the
manufacturer is unknown today. One of these is Round
Robin, sometimes called Accordion Pleats. It was pictured
as a luncheon set in the catalogs
of the late 1920s and 1930s and
offered in Green, Crystal, and
Iridescent Marigold.

### GREEN
Berry Bowl, 4 In. . . . . . . .5.50
Cup, Footed . . . . . .5.00 to 8.00
Cup & Saucer . . . . . . . . .13.00
Plate, Luncheon,
  8 In. . . . . . . . . . .4.50 to 7.00
Plate, Sherbet,
  6 In. . . . . . . . . . .3.00 to 6.00
Sherbet, Footed, 5 Oz. . . .10.00

### IRIDESCENT MARIGOLD
Berry Bowl, 4 In                5.00

Plate, Sherbet, 6 In. . . . . . .2.50
Saucer, 6 In. . . . . . . . . . . .2.50
Sherbet, Footed, 5 Oz. . . . .5.00

## ROYAL LACE

Royal Lace was made from
1934 to 1941. The popular pat-
tern by Hazel Atlas Glass
Company was made in Cobalt
Blue, Crystal, Green, and Pink,
and in limited quantities in
Amethyst. It is sometimes
called Gladiola or Rose Lace.
Reproductions have been made.
They are listed at the end of the
Depression Glass section.

### COBALT BLUE
Berry Bowl, Master,
  10 In. . . . . . .110.00 to 120.00
Bowl, Footed,
  10 In. . . . . . . . .59.00 to 95.00
Bowl, Rolled Edge,
  10 In. . . . .1200.00 to 1400.00
Bowl, Straight, Footed,
  10 In. . . . . . . . . . . . . . .105.00
Bowl, Vegetable, Oval,
  11 In. . . . . . . . . . . . . . .70.00
Butter, Cover . . . . . . . . .500.00
Cider Set, 7 Piece . . . .175.00 to
205.00
Cookie Jar,
  Cover . . . . . .340.00 to 495.00
Creamer . . . . . . .50.00 to 60.00
Cup . . . . . . . . .29.00 to 38.00

Cup & Saucer . .29.00 to 50.00
Grill Plate,
  9 7/8 In. . . . . . .42.00 to 45.00
Pitcher, Ice Lip,
  96 Oz.,
  8 1/2 In. . . . .325.00 to 495.00
Pitcher, Straight,
  48 Oz. . . . . .175.00 to 220.00
Plate, Dinner,
  9 7/8 In. . . . . . .37.00 to 55.00
Plate, Luncheon,
  8 1/2 In. . . . . . .40.00 to 47.00
Plate, Sherbet,
  6 In. . . . . . . . . .14.00 to 18.00
Salt &
  Pepper . . . . .315.00 to 325.00
Saucer . . . . . . .12.00 to 15.00
Sherbet, Footed . .42.50 to 53.00
Sherbet, Metal Holder,
  5 Piece . . . . . . . . . . . .125.00
Soup, Cream,
  4 3/4 In. . . . . . .40.00 to 48.00
Sugar . . . . . . . . . . . . . . .35.00
Sugar, Cover . . . . . . . . .225.00
Sugar &
  Creamer . . . .95.00 to 110.00
Sugar & Creamer,
  Cover . . . . . . . . . . . .295.00
Tumbler, 5 Oz.,
  3 1/2 In. . . . . . . . . . . . .55.00
Tumbler, 9 Oz.,
  4 1/8 In. . . . . . .42.00 to 55.00
Tumbler, 10 Oz.,
  4 7/8 In. . . . .165.00 to 270.00
Tumbler, 12 Oz.,
  5 3/8 In. . . . .130.00 to 155.00

### CRYSTAL
Berry Bowl, 5 In. . . . . . . .14.00
Bowl, Footed, 10 In. . . . . .23.00
Butter, Cover . . . . . . . . .63.00
Cookie Jar,
  Cover . . . . . . .38.00 to 45.00
Creamer . . . . . . . . . . . . .12.00
Creamer, Cover . . . . . . .32.00
Cup . . . . . . . . . . . . . . . . .7.50
Cup & Saucer . . . . . . . . .12.00
Pitcher, 68 Oz., 8 In. . . . . .3.00
Pitcher, 96 Oz., 8 1/2 In. . .60.00
Plate, Dinner, 9 7/8 In. . . .15.00
Plate, Luncheon,
  8 1/2 In. . . . . . . . . . . . .10.00
Sherbet, Footed . .16.00 to 19.00
Soup, Cream . . . .12.00 to 14.00

Sugar &
Creamer   ....22.00 to 32.00
Sugar & Creamer,
Cover .......40.00 to 45.00
Tumbler, 9 Oz.,
4 1/8 In. ......11.00 to 16.00

**GREEN**
Berry Bowl, Master,
10 In. ........30.00 to 75.00
Bowl, Ruffled, Footed,
10 In. .......65.00 to 165.00
Butter, Cover . .300.00 to 325.00
Cookie Jar,
Cover .......75.00 to 85.00
Cup ................20.00
Cup & Saucer   ..26.00 to 32.00
Nut Bowl ...........650.00
Pitcher, 86 Oz., 8 In. ....205.00
Pitcher, Ice Lip,
8 1/2 In.............130.00
Pitcher, Straight,
48 Oz.  .....100.00 to 125.00
Plate, Dinner,
9 7/8 In. ......28.00 to 36.00
Plate, Sherbet,
6 In. .........8.00 to 15.00
Platter, Oval,
13 In. ........35.00 to 55.00
Salt & Pepper  ..95.00 to 128.00
Saltshaker  ....60.00 to 65.00
Saucer ...............9.00
Sherbet, Footed . .34.00 to 36.00
Soup, Cream ....32.00 to 37.00
Sugar ........22.00 to 29.00
Sugar &
Creamer   ....30.00 to 45.00
Sugar & Creamer,
Cover ......90.00 to 132.00
Tumbler, 5 Oz.,
3 1/2 In.............37.00
Tumbler, Water, 9 Oz.,
4 1/8 In. .....35.00 to 44.00

**PINK**
Berry Bowl, 5 In. .......17.00
Berry Bowl, Master,
10 In. ........35.00 to 60.00
Bowl, Footed,
10 In. .......47.00 to 75.00
Bowl, Rolled Edge,
10 In. .............100.00
Bowl, Ruffled, 10 In. ....85.00
Candlestick, Rolled Edge,
Pair ..............110.00

Candlestick, Ruffled ....25.00
Console Set, Footed,
Rolled Edge, 3 Piece . .265.00
Cookie Jar,
Cover .......60.00 to 80.00
Cup ..........14.00 to 16.00
Cup & Saucer   ..22.00 to 29.00
Pitcher, 64 Oz.,
8 In. .......120.00 to 130.00
Pitcher, 86 Oz., 8 In. ....125.00
Pitcher, Straight, 48 Oz. . .95.00
Plate, Dinner,
9 7/8 In. ......21.00 to 27.00
Plate, Sherbet,
6 In. .........8.00 to 12.00
Platter, Oval,
13 In. ........30.00 to 60.00
Salt & Pepper ...70.00 to 80.00
Saucer ...............6.00
Sugar, Cover ..........75.00
Sugar & Creamer ......45.00
Tumbler, 9 Oz.,
4 1/8 In. ......30.00 to 39.00
Tumbler, 12 Oz.,
5 3/8 In.............60.00

## ROYAL RUBY

There is no reason to picture this pattern because it is the plain shape and bright red color that identifies it. Anchor Hocking Glass Corporation made it from 1939 to the 1960s and again in 1977. The same shapes were made in green and called by the pattern name Forest Green. Reproduction tumblers were made in 1977 and 1978.

❖

**A glass vase or bowl
can be cleaned with a
damp cloth. Try not to
wash the glass in a
sink—hitting the glass
on a faucet or the sink
is a common cause
of breakage.**

❖

Ashtray, Square, 4 1/4 In. . .6.00
Bowl, 4 1/2 In. . . .6.00 to 12.00
Bowl, 8 1/2 In. .........17.50
Bowl, Cereal, 5 1/4 In. . . .12.00
Bowl, Fruit, Deep,
10 In. ..............40.00
Creamer ............7.00
Cup, Round ...........6.00
Cup, Square ...........5.50
Cup & Saucer .........7.50
Goblet, 5 1/4 In. . .9.00 to 15.00
Pickle, 6 In. ..........15.00
Pitcher, Ball, Upright,
3 Qt. ..............45.00
Plate, Dinner, 9 1/8 In. ....9.00
Plate, Luncheon, 7 3/4 In. . .5.00
Plate, Square, 8 3/8 In. ....8.00
Punch Bowl, Base ......75.00
Punch Cup ............3.00
Punch Set,
10 Piece ....100.00 to 115.00
Punch Set, 14 Piece ....125.00
Saucer ...............3.00
Sherbet, Footed ....7.00 to 8.00
Soup, Dish,
7 1/2 In. ......14.00 to 18.00
Sugar ...............7.00
Sugar, Footed ..........5.00
Sugar &
Creamer .....12.00 to 16.00
Tumbler, 9 Oz.,
4 1/8 In..............4.75
Tumbler, 12 Oz.,
4 7/8 In..............5.00
Tumbler, 13 Oz.,
5 3/8 In. ........6.50 to 9.00
Tumbler, Cocktail,
3 1/2 In. .......5.50 to 12.50

Tumbler, Juice,
5 Oz., 3 In. . . . . . . . . . .5.00
Vase, 6 1/2 In. . . . .7.50 to 9.00
Vase, Ball Shape, 4 In. . . . .4.50
Vase, Bud, 7 1/2 In. . . . . .12.00

**RUSSIAN,** see Holiday

## S PATTERN

Macbeth-Evans Glass Company
made S Pattern, or Stippled
Rose Band, from 1930 to 1935.
It was made before 1932 in
Crystal, Pink, Topaz, and Crystal with gold, blue, or platinum
trim. The 1934 listing mentions
Red, Green, and Monax. Other
pieces were made in Amber,
Ritz Blue, and Crystal with
many colors of trim including
amber, green, rose, platinum,
red, silver, or white.

**AMBER**
Cake Plate, 13 3/4 In. . . . .70.00
Plate, Dinner, 9 1/4 In. . . . .6.50
Sherbet . . . . . . . . . . . . . .8.00
Tumbler, Iced Tea, 12 Oz.,
5 In. . . . . . . . . . . . . . .18.00

**CRYSTAL**
Bowl, Cereal, Amber Band,
5 1/2 In. . . . . . . . . . . . .6.00
Cake Plate, 11 In. . . . . . .45.00
Creamer, Amber Band,
Thin . . . . . . . . . . . . . . .5.00
Cup, Amber Band . . . . . . .4.00
Cup & Saucer, Platinum
Band, Thick . . . . . . . . . .4.50
Cup & Saucer, Red Band,
Thick . . . . . . . . . . . . . .7.50
Cup & Saucer, Thick . . . . .4.50
Cup & Saucer,
Thin . . . . . . . . . .4.50 to 5.00

Plate, Luncheon,
8 3/8 In. . . . . . . . .3.50 to 8.00
Plate, Sherbet,
6 In. . . . . . . . . . .4.00 to 4.50
Saucer, Amber Band . . . . . .4.00
Saucer, Red Band . . . . . . .2.50
Sugar, Footed, Amber
Band . . . . . . . . . . . . . .10.00
Sugar, Footed, Platinum
Band, Thick . . . . . . . . . .5.00
Sugar & Creamer,
Footed, Amber Band,
Thin . . . . . . . .10.00 to 12.00
Sugar & Creamer, Footed,
Platinum Band, Thick . .10.00
Sugar & Creamer, Footed,
Thin . . . . . . . . . . . . . . .8.50
Tumbler, Water, 9 Oz.,
4 In. . . . . . . . .10.00 to 12.00

**MONAX**
Plate, Sherbet,
6 In. . . . . . . . . .8.00 to 10.00

**YELLOW**
Cup, Platinum Band . . . . .5.00
Cup & Saucer, Thin . . . . .7.00
Plate, 8 In. . . . . . . . . . . .5.00
Sherbet, Footed . . . . . . . .7.00
Sugar & Creamer, Footed,
Thin . . . . . . . . . . . . . .10.00

**SAIL BOAT,** see White Ship

**SAILING SHIP,** see White Ship

## SANDWICH ANCHOR HOCKING

Many patterns were called
Sandwich. Each company
seemed to have one design with
that name. The most popular
were made by Anchor Hocking
Glass Corporation, Indiana
Glass Company, and Duncan &
Miller Glass Company. The
Anchor Hocking Sandwich pattern was made from 1939 to
1964 and can be distinguished
by the three lines around the
edge of each petal. Pink and
Royal Ruby were made about
1939; Crystal was made from
1939 to 1964; Forest Green and
White (opaque) date from the
1950s and 1960s; Desert Gold

from 1961 to 1964. A reproduction line was introduced in
1977 by another company in
Amber, Blue, Crystal, and
Royal Ruby.

**CRYSTAL**
Berry Bowl,
4 7/8 In. . . . . . . .3.00 to 5.00
Berry Bowl, Scalloped,
4 7/8 In. . . . . . .10.00 to 16.00
Bowl, Cereal,
6 1/2 In. . . . . . . .3.50 to 7.50
Bowl, Oval, 8 In. . . . . . . .6.00
Bowl, Scalloped,
5 1/4 In. . . . . . . .3.50 to 7.00
Bowl, Vegetable, Oval,
8 1/4 In. . . . . . . .5.00 to 6.00
Butter, Cover . . .40.00 to 48.00
Cookie Jar, Cover . . . . . . .36.00
Creamer . . . . . . . . . . . . .6.00
Cup . . . . . . . . . . . . . . . .2.00
Cup & Saucer . . . .3.00 to 6.00
Custard Cup . . . . .2.00 to 3.50
Custard Cup,
Ruffled . . . . . . . . . . . .12.00
Pitcher, Ice Lip,
1/2 Gal. . . . . . .70.00 to 90.00
Plate, Dessert, 7 In. . . . . .10.00
Plate, Dinner, 9 In. . . . . .17.00
Punch Set,
14 Piece . . . . .58.00 to 60.00
Saucer . . . . . . . . . . . . . .3.00
Sherbet, Footed . . . .7.00 to 8.00
Sugar . . . . . . . . . .3.00 to 6.00
Sugar & Creamer . . . . . . .12.00
Tumbler, Footed, 9 Oz.,
5 1/2 In. . . . . . . . . . . . .28.00
Tumbler, Juice, 3 Oz.,
3 3/4 In. . . . . . .14.00 to 16.00
Tumbler, Water, 9 Oz.,
4 1/2 In. . . . . . . .5.00 to 10.00

## DESERT GOLD

Berry Bowl, 4 7/8 In. . . . . .6.00
Bowl, Cereal,
   6 1/2 In. . . . . . .12.00 to 17.00
Bowl, Cereal, Scalloped,
   6 1/2 In. . . . . . . . . . . . .8.00
Cookie Jar, Cover . . . . . . .40.00
Cup . . . . . . . . . . . . . . . .5.00
Cup & Saucer . . . .4.50 to 6.75
Plate, Dinner,
   9 In. . . . . . . . . . .5.00 to 9.00
Sandwich Server, 12 In. . .14.00

## FOREST GREEN

Berry Bowl, 4 7/8 In. . . . . .3.00
Bowl, Cereal, 6 1/2 In. . . .70.00
Bowl, Salad, 7 In. . . . . . .125.00
Cup . . . . . . . . .22.00 to 24.00
Cup & Saucer . . . . . . . .44.00
Custard Cup
   Liner . . . . . . . . . .1.50 to 3.00
Pitcher, Juice, 6 In. . . . . .250.00
Plate, Dinner, 9 In. . . . . .115.00
Saucer . . . . . . .15.00 to 17.00
Sugar . . . . . . . . . . . . . .25.00
Sugar & Creamer . . . . . . .70.00
Tumbler, Juice, 3 Oz.,
   3 3/4 In. . . . . . . .4.00 to 5.00
Tumbler, Water, 9 Oz.,
   4 1/2 In. . . . . . . . . . . . .5.00

## ROYAL RUBY

Bowl, Scalloped,
   5 1/2 In. . . . . . .15.00 to 22.00
Bowl, Scalloped, 8 In. . . .38.00

## WHITE

Base, For Punch Bowl . . .12.00
Punch Cup, Gold Trim . . . . .45
Punch Set, 10 Piece . . . .35.00
Punch Set, 13 Piece . . . .24.00
Punch Set, Gold Trim,
   14 Piece . . . . . . . . . . . .50.00

# SANDWICH DUNCAN & MILLER

Sandwich Duncan & Miller is easy to recognize. It has long been said the pattern was designed by Mr. Heisey's son-in-law and that he added the diamond and H mark used by Heisey as part of the border design. New research suggests this is not true and that the diamon and H mark is really a mold flaw. The plates in this series have ground bottoms. The star in the center of the plate does not go to the edge of the circle. Duncan & Miller named pattern No. 41 Early American Sandwich Glass in 1925. The glass was made in Amber, Cobalt Blue, Crystal, Green, Pink, and Red. The pattern remained in production until 1955 when some of the molds were bought by other companies. Lancaster Colony made pieces in Blue, Green, and Amberina in the 1970s. Tiffin made Milk Glass pieces. Reproductions are listed at the end of the Depression Glass section.

## CRYSTAL

Bowl, Footed, 10 In. . . . . .55.00
Bowl, Fruit, Flared,
   12 In. . . . . . . .42.50 to 45.00
Bowl, Salad, 7 In. . . . . . .15.00
Candlestick, 4 In., Pair . . .35.00
Celery Dish, 10 In. . . . . . .25.00
Creamer . . . . . . . . . . . . .9.00
Pickle, 7 In. . . . . . . . . . .18.00
Sherbet, Footed . . . . . . . .20.00
Sugar . . . . . . . . . . . . . . .8.00
Tumbler, Iced Tea, 13 Oz.,
   5 1/4 In. . . . . . .18.00 to 20.00

## GREEN

Bonbon, Heart Shape,
   Handle, 5 1/2 In. . . . . . .25.00
Bowl, Fruit, 5 In. . . . . . . .20.00

# SANDWICH INDIANA

Another Sandwich pattern was made by the Indiana Glass Company, Dunkirk, Indiana, from the 1920s through the 1980s. It can be distinguished by the single line around the flower petals. Only the colors changed through the years. Amber was made from the late 1920s to the 1980s, Crystal from the late 1920s to the 1990s, Light Green and Pink from the 1920s to the 1930s, Red from 1933 to the 1970s, Teal Blue from the 1950s to the 1980s, Opaque White in the 1950s, and Smoky Blue in 1976 and 1977. The scroll design varies with the size of the plate. Tiara Home Products made Sandwich in Red (1969), Amber (1970), and Crystal (1978). They continued to make Amber, Chantilly Green, and Crystal in the 1980s. Tiara also made a few pieces from redesigned molds. A Teal Blue butter dish was also made. Reproductions are listed at the end of the Depression Glass section.

## AMBER

Candlestick, 3 1/2 In.,
   Pair . . . . . . . . . . . . . . .12.00

Cup . . . . . . . . . . . . . . . .2.50

**CRYSTAL**
Ashtray, Club Shape . . . . . .1.50
Ashtray, Spade Shape . . . . .1.50
Ashtray Set, 4 Piece . . . . .12.00
Berry Bowl, 4 1/4 In. . . . . .4.00
Berry Bowl, Master,
    8 1/4 In. . . . . . .11.00 to 12.00
Butter, Cover . . . . . . . . .65.00
Cake Plate, Frosted
    Edge, 13 In. . . . . . . . . .35.00
Candlestick, 3 1/2 In.,
    Pair . . . . . . . . . . . . . . .18.00
Candlestick, 7 In.,
    Pair . . . . . . . . . . . . . . .25.00
Celery Dish . . . . . . . . . .16.00
Console, Rolled Edge,
    11 1/2 In. . . . . .16.00 to 19.00
Cup . . . . . . . . . . .2.50 to 3.50
Cup & Saucer . . . .3.50 to 6.00
Dish, Mayonnaise,
    Flared . . . . . . . . . . . . .15.00
Goblet, Water, Footed,
    9 Oz., 5 In. . . . . . . . . .13.00
Goblet, Wine, 4 Oz.,
    3 In. . . . . . . . . . . . . . .11.00
Plate, Dinner,
    10 1/2 In. . . . . . .8.50 to 10.00
Plate, Luncheon,
    8 3/8 In. . . . . . . . .3.50 to 6.00
Plate, Sherbet, 6 In. . . . . . .3.00
Sandwich Server, Center
    Handle . . . . . . . . . . . . .20.00
Sherbet, Footed . . . .3.50 to 6.00
Sugar & Creamer,
    Cover . . . . . . . .18.00 to 30.00
Sugar & Creamer, Tray,
    3 Piece . . . . . . . . . . . .11.00
Tidbit, 2 Tiers . . . . . . . . .30.00
Tumbler, Cocktail,
    Footed, 3 Oz. . . . . . . . . .7.50

**LIGHT GREEN**
Ashtray . . . . . . . . . . . . .16.00
Bowl, Cereal, 6 In. . . . . .30.00
Bowl, Hexagonal,
    6 In. . . . . . . . . . . . . . .20.00
Candlestick, 3 1/2 In.,
    Pair . . . . . . . .45.00 to 50.00
Plate, Bread & Butter,
    7 In. . . . . . . . . . . . . . .12.00
Plate, Dinner,
    10 1/2 In. . . . . . . . . . . .20.00

Plate, Indentation, Oval,
    8 In. . . . . . . . . . . . . . .15.00
Sherbet, Footed . . . . . . . .15.00

**PINK**
Berry Bowl, Master,
    Scalloped, 8 1/2 In. . . . .40.00
Berry Bowl, Scalloped,
    4 1/4 In. . . . . . . . . . . . .10.00
Plate, Luncheon,
    8 3/8 In. . . . . . . . . . . . .16.00

**RED**
Berry Bowl,
    4 1/4 In . . . . . . . . . . . .14.00
Goblet, Water, 9 Oz.,
    5 In. . . . . . . . . . . . . . .25.00

**SAWTOOTH,** see English
    Hobnail

**SAXON,** see Coronation

**SHAMROCK,** see Cloverleaf

---

## SHARON

Sharon, or Cabbage Rose, was made by the Federal Glass Company from 1935 to 1939. The pattern was made in Amber, Crystal, Green, and Pink. A cheese dish was reproduced in 1976 in Amber, Blue, Dark Green, Light Green, and Pink. Other items have been reproduced in various colors. They are listed at the end of the Depression Glass section.

**AMBER**
Berry Bowl,
    5 In. . . . . . . . . . . .6.50 to 8.50
Berry Bowl, Master,
    8 1/2 In. . . . . . . . .4.00 to 5.00
Bowl, Cereal, 6 In. . . . . . .16.00
Bowl, Fruit,
    10 1/2 In. . . . . .15.00 to 22.00

Bowl, Vegetable, Oval,
    9 1/2 In. . . . . . .16.00 to 21.00
Butter, Cover . . .42.00 to 47.00
Cake Plate, Footed,
    11 1/2 In. . . . . .20.00 to 30.00
Candy Dish,
    Cover . . . . . . . .40.00 to 47.00
Creamer . . . . . . . . . . . . .14.00
Cup . . . . . . . . . . .6.00 to 8.00
Cup & Saucer . .10.00 to 17.00
Jam Jar, 7 1/2 In. . . . . . .30.00
Pitcher, Water, 80 Oz. . .135.00
Plate, Bread & Butter,
    6 In. . . . . . . . . . . .3.00 to 8.00
Plate, Dinner,
    9 1/2 In. . . . . . . .8.00 to 12.00
Plate, Salad,
    7 1/2 In. . . . . . .12.00 to 16.00
Platter, Oval,
    12 1/2 In. . . . . .13.00 to 20.00
Salt & Pepper . . .30.00 to 45.00
Saucer . . . . . . . . . . . . . . .5.00
Sherbet, Footed . .10.00 to 12.00
Soup, Cream,
    5 In. . . . . . . . . .20.00 to 28.00
Sugar . . . . . . . . . . . . . . .7.00
Sugar, Cover . . . .25.00 to 31.00
Sugar & Creamer . . . . . .20.00
Sugar & Creamer,
    Cover . . . . . . . . . . . . . .45.00
Tumbler, Iced Tea,
    Footed, 15 Oz.,
    6 1/2 In. . . . . .95.00 to 120.00
Tumbler, Water, Thin, 9 Oz.,
    4 1/8 In. . . . . .25.00 to 28.00

**GREEN**
Berry Bowl,
    5 In. . . . . . . . .11.50 to 15.00
Bowl, Fruit,
    10 1/2 In. . . . . .33.00 to 38.00
Bowl, Vegetable, Oval,
    9 1/2 In. . . . . . .29.00 to 35.00
Butter, Cover . . . . . . . .125.00
Creamer, Footed .17.00 to 20.00
Cup . . . . . . . . . .18.00 to 19.00
Cup & Saucer . . . . . . . .23.00
Jam Jar, 7 1/2 In. . . . . . .65.00
Plate, Bread & Butter,
    6 In. . . . . . . . . . .6.00 to 8.00
Plate, Dinner,
    9 1/2 In. . . . . . .19.00 to 23.00
Plate, Salad,
    7 1/2 In. . . . . . .17.00 to 21.00

Platter, Oval,
  12 1/2 In. . . . . .27.00 to 29.00
Salt & Pepper . . .69.00 to 70.00
Saucer . . . . . . . . . . . . . .10.00
Sugar . . . . . . . . . . . . . . .16.00

### PINK
Berry Bowl,
  5 In. . . . . . . . .11.00 to 12.50
Berry Bowl, Master,
  8 1/2 In. . . . . . .27.00 to 45.00
Bowl, Cereal,
  6 In. . . . . . . . .21.00 to 25.00
Bowl, Fruit,
  10 1/2 In. . . . . .36.00 to 40.00
Bowl, Vegetable, Oval,
  9 1/2 In. . . . . . .24.00 to 30.00
Butter, Cover . . .40.00 to 52.50
Cake Plate, Footed,
  11 1/2 In. . . . . . . . . . . .25.00
Candy Jar,
  Cover . . . . . . .31.00 to 50.00
Creamer,
  Footed . . . . . .17.00 to 20.00
Cup . . . . . . . . . .14.00 to 19.00
Cup & Saucer . .21.00 to 27.00
Pitcher, Ice Lip,
  80 Oz. . . . . .144.00 to 170.00
Plate, Bread &
  Butter, 6 In. . . . .6.00 to 14.00
Plate, Dinner,
  9 1/2 In. . . . . . .17.00 to 25.00
Plate, Salad,
  7 1/2 In. . . . . . .23.00 to 31.00
Platter, Oval,
  12 1/2 In. . . . . .24.00 to 35.00
Salt & Pepper . . .50.00 to 60.00
Saucer . . . . . . .12.00 to 15.00
Sherbet, Footed . .12.00 to 19.00
Soup, Cream,
  5 In. . . . . . . . .41.00 to 42.00
Soup, Dish,
  7 1/2 In. . . . . . .43.50 to 53.00
Sugar . . . . . . . .10.00 to 14.00
Sugar, Cover . . . . . . . . . .39.00
Sugar & Creamer . . . . . . .62.00
Sugar & Creamer,
  Cover . . . . . . . . . . . .225.00
Tumbler, Iced Tea,
  Footed, 15 Oz.,
  6 1/2 In. . . . . . .20.00 to 50.00
Tumbler, Water, Thick,
  9 Oz., 4 1/8 In. . . . . . .34.00
Tumbler, Water, Thin, 9 Oz.,
  4 1/8 In. . . . . . .26.00 to 40.00

Tumbler, Water, Thin, 12 Oz.,
  5 1/4 In. . . . . . . . . . . .42.50

**SHEFFIELD,** see Chinex Classic

**SHELL,** see Petalware

**SHIPS,** see White Ship

## SHIRLEY TEMPLE
Shirley Temple is not really a pattern, but the dishes with the white enamel decoration picturing Shirley have become popular with collectors. The most famous were made as giveaways with cereal from 1934 to 1942. Several companies, including Hazel Atlas Glass Company and U.S. Glass, made the glassware. Sugars and creamers, bowls, plates, and mugs were made. The milk pitcher and mug have been reproduced since 1982 and the bowl has been reproduced since 1986. Other items with the Shirley Temple decal include a Fostoria Mayfair Green sugar bowl and tea cup, a White mug, and an 8 7/8-inch Moderntone Cobalt Blue plate. In 1972 Libbey Glass Company made six different sized tumblers.

### BLUE
Bowl, Cereal,
  6 1/2 In. . . . . . .50.00 to 60.00
Creamer . . . . . . . . . . . . .45.00
Mug, 3 3/4 In. . . .50.00 to 60.00
Plate . . . . . . . . . . . . . .300.00
Sugar . . . . . . . . . . . . . . .50.00

## SIERRA
Sierra, or Pinwheel, was made by Jeannette Glass Company from 1931 to 1933. It is found in Green, Pink, and Ultramarine.

### GREEN
Berry Bowl, Master,
  8 1/2 In. . . . . . .26.00 to 28.00
Bowl, Cereal,
  5 1/2 In. . . . . . .12.00 to 18.50
Butter . . . . . . . . . . . . . .75.00
Creamer . . . . . . . . . . . . .22.50
Cup & Saucer . .17.00 to 24.00
Pitcher, 6 1/2 In. . . . . . .150.00
Plate, Dinner,
  9 In. . . . . . . . .18.00 to 25.00
Platter, Oval,
  11 In. . . . . . . . . . . . . .50.00

### PINK
Berry Bowl, Master,
  8 1/2 In. . . . . . .30.00 to 34.50
Bowl, Cereal,
  5 1/2 In. . . . . . .12.50 to 14.00
Creamer . . . . . . . . . . . . .15.00
Cup . . . . . . . . . .11.00 to 14.00
Cup & Saucer . . . . . . . .19.00
Pitcher,
  6 1/2 In. . . . . . .75.00 to 80.00

Plate, 6 In. . . . . . . . . . . . .8.00
Plate, Dinner,
9 In. . . . . . . . .17.00 to 23.00
Sandwich Server,
10 1/4 In. . . . . . . . . . . .20.00
Saucer . . . . . . . . . . . . . . .6.00
Sherbet . . . . . . . . . . . . .15.00
Tumbler, Footed, 9 Oz.,
4 1/2 In. . . . . . .75.00 to 80.00

**SMOCKING,** see Windsor

**SNOWFLAKE,** see Doric

## SPIRAL

It is easy to confuse Spiral, a Hocking Glass Company pattern, with Twisted Optic, made by Imperial Glass Company. Ask to be shown examples of each, because even a picture will not be much help. Looking from the top to the base, Twisted Optic spirals right to left; Spiral twists left to right. There are a few pieces that are exceptions. Spiral pattern beverage and luncheon sets were manufactured from 1928 to 1930 in Crystal, Green, and Pink. It is also sometimes called Spiral Optic or Swirled Big Rib.

**CRYSTAL**
Plate, Luncheon, 8 In. . . . . .1.00
**GREEN**
Berry Bowl, Master,
8 1/2 In. . . . . . . . . . . .17.50
Cup . . . . . . . . . . . . . . . .5.00
Pitcher, 8 1/2 In. . . . . . . .22.00
Plate, Luncheon, 8 In. . . . . .3.75
Preserve, Cover . . . . . . . .30.00
Salt & Pepper . . . . . . . .30.00
Sherbet, Footed . . . . . . . .4.00
Tumbler, Footed,
5 7/8 In. . . . . . . . . . . . .16.00

**To remove the remains of sticky glue and tape from antiques, try rubbing peanut butter on the sticky area until the glue is gone. Do not use this method on porous materials since the oil from the peanut butter could leave a stain.**

**PINK**
Plate, Luncheon,
8 In. . . . . . . . . . . . . . . .4.50

## SPIRAL FLUTES

Duncan & Miller Glass Company, Washington, Pennsylvania, made Spiral Flutes pattern. It was made of Amber, Crystal, and Green glass in 1924; Pink in 1926. A few pieces are reported with gold trim and in Blue or Vaseline-Colored glass.

**AMBER**
Cup & Saucer . . . . . . . .12.00
Nut Dish, Footed . . . . . .12.00
Pitcher, Water,
1/2 Gal. . . . . . . . . . . .175.00
Sugar, Oval . . . . . . . . . . .9.00
Toothpick . . . . . . . . . . .27.00
**CRYSTAL**
Nut Dish, Footed,
Gold Trim . . . . . . . . . .12.00
Soup, Cream . . . . . . . . . .10.00
**GREEN**
Console, Flared,
11 3/8 In. . . . . . . . . . . .30.00
Goblet, Water, 7 Oz.,
6 1/4 In. . . . . . . . . . . . .15.00

Ice Tub, Handles . . . . . .20.00
Nut Dish, Footed . . . . . .12.00
Vase, 6 1/2 In. . . . . . . . .15.00
**PINK**
Bouillon, 3 1/4 In. . . . . . .15.00

**SPIRAL OPTIC,** see Spiral

**SPOKE,** see Patrician

## SPORTSMAN SERIES

Hazel Atlas Glass Company made an unusual Depression glass pattern in the 1940s. It was made of Cobalt Blue, Amethyst, or Crystal with fired-on decoration. Although the name of the series was Sportsman, designs included golf, sailboats, hunting, angelfish, and a few strange choices like windmills. We list Windmill and White Ship separately, although they are sometimes considered part of this pattern.

**COBALT BLUE**
Bowl, Angelfish, 6 In. . . .67.50
Cocktail Shaker,
Angelfish . . . . . . . . . .80.00
Cocktail Shaker, Polo . . . .65.00
Pitcher, Water,
Angelfish . . . . . . . . . . .85.00
Tumbler, Juice,
Fox Hunt . . . . . . . . . . .11.00
Tumbler, Water,
Angelfish, 4 5/8 In. . . . .10.00

**SQUARE,** see Charm

## STARS AND STRIPES

Stars and Stripes was a clear glass pattern made about 1942 by Anchor Hocking Glass Corporation. The pieces had appropriate wartime patriotic designs of stars, stripes, and eagles.

**CRYSTAL**
Sherbet . . . . . . . . . . . . . .14.00

**STIPPLED ROSE BAND,** see
S Pattern

## STRAWBERRY

Strawberry and Cherry-Berry are similar patterns. The U.S. Glass Company made luncheon sets in this pattern in the early 1930s with strawberry decoration. Pink and Green were the most commonly used colors, although Crystal and Iridescent Marigold pieces were also made.

**GREEN**
Berry Bowl, Deep,
7 1/2 In. . . . . . .19.00 to 35.00
Sherbet, Footed . . . . . . . .7.50
Sugar, Cover, Large . . . . .89.00
Sugar, Small . . . . . . . . . .32.00

**PINK**
Berry Bowl,
4 In. . . . . . . . . .8.50 to 13.00
Berry Set, 7 Piece . . . . . . .75.00
Pitcher, 7 3/4 In. . . . . . .195.00
Plate, Salad,
7 1/2 In. . . . . .11.00 to 18.00
Sherbet . . . . . . . . . . . . . .7.00

**STRAWBERRY,** see also Cherry-Berry

## SUNBURST

Crystal dinner sets were made in Sunburst pattern from 1938 to 1941 by Jeannette Glass Company of Jeannette, Pennsylvania.

**CRYSTAL**
Candlestick,
2-Light, Pair . . . . . . . .25.00
Cup & Saucer . . . . . . . . .7.00
Plate, Dinner, 9 1/2 In. . . .14.00
Relish, Oval, 8 3/4 In . . . . .8.00

## SUNFLOWER

Sunflower was made by Jeannette Glass Company, Jeannette, Pennsylvania, in the late 1920s and early 1930s. It is most commonly found in Pink and two shades of Green. The darker green was used for Cake Plates given as a premium in sacks of flour. Small quantities of Delphite pieces also were made.

**GREEN**
Ashtray, 5 In. . . .11.00 to 15.00

Cake Plate, Footed,
10 In. . . . . . . . .8.00 to 15.00
Cup . . . . . . . . .12.00 to 15.00
Cup & Saucer . .20.00 to 27.00
Plate, Dinner,
9 In. . . . . . . . .14.00 to 23.00
Sugar, Footed . . .18.00 to 21.00
Tumbler, Footed, 8 Oz,
4 3/4 In. . . . . . . . . . . . .45.00

**PINK**
Ashtray, 5 In. . . . . . . . . . .9.00
Cake Plate, Footed,
10 In. . . . . . . . .9.00 to 20.00
Creamer, Footed . . . . . . .18.00
Cup . . . . . . . . . . . . . . . .12.00
Cup & Saucer . .20.00 to 22.00
Plate, Dinner,
9 In. . . . . . . . .15.00 to 19.00
Sugar, Footed . . .18.00 to 19.00
Tumbler, Footed, 8 Oz.,
4 3/4 In. . . . . . .25.00 to 31.00

## SWANKYSWIGS

In October 1933, Kraft Cheese Company began to market cheese spreads in decorated, reusable glass tumblers. The tumbler was made in a 5-ounce size. It had a smooth beverage lip and a permanent color decoration. The designs were tested and changed as public demand indicated. Hazel Atlas Glass Company made the glasses, which were decorated by hand by about 280 girls, working in shifts around the clock. In 1937 a silk screen process was developed and the Tulip design was made by this new, faster method. The glasses were made thinner and lighter in weight. The decorated Swankyswigs were discontinued from 1941 to 1946, the war years. They were made again in 1947 and were continued through 1958. Then plain glasses were used for most of the cheese, although a few specially decorated Swankyswigs have been made since that time.

### ANTIQUE NO. 1
Brown . . . . . . . . . . . . . . . .4.00
Green . . . . . . . . . .2.75 to 4.00
Red . . . . . . . . . . . . . . . . . .2.00

### ANTIQUE NO. 2
Blue . . . . . . . . . . . . . . . . .5.00
Orange . . . . . . . . . .2.75 to 4.00
Red . . . . . . . . . . . . . . . . . .2.00

### BAND NO. 1
Blue & White . . . . . . . . . .3.00

### BAND NO. 2
Red & Black . . . . . . . . . . .2.50

### BAND NO. 3
Blue & White . . . .3.00 to 4.00

### BUSTLIN' BETSY
Blue . . . . . . . . . . . .2.00 to 5.00
Brown . . . . . . . . . .2.00 to 6.00
Green . . . . . . . . . . .2.00 to 4.00
Orange . . . . . . . . . . . . . . .4.00
Red . . . . . . . . . . . .2.75 to 4.00
Yellow . . . . . . . . . .3.00 to 4.00

### CARNIVAL
Blue . . . . . . . . . . .6.00 to 17.00
Green . . . . . . . . . .4.50 to 6.00
Red . . . . . . . . . . . .3.00 to 4.00
Yellow . . . . . . . . . . . . . . .3.00

### CHECKERBOARD
Red & White . . . . . . . . . .25.00

### CIRCLE & DOT
Black . . . . . . . . . . . . . . . .4.25
Blue . . . . . . . . . . . . . . . . .4.25
Red . . . . . . . . . . . . . . . . . .4.25

### DAISY
Red, White & Green,
    3 3/4 In. . . . . . . . . . . . . .2.00
Red, White & Green,
    4 1/2 In. . . . . . . . . . . . . .15.00

### FORGET-ME-NOT
Dark Blue . . . . . . .2.00 to 7.00

Light Blue,
    3 1/2 In. . . . . . . . .2.00 to 8.00
Light Blue, 3 1/4 In. . . . . .15.00
Red . . . . . . . . . .2.00 to 5.00
Yellow . . . . . . . . .2.00 to 3.00

### KIDDIE KUP
Black, Duck &
    Horse . . . . . . . . .2.75 to 6.00
Black, Duck &
    Horse, 3 3/4 In. . . . . . .15.00
Brown, Deer &
    Squirrel . . . . . . .2.75 to 4.00
Green, Kitten &
    Rabbit . . . . . . . . .3.00 to 4.00
Orange, Dog & Rooster,
    3 1/4 In. . . . . . . . . . . . . .15.00
Orange, Dog & Rooster,
    3 3/4 In. . . . . . . . . . . . . .2.75
Red, Bird & Elephant,
    3 3/4 In. . . . . . . . . . . . . .15.00

### POSY CORNFLOWER
No. 1, Light Blue,
    3 1/2 In. . . . . . . . .2.00 to 9.00
No. 2, Dark Blue . . .2.50 to 8.00
No. 2, Light Blue . .2.00 to 5.00
No. 2, Red . . . . . . . . . . . .4.00
No. 2, Yellow,
    3 1/2 In. . . . . . . . .2.00 to 5.00

### POSY CORNFLOWER NO. 2
Blue, 3 1/4 In. . . . . . . . . .15.00
Yellow, 3 1/4 In. . . . . . . .15.00

### POSY JONQUIL
Yellow, 3 1/2 In. . . . . . . .4.00

### POSY TULIP
No. 1, Blue,
    3 1/2 In. . . . . . . . .2.75 to 4.00
No. 1, Blue, 4 1/2 In. . . . . .8.50
No. 1, Green, 3 1/2 In. . . . .2.75
No. 1, Green, 4 1/2 In. . . . .8.00
No. 1, Red,
    3 1/2 In. . . . . . . . .2.75 to 5.00
No. 1, Red, 4 1/2 In. . . . . .15.00
No. 2, Green, 3 1/2 In. . . .22.50
No. 3, Light Blue,
    3 1/4 In. . . . . . . . . . . . . .15.00
No. 3, Light Blue,
    3 3/4 In. . . . . . . . .2.75 to 3.00
No. 3, Red, 3 1/4 In. . . . . .15.00
No. 3, Red, 4 1/2 In. . . . . .15.00
No. 3, Yellow, 3 1/4 In. . .15.00

### POSY VIOLET
Blue . . . . . . . . . . .3.00 to 5.00

### SAILBOAT
No. 2, Blue, 4 1/2 In. . . .16.00
No. 2, Green, 4 1/2 In. . . .16.00
No. 2, Red,
    4 1/2 In. . . . . . .12.00 to 16.00

### STAR
Blue, 3 1/2 In. . . . . . . . . . .4.00
Blue, 4 3/4 In. . . . . . . . . .15.00
Red, 3 1/2 In. . . . . . . . . . .4.00
Red, 4 3/4 In. . . .11.00 to 15.00

**SWEET PEAR,** see Avocado

## SWIRL

Swirl, sometimes called Double Swirl or Petal Swirl, was made by Jeannette Glass Company during 1937 and 1938. Ultramarine, in a variety of shades, was the most commonly used color, but Amber, Delphite, Ice Blue, and Pink were also used. Some pieces have a smooth edge while others have a flower petal rim.

### DELPHITE
Bowl, Cereal,
    5 1/4 In. . . . . . .13.00 to 14.00
Bowl, Salad, 9 In. . . . . . .34.00
Cup & Saucer . . . . . . . .20.00
Plate, Dinner, 9 1/4 In. . . .16.00
Plate, Sherbet, 6 1/2 In. . . .7.50
Platter, Oval, 12 In. . . . . .46.00

## ICE BLUE
Sugar, Cover . . . . . . . . . . .12.50

## PINK
Butter . . . . . . .150.00 to 170.00
Candy Dish, Footed . . . . .15.00
Coaster . . . . . . . . . . . . .15.00
Cup . . . . . . . . . . . . . . . .4.00
Cup & Saucer . . . . . . . . .14.00
Plate, Sherbet, 6 1/2 In. . . .7.50
Saucer . . . . . . . . . . . . . .1.00
Sherbet, Footed . . . . . . . .12.00
Soup, Dish, Tab
  Handles . . . . . . . . . . . .18.00
Sugar, Footed . . . . . . . . .10.00
Vase, Ruffled, Footed,
  6 1/2 In. . . . . . . . . . . . .24.00

## ULTRAMARINE
Bowl, Cereal,
  5 1/4 In. . . . . . .14.00 to 16.00
Bowl, Salad,
  9 In. . . . . . . . .24.00 to 25.00
Candlestick, 2-Light,
  Pair . . . . . . . .40.00 to 45.00
Candy Dish,
  Cover . . . . .125.00 to 175.00
Candy Dish, Footed . . . . .24.00
Console, Handles, Footed,
  10 In. . . . . . .27.00 to 29.00
Creamer,
  Footed . . . . . .15.00 to 17.50
Cup . . . . . . . . . . . . . . .17.00
Cup & Saucer . .14.00 to 20.00
Plate, Dinner,
  9 1/4 In. . . . . . .16.00 to 19.00
Plate, Sherbet,
  6 1/2 In. . . . . . . .6.00 to 8.00
Salt & Pepper . . . . . . . .48.00
Sandwich Server,
  12 1/2 In. . . . . .25.00 to 40.00
Soup, Dish, Tab
  Handles . . . . . . . . . . . .32.00
Sugar, Footed . . . . . . . . .17.00
Sugar & Creamer . . . . . .37.00

---

All outside doors should
be made of solid wood
or metal so they are
difficult to kick in.

---

Sugar & Creamer,
  Footed . . . . . . . . . . . . .27.00
Tumbler, Footed, 9 Oz.,
  4 5/8 In. . . . . . .34.00 to 45.00
Vase, Footed,
  8 1/2 In. . . . . . .18.00 to 30.00

## SWIRL FIRE-KING
Swirl Fire-King is named for its
wide swirled border. In the
1950s it was made in Azurite
(blue), Ivory White with or
without trim (later changed to
Anchor White), and Pink. From
1960 to 1975 it was made in
Jadite, Iridescent Lustre, and
Anchor White with or without
gold trim. Other related sec-
tions in this book are Alice,
Charm, Fire-King, Fleurette,
Game Bird, Gray Laurel,
Jadite, Jane-Ray, Peach Lustre,
Philbe, Turquoise Blue, and
Wheat.

## AZURITE
Creamer . . . . . . . . . . . . .6.00

## IVORY
Cup . . . . . . . . . . . . . . . .3.00
Mixing Bowl, 9 In. . . . . . .13.00
Plate, Dinner, 10 In. . . . . .4.50
Saucer, 5 3/4 In. . . . . . . . .1.00
Soup, Dish . . . . . . . . . . . .8.00

## JADITE
Mixing Bowl, 6 In. . . . . . .12.00
Mixing Bowl, 7 In. . . . . . .14.00
Mixing Bowl, 9 In. . . . . . .16.00
Plate, Dinner, 10 In. . . . . .11.00
Soup, Dish, 7 5/8 In. . . . . .12.00
Sugar, Cover, Footed . . . .49.00

## PINK
Creamer . . . . . . . . . . . . .8.50
Cup . . . . . . . . . . . . . . . .5.00
Sandwich Server, 11 In. . .20.00
Saucer . . . . . . . . . . . . . .2.00

---

Soup, Dish, 7 5/8 In. . . . . .10.00
Sugar, Cover, Tab
  Handles . . . . . . . . . . . .12.50

## WHITE
Bowl, Vegetable,
  8 1/4 In. . . . . . . . . . . . . .8.00
Casserole, Tab Handles,
  Individual, 5 x 1 3/4 In. . .8.00
Creamer, Footed . . . . . . . .4.00
Plate, Dinner, 10 In. . . . . . .5.00
Saucer, 5 3/4 In. . . . . . . . .1.00
Sugar, Footed, Open
  Handles . . . . . . . . . . . . .4.00
Sugar & Creamer,
  Cover . . . . . . . .8.00 to 15.00

**SWIRLED BIG RIB,** see Spiral

**SWIRLED SHARP RIB,** see Diana

---

## SYLVAN
Sylvan is often called Parrot or
Three Parrot because of the
center pattern on the plates. It
was made by Federal Glass
Company in 1931 and 1932 in
Amber, Blue, Crystal, and
Green. The molds were later
used for the Madrid pattern.

## AMBER
Berry Bowl, 5 In. . . . . . . .22.00
Bowl, Vegetable,
  Oval, 10 In. . . . . . . . . .32.00
Butter . . . . . . . . . . . . . .85.00
Creamer . . . . . . . . . . . . .11.00
Cup . . . . . . . . . . . . . . . .40.00
Cup & Saucer . . . . . . . . .17.00
Grill Plate, Round,
  10 1/2 In. . . . . .12.00 to 14.00
Plate, Dinner, 9 In. . . . . . .49.00
Plate, Sherbet,
  6 In. . . . . . . . .20.00 to 22.00
Platter, Oblong,
  11 1/4 In. . . . . . . . . . . .27.00
Saucer . . . . . . . . . . . . . .18.00

Sherbet, Cone,
Footed . . . . . . .27.00 to 28.50

Soup, Dish, 7 In. . . . . . . . .32.50

Tumbler, Footed,
10 Oz., 4 1/4 In. . . . . . .32.00

Tumbler, Footed, 12 Oz.,
5 1/2 In. . . . . . .45.00 to 50.00

### CRYSTAL
Grill Plate, Square,
10 1/2 In. . . . . .30.00 to 32.00

### GREEN
Bowl, Vegetable, Oval,
10 In. . . . . . . . .57.00 to 60.00

Butter, Cover . .350.00 to 375.00

Cup . . . . . . . . . . . . . . .40.00

Cup & Saucer . . . . . . . .55.00

Hot Plate, Pointed Edge,
5 In. . . . . . . . . . . . . . .900.00

Plate, Dinner, 9 In. . . . . .50.00

Plate, Salad, 7 1/2 In. . . . .40.00

Platter, Oblong,
11 1/4 In. . . . . .50.00 to 55.00

Salt & Pepper . . . . . . . .300.00

Saltshaker . . . . . . . . . .135.00

Sugar . . . . . . . .30.00 to 40.00

Sugar & Creamer,
Cover . . . . . . . . . . . .285.00

Tumbler, Footed,
5 3/4 In. . . . . . . . . . . .175.00

**TASSELL,** see Princess

## TEA ROOM
The very Art Deco design of Tea Room has made it popular with a group of collectors; it is even called Moderne Art by some. The Indiana Glass Company, Dunkirk, Indiana, made it from 1926 to 1931. Dinner sets were made of Amber, Crystal, Green, and Pink glass.

### AMBER
Pitcher,
64 Oz. . . . . .500.00 to 900.00

Sugar &
Creamer . . .200.00 to 290.00

Tumbler, Footed, 8 Oz.,
5 1/4 In. . . . .100.00 to 200.00

### CRYSTAL
Relish, 2 Sections,
8 1/2 In. . . . . . . . . . . . .20.00

Sugar & Creamer . . . . . .40.00

Tumbler, Iced Tea, Footed,
11 Oz., 6 1/16 In. . . . . .50.00

Vase, Block, Frosted,
9 1/2 In. . . . . . . . . . . .175.00

Vase, Ruffled, 9 1/2 In. . . .50.00

Vase, Ruffled, 11 In. . . . .175.00

### GREEN
Bowl, Salad, Deep,
8 3/4 In. . . . . . . . . . . .150.00

Bowl, Vegetable, Oval,
9 1/2 In. . . . .63.00 to 75.00

Candlestick, Pair . . . . . . .48.00

Lamp, Electric,
9 In. . . . . . .165.00 to 200.00

Pitcher, 64 Oz. . . . . . . .175.00

Salt & Pepper,
Footed . . . . . .60.00 to 75.00

Saltshaker . . . . . . . . . . .25.00

Sugar, Cover . . . . . . . . .295.00

Sugar, Footed,
4 In. . . . . . . . .18.00 to 20.00

Sugar & Creamer . . . . . .32.00

Sugar & Creamer,
Tray . . . . . . .65.00 to 105.00

Sundae, Footed . . . . . . . .70.00

Vase, Ruffled, 6 1/2 In. . .145.00

Vase, Ruffled,
9 1/2 In. . . . .135.00 to 175.00

Vase, Ruffled,
11 In. . . . . . .310.00 to 350.00

Vase, Straight,
11 In. . . . . . .120.00 to 150.00

### PINK
Candlestick, Pair . . . . . . .50.00

Pitcher, Footed, 64 Oz. . .135.00

Salt & Pepper . . .60.00 to 75.00

Sugar & Creamer, Tray . . .87.50

Sundae,
Footed . . . . .145.00 to 150.00

Tray, Center Handle . . . .190.00

Tumbler, 9 Oz.,
5 1/8 In. . . . . . . . . . . . .32.00

Vase, Ruffled, 6 1/2 In. . .125.00

Vase, Ruffled, 11 In. . . . .145.00

Vase, Straight, 11 In. . . . .96.00

## TEAR DROP
Tear Drop, a pattern available in full dinnerware sets, was made by Duncan & Miller Glass Company, Washington, Pennsylvania, from 1934 to 1955. It was made only in Crystal.

### CRYSTAL
Bowl, 12 In. . . . . . . . . . .24.00

Cake Stand, 13 In. . . . . .40.00

Candy Dish, Heart Shape,
7 1/2 In. . . . . . . . . . . . .23.50

Celery Dish, Handles,
6 x 12 In. . . . . . . . . . . .18.00

Creamer . . . . . . . . . . . . .6.00

Cruet, Oil, 3 Oz.,
4 3/4 In. . . . . . . . . . . . .20.00

Cup & Saucer . . .7.00 to 10.00

Dish, Mayonnaise,
Footed, Spoon . . . . . . . .18.00

Goblet, Champagne,
5 Oz., 3 In. . . . . . . . . . .7.00

Goblet, Cocktail, 3 1/2 Oz.,
4 1/2 In. . . . . . .10.00 to 15.00

Goblet, Wine, 3 Oz.,
4 1/4 In. . . . . . . . . . . . .14.00

Jam Jar, Cover . .28.00 to 30.00

Mustard, 4 1/2 In. . . . . . .30.00

Oyster Cocktail, Footed,
3 1/2 Oz., 3 3/4 In. . . . . .8.00
Pitcher, Water, Ice Lip,
64 Oz., 8 1/2 In. . . . . . .110.00
Relish, 5 Sections, 12 In. .22.00
Saucer, After Dinner . . . . .3.50
Sugar . . . . . . . . . . . . . . .6.00
Sugar & Creamer . . . . . .21.00
Sugar & Creamer, Tray,
8 In. . . . . . . . . . . . . . . .7.50
Tumbler, Iced Tea, 14 Oz.,
6 In. . . . . . . . .10.00 to 18.00

## THISTLE

Thistle pattern was made by
Macbeth-Evans Glass Company
from 1929 to 1930. The pattern
pictures large thistles primarily
on Pink pieces, but Green,
Crystal, and Yellow dishes also
were made. Reproductions have
been made. They are listed at
the end of the Depression Glass
section.

### CRYSTAL
Plate, Luncheon, 8 In. . . . . .8.00
### GREEN
Bowl, Cereal, 5 1/2 In. . . .27.00
Bowl, Fruit, 10 1/2 In. . .350.00
Cup & Saucer . . . . . . . .37.00
Plate, Luncheon,
8 In. . . . . . . . .23.00 to 30.00
### PINK
Bowl, Cereal,
5 1/2 In. . . . . . .25.00 to 30.00
Cup . . . . . . . . .22.00 to 28.00

Cup & Saucer . . . . . . . .36.00
Plate, Luncheon,
8 In. . . . . . . . .15.00 to 22.50
Saucer . . . . . . . . . . . . .13.00

**THREADING,** see Old English

**THREE PARROT,** see Sylvan

## TRADITION

Imperial Glass Company of
Bellaire, Ohio, made Tradition
pattern glass in the 1930s. It
was made in Amber, Amethyst,
Blue, Crystal, Green, Pink, and
Red.

### AMBER
Goblet, Juice, Footed,
5 Oz. . . . . . . . . . . . . . . .9.00
Goblet, Water, 10 Oz. . . . .10.00
Goblet, Wine, 4 Oz. . . . . .7.00
Sherbet, Footed, 4 1/8 In. . .6.50
Tumbler, Iced Tea,
12 Oz., 6 In. . . . . . . . . .7.00
### AMETHYST
Goblet, Juice, Footed,
5 Oz. . . . . . . . . . . . . . . .7.00
Goblet, Water, 10 Oz. . . . .16.00
Goblet, Wine, 4 Oz. . . . . .20.00
### BLUE
Finger Bowl, 4 1/2 In. . . .35.00

Goblet, Juice, Footed,
5 Oz. . . . . . . . . . . . . . .25.00
Goblet, Water, 10 Oz. . . . .20.00
Goblet, Wine, 4 Oz. . . . . .30.00
Sherbet, Footed . . . . . . . .15.00
Tumbler, Iced Tea, Footed,
12 Oz. . . . . . .22.00 to 25.00
### CRYSTAL
Plate, Handles, 9 1/2 In. . .30.00
Plate, Salad, 8 In. . . . . . .15.00
Salt & Pepper . . . . . . . .17.00
### GREEN
Goblet, Juice, Footed,
5 Oz. . . . . . . . . . . . . . .21.00
Goblet, Water, 10 Oz. . . . .12.00
Goblet, Wine,
4 Oz. . . . . . . . .16.00 to 20.00
Sherbet, Footed . . . . . . . .10.00
Tumbler, Iced Tea,
12 Oz. . . . . . . . . . . . . .16.00
### PINK
Goblet, Water,
10 Oz. . . . . . .20.00 to 22.00
Plate, Salad, 8 In. . . . . . .20.00
### RED
Sherbet, Footed . . . . . . . .16.00

## TROJAN

The Fostoria Glass Company
made Trojan. The etched glass
dishes were made in Rose from
1929 to 1935, Topaz from 1929
to 1938, and Gold Tint from
1938 to 1944. It also was made
in Green. Crystal bases were
used on some pieces from 1931
to 1944.

## ROSE

Lunch Tray, Center
   Handle . . . . . . . . . . . . .75.00
Plate, Luncheon, 9 In. . . . .65.00

## TOPAZ

Bowl, Dessert, Handle,
   Large . . . . . . . . . . . . . .95.00
Bowl, Vegetable, Oval,
   12 In. . . . . . . . . . . . . . .95.00
Candlestick, 3 In., Pair . . .65.00
Cup & Saucer   . .22.00 to 24.00
Finger Bowl Liner,
   6 1/2 In. . . . . . . . . . . . .10.00
Goblet, Water, Footed,
   9 Oz. . . . . . . . . . . . . . .32.50
Parfait  . . . . . . . . . . . . . .65.00
Plate, Breakfast,
   7 1/2 In. . . . . . . . . . . . .10.00
Plate, Cheese & Cracker . .60.00
Plate, Dessert, 6 In. . . . . . .8.00
Plate, Lemon, Handles  . . .24.00
Plate, Luncheon,
   8 1/2 In. . . . . . . . . . . . .16.50
Soup, Dish, 7 In. . . . . . . .195.00
Tumbler, Juice, Footed,
   5 Oz. . . . . . . . . . . . . . .19.50
Vase, Bulbous, 8 In. . . . .395.00

## TULIP

Tulip pattern pictures the side
of a tulip in a very stylized border. It was made by the Dell
Glass Company of Millville,
New Jersey, during the 1930s.
Amber, Amethyst, Blue, Crystal, and Green pieces were
made. Fire-King also made a
pattern called Tulip.

## AMETHYST

Cup  . . . . . . . . . . . . . . . .20.00

---

**If two tumblers get
stuck when stacked, try
putting cold water in
the inside glass, then
put both into hot water
up to the lower rim.**

---

### BLUE
Cup & Saucer  . . . . . . . .24.00
Plate, Dessert, 6 In. . . . . .10.00

### GREEN
Creamer . . . . . . . . . . . . .20.00
Cup & Saucer   . .23.00 to 26.00
Plate, Dessert,
   6 In. . . . . . . . . . .8.50 to 9.00
Plate, Dinner,
   9 In. . . . . . . . . .22.00 to 34.00
Plate, Salad,
   7 1/4 In. . . . . . . . . . . . .15.00
Sugar  . . . . . . . . . . . . . . .20.00

## TURQUOISE BLUE

Turquoise Blue, one of the pat-
terns made by Anchor Hocking
Glass Corporation, is a plain
pattern named for its color.
Mixing bowls were made in 1-
pt., 1-qt., 2-qt., and 3-qt. sizes.
It was made in the 1950s.
Related sections in this book
are Alice, Charm, Fire-King,
Gray Laurel, Jadite, Jane-Ray,
Peach Lustre, Philbe, Swirl
Fire-King, and Wheat.

Berry Bowl,
   4 1/2 In. . . . . . . . .5.00 to 6.00
Bowl, 4 1/2 In. . . . . . . . . .5.00
Bowl, Cereal,
   5 In. . . . . . . . . .6.00 to 13.00
Bowl, Vegetable,
   8 In. . . . . . . . . .8.00 to 15.00
Creamer  . . . . . . . .4.00 to 5.50
Cup  . . . . . . . . . . .2.00 to 2.50
Cup & Saucer   . . .3.50 to 6.00
Mug  . . . . . . . . . . .4.00 to 5.75
Plate, Bread & Butter,
   7 In. . . . . . . . . . . . . . . .8.00

---

Plate, Dinner, 10 In. . . . .27.50
Plate, Indentation, Gold
   Trim, 9 In. . . . . . .5.25 to 8.50
Plate, Salad,
   7 In. . . . . . . . . .8.00 to 11.00
Relish, 3 Sections,
   11 1/2 In. . . . . .8.00 to 10.00
Relish, 3 Sections, Oval,
   11 1/2 In. . . . . . . . . . . .10.00
Saucer  . . . . . . . . .1.00 to 2.00
Soup, Dish,
   6 5/8 In. . . . . . .14.25 to 20.00
Sugar . . . . . . . . . . . . . . .5.25
Sugar & Creamer . . . . . . .9.00

## TWISTED OPTIC

Twisted Optic is the pattern
sometimes confused with Spi-
ral. Be sure to look at the infor-
mation about that pattern.
Imperial Glass Company of
Bellaire, Ohio, made Twisted
Optic luncheon sets from 1927
to 1930 in Amber, Blue,
Canary Yellow, two shades of
Green, and Pink.

### GREEN
Candy Dish,
   Cover . . . . . . . .30.00 to 35.00
Cup & Saucer  . . . . . . . . .7.00
Plate, Luncheon,
   8 In. . . . . . . . . . .4.00 to 7.50
Plate, Sherbet,
   6 In. . . . . . . . . . .3.00 to 3.50
Vase, Footed, 2 Handles,
   8 In. . . . . . . . . . . . . . .37.00

### PINK
Bowl, Cereal, 5 In. . . . . . .17.00
Creamer . . . . . . . .6.00 to 11.00
Cup  . . . . . . . . . . . . . . . .6.00
Plate, Sherbet, 6 In. . . . . .3.00

Sandwich Server,
2 Handles, 8 In. . . . . . . .25.00
Sherbet . . . . . . . . . . . . .6.00
Vase, Footed, 2 Handles,
8 In. . . . . . . . . . . . . . .37.00

## VERSAILLES

Versailles by Fostoria Glass
Company was made in many
colors during the years of its
production, 1928 to 1944.
Azure Blue, Green, and Rose
were made from 1928 to 1944,
Topaz from 1929 to 1938, and
Gold Tint from 1938 to 1944.
Crystal bases were used with
colored glass from 1931 to
1944.

**BLUE**
Candlestick, 2 In., Pair . . .55.00
Chop Plate, 13 In. . . . . . .195.00
Console, Round, 11 In. . .145.00
Cup & Saucer . . . . . . . .49.00
Finger Bowl, Liner . . . . .125.00
Goblet, Champagne . . . . .35.00
Goblet, Water . . . . . . . . .65.00
Ice Bucket . . . . . . . . . .225.00
Nut Dish, Individual . . . . .65.00
Plate, Bread & Butter,
6 In. . . . . . . . . . . . . . .12.50
Plate, Dinner,
10 1/2 In. . . . . . . . . . .135.00
Sugar . . . . . . . . . . . . . .37.50
Sugar & Creamer . . . . . . .75.00
Tumbler, Footed, 9 Oz. . . .35.00
Tumbler, Iced Tea, Footed,
12 Oz., 6 In. . . .50.00 to 65.00
Tumbler, Juice, Footed,
2 1/2 Oz. . . . . . . . . . . .45.00
Tumbler, Water, Footed . .45.00

**GREEN**
Finger Bowl Liner . . . . . .15.00
Goblet, Champagne . . . . .37.50
Goblet, Cocktail, 3 Oz.,
5 1/4 In. . . . . . . . . . . .47.50
Gravy Boat, Liner . . . . . .250.00
Ice Bucket . . . . . . . . . .175.00
Ice Dish Liner . . . . . . . .22.50
Pail, Whipped Cream,
Handle . . . . . . . . . . . .125.00
Plate, Dinner, 9 In. . . . . .18.00
Platter, 12 In. . . . . . . . . .75.00
Sugar & Creamer . . . . . . .55.00
Sweetmeat, Loop
Handle . . . . . . . . . . . . .35.00
Tray, Service &
Lemon . . . . . . . . . . . .375.00

**ROSE**
Bowl, Cereal, 6 In. . . . . . .85.00
Goblet, Cocktail, 3 Oz.,
5 1/4 In. . . . . . . . . . . .55.00
Goblet, Cordial, Footed,
3/4 Oz., 4 In. . . . . . . . .125.00
Goblet, Water, 9 Oz. . . . . .65.00
Goblet, Wine, 3 Oz.,
5 1/2 In. . . . . . .45.00 to 95.00
Ice Dish Liner . . . . . . . .25.00
Pail, Whipped Cream,
Handle . . . . . . . . . . . .275.00
Pitcher . . . . . . . . . . . . .675.00
Plate, Bread & Butter,
6 In. . . . . . . . . . . . . . . .4.50
Plate, Luncheon,
8 3/4 In. . . . . . . . . . . . .18.00
Sherbet, 4 1/4 In. . . . . . .37.50
Sherbet, 6 In. . . . . . . . . .19.00
Soup, Cream, Footed . . . .75.00
Tumbler, Juice, Footed,
5 Oz., 4 1/2 In. . . . . . . .47.50

**TOPAZ**
Bowl, Footed, 12 In. . . . . .55.00

---

**If you are moving,
remember there is no
insurance coverage for
breakage if the items
are not packed by the
shipper.**

---

Bowl, Fruit, 5 In. . . . . . . .35.00
Bowl, Whipped Cream,
Handle . . . . . . . . . . . . .35.00
Candlestick, 3 In., Pair . . .28.00
Goblet, Cordial, 3/4 Oz.,
4 In. . . . . . . . .75.00 to 125.00
Goblet, Water, 10 Oz.,
8 1/4 In. . . . . . . . . . . . .25.00
Sherbet, 4 1/2 In. . . . . . .20.00
Sherbet, 6 In. . . . .20.00 to 25.00
Soup, Dish, 7 In. . . . . . . .85.00
Sugar, Individual . . . . . . .42.00

**VERTICAL RIBBED,** see Queen
Mary

## VESPER

Vesper was made by the
Fostoria Glass Company of
Ohio and West Virginia from
1926 to 1934. Dinner sets were
made in Amber, Blue, and
Green.

**AMBER**
Bowl, Footed, 10 In. . . . . .85.00
Compote, Twisted Stem,
8 In. . . . . . . . . . . . . . .45.00
Cup & Saucer . .18.00 to 25.00
Finger Bowl Liner, 6 In. . .10.00
Goblet, Champagne . . . . .25.00
Goblet, Cocktail . . . . . . .27.50
Goblet, Water . . . . . . . . .28.00
Gravy Boat Liner . . . . . . .40.00
Ice Bucket, Handle . . . . .95.00
Pitcher, Footed . . . . . . .345.00
Plate, Dinner,
9 1/2 In. . . . . . .15.00 to 25.00
Plate, Luncheon, 8 1/2 In. . .8.00
Plate, Salad, 7 1/2 In. . . . . .6.00
Sandwich Server, Center
Handle, 11 In. . . . . . . . .38.00
Saucer . . . . . . . . . . . . . .10.00
Sherbet . . . . . . . . . . . . .15.00
Sugar & Creamer . . . . . . .45.00

Tumbler, Footed, 9 Oz. . . .20.00

**GREEN**

Candy Jar, Cover,
1/2 Lb. . . . . . . . . . . . .115.00
Compote, Footed, 8 In. . . .24.00
Console, 11 In. . . . . . . . .35.00
Cup & Saucer . . . . . . . .18.00
Cup & Saucer, After
Dinner . . . . . . . . . . . .49.50
Goblet, Water . . . . . . . .29.00
Goblet, Wine . . . . . . . . .45.00
Plate, Bread & Butter,
6 In. . . . . . . . . . . . . . .9.00
Plate, Dinner, 9 1/2 In. . . . .8.00
Plate, Dinner, 10 1/2 In. . .35.00
Sandwich Server, Center
Handle . . . . . . . . . . . .35.00
Saucer . . . . . . . . . . . . .4.50
Sherbet . . . . . . . . . . . .15.00
Soup, Cream . . . .25.00 to 29.50

---

## VICTORY

The Diamond Glass-Ware Company, Indiana, Pennsylvania, made Victory pattern from 1929 to 1932. It is known in Amber, Black, Cobalt Blue, Green, and Pink. A few pieces have gold trim.

**AMBER**

Bowl, Cereal, 6 1/2 In. . . . .5.00
Candlestick, Gold Trim,
3 In., Pair . . . . . . . . . .22.00
Cup . . . . . . . . . . . . . . .4.50

**GREEN**

Bowl, Cereal, 6 1/2 In. . . .12.00
Creamer . . . . . . . . . . . .11.00
Cup . . . . . . . . . . . . . . .6.50
Cup & Saucer . . .9.75 to 14.00
Plate, Dinner, 9 In. . . . . .18.00
Plate, Luncheon, 8 In. . . . .7.00
Sugar . . . . . . . . . . . . .14.00

**PINK**

Cup . . . . . . . . . . . . . . .8.50
Cup & Saucer . . .12.00 to 14.00

Plate, Dinner, 9 1/4 In. . . .23.50
Plate, Luncheon,
8 In. . . . . . . . . . .7.00 to 8.00
Sandwich Server, Center
Handle . . . . . .28.00 to 30.00
Saucer . . . . . . . . . . . . .2.00

---

## VITROCK

Vitrock is both a kitchenware and a dinnerware pattern. It has a raised flowered rim and so is often called Floral Rim or Flower Rim by collectors. It was made by Hocking Glass Company from 1934 to 1937 and resembles embossed china. It was made in White, sometimes with fired-on colors, in solid Red or Green, and with decal-decorated centers.

**WHITE**

Berry Bowl, 4 In. . . .4.50 to 7.50
Bowl, Cereal, 6 In. . . . . . .5.50
Bowl, Vegetable,
9 1/2 In. . . . . . . . . . . .16.00
Canister, Tea, Screw
Cover, 20 Oz. . . . . . . .27.00
Cup . . . . . . . . . . . . . . .4.00
Cup & Saucer . . . . . . . .7.50
Plate, Luncheon,
8 3/4 In. . . . . . . .4.50 to 5.00
Platter . . . . . . . . . . . . .20.00
Saucer . . . . . . . . . . . . .2.50
Soup, Cream,
5 1/2 In. . . . . . .15.00 to 17.00

**VIVID BANDS,** see Petalware

**WAFFLE,** see Waterford

---

## WATERFORD

Waterford, or Waffle, pattern was made by Anchor Hocking Glass Corporation from 1938 to 1944. Crystal and Pink are the most common colors; Yellow and White were used less extensively. Some of the Opaque White pieces also have fired-on pink and green. In the 1950s some Forest Green pieces were made.

**CRYSTAL**

Berry Bowl, 4 1/2 In. . . . . .6.00
Berry Bowl, Master,
8 1/4 In. . . . . . . .8.00 to 9.00
Butter, Cover . . .23.00 to 24.00
Cake Plate, Handle,
10 1/4 In. . . . . . .6.00 to 8.00
Candy Dish, 2 Sections, Gold
Trim, 6 1/2 In. . . . . . . . .4.00
Coaster . . . . . . . .1.50 to 4.00
Creamer . . . . . . . .4.00 to 4.50
Cup . . . . . . . . . . . . . . .5.00
Cup & Saucer . . . . . . . . .8.00
Goblet, Water, 5 1/4 In. . .20.00
Pitcher, Ice Lip, Tilted,
80 Oz. . . . . . . . . . . . . .25.00

Pitcher, Juice, Tilted,
42 Oz. . . . . . . . . . . . . .18.00
Plate, Dinner,
9 5/8 In. . . . . . .6.00 to 11.00
Plate, Salad,
7 1/8 In. . . . . . . .4.00 to 6.00
Plate, Sherbet, 6 In. . . . . .3.00
Salt & Pepper,
Large . . . . . . . . .4.00 to 9.00
Salt & Pepper,
Small . . . . . . . . .4.00 to 8.00
Sandwich Server,
13 3/4 In. . . . . .8.00 to 12.00
Saucer . . . . . . . . . . . . . . .2.00
Sherbet, Footed . . . .2.25 to 4.00
Sugar . . . . . . . . . . . . . . . .4.00
Sugar, Cover . . . . .8.00 to 15.00
Sugar & Creamer .9.50 to 14.00
Tumbler, Footed, 10 Oz.,
4 7/8 In. . . . . . . .9.00 to 12.00

### PINK

Ashtray . . . . . . . . . . . . . .3.50
Butter, Cover . . . . . . . . .200.00
Cake Plate, Handles,
10 1/4 In. . . . . .13.00 to 21.00
Plate, Dinner, 9 5/8 In. . . .24.00
Sandwich Server,
13 3/4 In. . . . . .30.00 to 35.00
Sherbet . . . . . . . . . . . . .12.00
Tumbler, 10 Oz. . . . . . . . .20.00

**WEDDING BAND,** see
Moderntone

## WHEAT

Wheat glass was made by
Anchor Hocking Glass Corporation from 1962 to about 1967.
It is part of the Fire-King Oven
Ware line. It is a white opaque
glass decorated with a natural-
looking spray of wheat. A few
pieces were given added decoration. Another pattern of glass
called Wheat was made by
Federal Glass Company in the
1930s, but only the Anchor
Hocking glass is listed here.

Baking Pan,
8 x 12 1/2 In. . . . . . . . . .6.00
Bowl, Dessert,
4 5/8 In. . . . . . . . .3.00 to 3.75
Casserole, 1 Qt. . . . . . . . .6.00

Creamer . . . . . . . . . . . . .3.00
Cup . . . . . . . . . . . . . . . .4.25
Custard, 6 Oz. . . . . . . . . .3.75
Plate, Dinner,
10 In. . . . . . . . . .5.00 to 5.25
Platter . . . . . . . . . . . . . .10.00
Platter, Oval . . . . . . . . . . .6.00
Snack Set, Cup, Rectangular
Plate, 2 Piece . . . . . . . . .1.50
Soup, Dish, 6 5/8 In. . . . . .5.75
Sugar . . . . . . . . . . . . . . .4.25
Tray, Snack, 11 x 6 In. . . . .5.00

**WHITE SAIL,** see White Ship

## WHITE SHIP

White Ship, also called Sailing
Ship, Sail Boat, or White Sail,
is really part of the Sportsman
series made by Hazel Atlas
Glass Company in 1938. The
ships are enamel decorations on
Cobalt Blue, Crystal, or Amethyst glass. The enamel decorations are sometimes in color.

### COBALT BLUE

Cocktail
Shaker . . . . . . .33.00 to 60.00
Ice Bowl . . . . .30.00 to 45.00
Pitcher, Ice Lip, 86 Oz. . . .64.00
Tray, Round, 12 In. . . .100.00
Tumbler, Iced Tea, 10 1/2 In.,
4 7/8 In. . . . . .10.00 to 18.00
Tumbler, Juice, 5 Oz.,
3 1/2 In. . . . . . . . . . . . . .6.00
Tumbler, Old Fashioned, 8 Oz.,
3 5/8 In. . . . . . .14.00 to 31.00
Tumbler, Roly Poly,
4 1/2 Oz. . . . . . . . . . . .10.00
Tumbler, Roly Poly,
6 Oz. . . . . . . . . . . . . . . .8.00
Tumbler, Water, 9 Oz.,
3 3/4 In. . . . . . .11.00 to 16.00

**WILDFLOWER,** see No. 618
**WILDROSE,** see Dogwood
**WILDROSE WITH APPLE
BLOSSOM,** see Flower Garden
with Butterflies

## WINDMILL

Windmill, or Dutch, is a part of
the Sportsman series made by
Hazel Atlas Glass Company in
1938. Of course, it pictures a
landscape with a windmill. The
windmills are enamel decorations on Cobalt Blue, Crystal,
or Amethyst glass.

Cocktail Set, Chrome Tray,
6 Tumblers, 8 Piece . . .175.00
Cocktail Shaker . . . . . . . .25.00
Ice Bowl . . . . .25.00 to 30.00
Ice Bowl Set, Tumblers,
Stirrers, Wire Carrier,
14 Piece . . . . . . . . . . .130.00
Tumbler, Roly Poly,
6 Oz. . . . . . . . . .7.50 to 10.00

Tumbler, Water, 9 Oz.,
4 5/8 In. . . . . . . . . . . . .10.00

## WINDSOR

Windsor pattern, also called Diamond, Smocking, or Windsor Diamond, was made by Jeannette Glass Company, Jeannette, Pennsylvania, from 1936 to 1946. The pattern is most easily found in Crystal, Green, and Pink, although pieces were made in Amberina Red, Ice Blue, and Delphite.

### CRYSTAL
Berry Bowl, 4 3/4 In. . . . . .3.00
Bowl, Boat Shape,
7 x 11 3/4 In. . . . . . . . .18.00
Bowl, Footed, 7 1/8 In. . . . .7.00
Butter, Cover . . . . . . . . .20.00
Butter, Pointed Edge . . . . .25.00
Candlestick,
3 In. . . . . . . . .10.00 to 12.00
Candlestick, 3 In.,
Pair . . . . . . . .20.00 to 22.00
Chop Plate, 13 5/8 In. . . . .32.00

Creamer . . . . . . . . . . . . .4.00
Cup . . . . . . . . . . . . . . . .3.00
Pitcher, 16 Oz.,
4 1/2 In. . . . . . .13.00 to 15.00
Powder Jar . . . . . . . . . . .15.00
Relish, Oval, 11 1/2 In. . . .10.00
Sandwich Server, Closed
Handles, 10 1/4 In. . . . .10.00
Sandwich Server,
Handles, 10 In. . . . . . . .5.50
Sherbet, Footed . . . . . . . .3.00
Sugar, Cover . . . . .8.00 to 17.50
Tray, Handles, 8 1/2 In. . .13.00
Tumbler, Footed,
4 In. . . . . . . . . . .5.00 to 7.00
Tumbler, Footed,
12 Oz., 5 In. . . . . . . . .10.00

### GREEN
Bowl, Vegetable, Oval,
9 1/2 In. . . . . . . . . . . . .27.00
Butter, Cover . . . . . . . . .92.00
Chop Plate,
13 3/4 In. . . . . .40.00 to 45.00
Cup & Saucer . . . . . . . .18.50
Pitcher, Water, 52 Oz.,
6 3/4 In. . . . . . . . . . . . .50.00
Plate, Salad, 7 In. . . . . . .27.50
Plate, Sherbet, 6 In. . . . . .8.00
Salt & Pepper . .45.00 to 50.00
Sandwich Server, Handles,
10 1/4 In. . . . . .16.00 to 18.00
Saucer . . . . . . . . . . . . . .6.00
Sherbet . . . . . . . . . . . . .15.00
Sugar, Cover . . . . . . . . . .37.00
Tumbler, 4 In. . . . . . . . . .29.00
Tumbler, Footed, 12 Oz.,
5 In. . . . . . . . .34.00 to 45.00

### PINK
Ashtray . . . . . . .37.00 to 45.00
Berry Bowl,
4 3/4 In. . . . . . .9.00 to 12.50

Berry Bowl, Master,
8 1/2 In. . . . . . .20.00 to 22.00
Bowl, Boat Shape,
7 x 11 3/4 In. . .35.00 to 37.50
Bowl, Footed, 10 1/2 In. . .40.00
Butter, Cover . . .50.00 to 58.00
Cake Plate, Footed,
10 3/4 In. . . . . .20.00 to 25.00
Chop Plate,
13 5/8 In. . . . . .35.00 to 45.00
Compote, 6 In. . . . . . . . .11.00
Console, 12 1/2 In. . . . . .107.00
Creamer . . . . . . . . . . . . .12.50
Cup & Saucer . . . . . . . .14.00
Pitcher, 52 Oz.,
6 3/4 In. . . . . . .27.00 to 32.00
Plate, Dinner,
9 In. . . . . . . . .18.00 to 24.00
Plate, Sherbet,
6 In. . . . . . . . . .4.00 to 5.00
Platter, Oval,
11 1/2 In. . . . . .20.00 to 22.00
Punch Cup . . . . . . . . . . .2.75
Salt & Pepper . .37.00 to 40.00
Saltshaker . . . . .18.00 to 20.00
Sandwich Server, Handles,
10 1/4 In. . . . . .12.50 to 16.00
Saucer . . . . . . . . .6.00 to 8.00
Sherbet . . . . . . .8.00 to 12.00
Sugar, Cover . . . .25.00 to 30.00
Sugar, Holiday . . . . . . . .50.00
Tray, 2 Handles . . . . . . . .18.00
Tumbler, 4 In. . . .12.50 to 20.00
Tumbler, 5 Oz.,
3 1/4 In. . . . . . .24.00 to 25.00
Tumbler, Footed, 12 Oz.,
5 In. . . . . . . . . . . . . . . .30.00

**WINDSOR DIAMOND,** see
Windsor

**WINGED MEDALLION,** see Madrid

# Reproductions

| PATTERN | ITEM | COLORS | DATES |
|---------|------|--------|-------|
| Adam | Butter dish | Green, Pink | 1981 |
| American | Two-piece candle night-light | Crystal | 1987 |
| American | Almost all items have been reproduced | Crystal | 1992 |
| American | Nappy, footed punch bowl, salad bowl, torte plate | Red | 1992 |
| Avocado | Cup & saucer, handled dish, nappy, pickle, pitcher, sugar & creamer | Blue, Frosted Pink, Pink, Red, Amethyst, Yellow, Dark Green, Frosted Green | 1974 |
| Avocado | Pitcher, 64 oz. | Dark Green | 1979 |
| Avocado | Berry bowl, olive, 5 1/2-in. plate, relish, sundae, tumbler | Amber, Amethyst, Blue, Frosted Pink, Green, Pink, Red Amethyst, Red-Yellow | 1974 |
| Avocado | Pitcher, tumbler set, olive dish, cup & saucer, sugar & creamer, pickle, 6-in. & 8-in. plate, nappy, sherbet | Amber | 1978–1982 |
| Avocado | Pitcher, tumbler set, 5-piece beverage set | Pink | 1973 |
| Avocado | Pitcher, tumblers | Frosted Pink | |
| Avocado | Pitcher, 9 oz. tumbler, 5-piece beverage set | Purple | 1975 |
| Bubble | Square ashtray, 4-in. & 8-in. bowl, ivy ball, punch cup, 3 3/4-in. vase | Red | 1977–1978 |
| Cameo | Water set, ice bucket, tumblers, covered sugar & creamer | Pink, Yellow, Green | 1996 |
| Cameo | Children's dishes from Taiwan & China | Green, Pink, Yellow | 1996 |

| PATTERN | ITEM | COLORS | DATES |
|---|---|---|---|
| Cameo | Children's dishes called Jennifer Line | Green, Pink, Yellow | 1982–1996 |
| Cameo | Salt & pepper shakers | Green, Pink, Cobalt Blue | 1982 |
| Candlewick | Bowl, candelabra, cup & saucer, sugar & creamer, 2-handled jelly, plate, basket | Alexandrite, Blue, Pink (1987); Crystal, Cobalt Blue, Emerald Green, Red, Black (1990); Cranberry Mist (1993) | 1987–1993 |
| Cape Cod | Cruet | | 1986 |
| Cape Cod | Dinner set | | 1978 |
| Caprice | Bashful Charlotte, butter, sugar & creamer, footed juice, footed water tumbler, nut, relish, seashell ashtray, swan | Cobalt Blue, Light Blue; Rubina (called Sunset) (1950s) | 1985 |
| Cherry Blossom | Almost all items have been reproduced in various colors since 1972 | Blue, Cobalt Blue, Delphite, Iridescent, Green, Pink, Red | 1973 |
| Cherry Blossom | Salt & pepper shakers | Pink, Green, Delphite | 1977 |
| Cherry Blossom | Pitcher | Blue | 1979 |
| Cherry Blossom | Salt & pepper shakers | Cobalt Blue, Pink, Green | 1989 |
| Cherry Blossom | Cake plate, 13-in. platter | Pink, Green, Blue, Delphite | 1982 |
| Cherry Blossom | Pitcher | Blue | 1979 |
| Cherry Blossom | Water set | Amethyst Carnival glass | 1996 |
| Colony | Reamer, 2 spouts | White, Crystal | |
| Diana | Bowl | Pink | 1986 |
| English Hobnail | 18 pieces | Red | 1980 |
| English Hobnail | 26 pieces | Pink | 1982–1983 |
| English Hobnail | Pedestal salt dip | Crystal | 1986 |
| Floral | Salt & pepper shakers, footed | Cobalt Blue, Dark Green, Pink, Red | 1989 |
| Florentine No. 1 | Salt & pepper shakers, footed | Cobalt Blue, Pink, Red | 1989 |
| Florentine No. 2 | Water pitcher, tumbler | Blue, Pink, Deep Opaque Green | 1995 |
| Georgian | Tumblers: 5-oz., 12-oz., & 15-oz. | Ruby | 1978 |
| Hazel Atlas Quilt | Kitchen shaker | Pink | 1987 |
| Heritage | 5-in. bowl | Amber, Crystal | 1987 |
| Heritage | 5-in. bowl, 9-in. footed bowl, cake plate, goblets: iced tea, 10-in. plate | Crystal | 1992 |
| Heritage | Goblets: iced tea, wine | Blue, Pink | 1992 |

| PATTERN | ITEM | COLORS | DATES |
|---------|------|--------|-------|
| Ipswich | Candlestick | Forest Green, Ruby | 1994 |
| Iris | Candy dish (bottom only), vase | Multicolored over Crystal | 1976 |
| Iris | Various items | Crystal | 1969 |
| Iris | Various items | Milk glass & sprayed-on colors | 1970 |
| Iris | Candy dish | Crystal | 1970 |
| Iris | Vase | Crystal | 1982 |
| June | Bottom's-Up tumbler | Black, Jade, Custard | 1979 |
| June | Goblets: 4-oz., 6-oz., 9-oz., 12-oz. | Blue, Crystal, Yellow | 1979 |
| Madrid | Candleholder | Black | 1977 |
| Madrid | Candleholder, sugar & creamer | Crystal | 1977 |
| Madrid | Butter, 9 1/2-in. bowl, sugar & creamer | Amber | 1977 |
| Madrid | Covered butter dish | Crystal | 1979 |
| Madrid | Dinner set | Amber | 1982 |
| Madrid | Dinner set | Amber | 1976 |
| Madrid | Salt & pepper shakers | Crystal | 1978 |
| Madrid (called Recollection) | Various items | Amber, Blue, Crystal, Yellow, Pink, Teal, frosted & other colors later | 1976–1977 |
| Mayfair Open Rose | Cookie jar | Amethyst, Green, Pink, Cobalt Blue, Red | 1982 |
| Mayfair Open Rose | Cookie jar | Cobalt Blue | 1990 |
| Mayfair Open Rose | Juice pitcher | Cobalt Blue, Pink | 1993 |
| Mayfair Open Rose | Salt & pepper shakers | Cobalt Blue, Pink, Red | 1988 |
| Mayfair Open Rose | Salt & pepper shakers | Green, Pink | 1989 |
| Mayfair Open Rose | Whiskey | Green, Pink, Cobalt Blue | 1977 |
| Miss America | Butter dish | Amberina, Crystal, Green, Ice Blue, Pink, Red | 1977 |
| Miss America | Water pitcher, tumbler | Crystal, Cobalt Blue, Green, Ice Blue, Pink, Amberina | 1970–1980 |
| Miss America | Pitcher, tumbler | Crystal, Green, Pink | 1982 |

| PATTERN | ITEM | COLORS | DATES |
|---------|------|--------|-------|
| Miss America | Salt & pepper shakers | Crystal, Green, Pink | 1977 |
| Miss America | Various items | Cobalt Blue | 1987 |
| Moonstone | Goblets: iced tea, wine | Dark & Light Blue | 1992 |
| Newport | Tumblers: 7-oz., 9-oz., 12-oz., 16-oz. | Cobalt Blue | 1977 |
| No. 610 | Berry bowl, relish, tray, tumbler | Black, Blue | 1974 |
| Princess | Candy jar | Pink, Blue | |
| Princess Feather | 1-piece & 2-piece reamers, "Gillespie" measuring cup | Various colors | 1986 |
| Royal Lace | 5-oz. tumbler | Cobalt Blue | 1996 |
| Royal Ruby | Tumblers: 7-oz., 9-oz., 12-oz., 16-oz. | Red | 1977–1978 |
| Royal Ruby | Bread & butter plate, salad plate, 4-in. bowl, tumblers: 7-oz., 9-oz., 12-oz., 16-oz. | Red | 1978 |
| Sandwich Anchor Hocking | Covered cookie jar | Crystal | 1978 |
| Sandwich Duncan & Miller | Ashtray, basket, berry set, boxes, bowl, bridge set, candleholder, napkin holder, platter, pitcher, snack set, 3-part relish, tidbit, tumbler, vase | Amber, Light Green, Crystal | 1982 |
| Sandwich Indiana | Basket, bridge set, candle-holder, goblet, napkin holder, nappy, punch set, snack set, tidbit, vase, wine set | Amber | 1982 |
| Sandwich Indiana | Cookie jar | Crystal | 1989 |
| Sandwich Indiana | Sugar & creamer, 6-in. & 8-in. sherbet | Avocado, some frosted | 1981 |
| Sandwich Indiana | Child's set, nappy, pickle, plate, mug, bowl, 6-oz. tumbler, 5-in. pitcher (Marjorie Daw) | Avocado | 1977–1985 |
| Sandwich Indiana | Butter dish | Teal | 1981 |
| Sandwich Indiana | Basket, candleholder, snack set, wine set | Light Green | 1982 |
| Sandwich Indiana | Dinner set | Amber, Crystal, Dark Blue, Red | 1969 |
| Sandwich Indiana | Various items | Amber, Blue, Crystal, Green, Red | |

| PATTERN | ITEM | COLORS | DATES |
|---|---|---|---|
| Sharon | Butter dish | Amber, Blue, Dark Green, Light Green, Pink | 1976 |
| Sharon | Covered candy dish | Pink | 1984 |
| Sharon | Covered candy dish | Cobalt Blue | 1976 |
| Sharon | Cheese dish | Blue, Amber, Dark Green, Light Green, Pink | 1977 |
| Sharon | Measuring cup, candy dish | Pink | 1984 |
| Sharon | Covered sugar & creamer | Light Pink | 1977 |
| Sharon | Salt & pepper shakers | Green, Pink, & other colors | 1980 |
| Sharon | Covered sugar & creamer | Pink, Green | 1983 |
| Shirley Temple | Milk pitcher, mug | Cobalt Blue | 1982 |
| Shirley Temple | 6 1/2-in. bowl | Cobalt Blue | 1986 |
| Thistle | Large bowl, pitcher, tumbler, platter | Pink | 1996–1997 |

# DEPRESSION GLASS FACTORIES, PATTERNS, AND BIBLIOGRAPHY

*Kovels' Depression Glass & Dinnerware Price List* is a concise guide to price and age information. This is a list that will help collectors learn more about Depression glass patterns. Each glass factory is listed separately with the location and the dates of operation. A list of books that specialize in this type of glass is also included. These books often have many color pictures of the glass, reprints of early advertising, and other information. Also included under each factory name is a list of the best-known patterns made by the firm. Not all of these are included in the main body of our book. General reference books on Depression glass are included at the end of this section.

## Akro Agate Company, Clarksburg, West Virginia, 1914–1951

### REFERENCE BOOKS
Archer, Margaret and Douglas. *Imperial Glass*. Paducah, Kentucky: Collector Books, 1978.
Florence, Gene. *Collector's Encyclopedia of Akro Agate*. Revised edition. Paducah, Kentucky: Collector Books, 1975. Revised 1992 prices.
Hardy, Roger and Claudia. *The Complete Line of the Akro Agate Co.* Privately printed, 1992 (10 Bailey St., Clarksburg, WV 26301-2524).

### PATTERNS
Akro Agate tableware, 1932–1951

## Anchor Hocking Glass Corporation, Lancaster, Ohio, 1905–present (Hocking Glass Company, 1905–1937; Anchor Hocking Glass Corporation, 1937–1969; Anchor Hocking Corporation, 1969–present)

### REFERENCE BOOKS
Kilgo, Garry and Dale; Jerry and Gail Watkins. *A Collector's Guide to Anchor Hocking Fire-King Glassware*. 2nd Edition. Privately printed, 1997 (K & W Collectibles, P.O. Box 473, Addison, AL 35540).

### PATTERNS
Alice, 1940s
Arctic, 1932
Bibi, 1940s
Block Optic, 1929–1933
Boopie, late 1940s–1950s

Bubble, 1934–1965
Burple, 1940s
Cameo, 1930–1934
Chariot, 1932
Charm, 1950–1954

Circle, 1930s
Colonial, 1934–1938
Coronation, 1936–1940
Dancing Girl (Sunrise Medallion), late 1920s–early 1930s
Debbra, 1931–1933
Fire-King Oven Glass, 1942–1960s
Fire-King Oven Ware, 1950s
Fleurette, 1958–1960
Forest Green, 1950–1957
Fortune, 1937–1938
Frosted Ribbon, 1940
Game Bird, c.1959–1963
Georgian, 1935
Hobnail, 1934–1936
Jane-Ray, 1945–1963
Lace Edge, 1935–1938
Lake Como, 1934–1937
Little Bo Peep, 1940
Manhattan, 1938–1941
Mayfair Open Rose, 1931–1937
Miss America, 1933–1936
Monarch, 1970s–1985
Moonstone, 1941–1946
Old Cafe, 1936–1938
Oyster & Pearl, 1938–1940

Panelled Ring-Ding, 1932
Pantryline, 1920s–1930s
Peach Lustre, 1952–1963
Philbe, 1937–1940s
Pillar Optic, 1935
Polar Bear, 1932
Primrose, 1960–1962
Princess, 1931–1935
Queen Anne, late 1930s
Queen Mary, 1936–1940
Ring, 1927–1932
Ring-Ding, 1932
Roulette, 1935–1939
Royal Ruby, 1939–1960s
Sandwich Anchor Hocking, 1939–1964
Spiral, 1928–1930
Stripe, 1932
Stars and Stripes, c.1942
Swirl Fire-King, 1955–1960s
Three Bands, 1930s
Turquoise Blue, 1950s
Vitrock, 1934–1937
Waterford, 1938–1944; 1950s
Wheat, 1960s
Whirly-Twirly, 1940s

---

## Bartlett-Collins, Sapulpa, Oklahoma, 1914–present

### REFERENCE BOOKS

Warner, Ian. *Swankyswigs: A Pattern Guide and Check List.* Privately printed, 1982 (P.O. Box 57, Otisville, MI 48463).

Weatherman, Hazel Marie. *Decorated Tumbler.* Privately printed, 1978 (P.O. Box 280, Springfield, MO 65721).

———. *Price Guide to the Decorated Tumbler.* Privately printed, 1979 (P.O. Box 280, Springfield, MO 65721).

### PATTERNS

Sheraton, 1930s
Swankyswigs, 1956–1958; 1975

Twitch, early 1930s

## Belmont Tumbler Company, Bellaire, Ohio, c.1920–1952

**PATTERNS**

ABC Stork                                            Rose Cameo, 1933

Belmont Ship Plate

## Cambridge Glass Company, Cambridge, Ohio, 1901–1958

**REFERENCE BOOKS**

*Cambridge Glass Co.* (catalog reprint). Privately printed, 1976 (P.O. Box 416, Cambridge, OH 43725).

*Fine Handmade Table Glassware* (catalog reprint). Privately printed, 1978 (P.O. Box 416, Cambridge, OH 43725).

National Cambridge Collectors, Inc. *Colors in Cambridge Glass.* Paducah, Kentucky: Collector Books, 1984.

National Cambridge Collectors, Inc. *Etchings by Cambridge.* Volume 1. Privately printed, 1997 (Brookville Publishing, P.O. Box 3, Brookville, OH 45309-0003).

Smith, Bill and Phyllis. *Cambridge Glass 1927–1929.* Privately printed, 1986 (4003 Old Columbus Rd., Springfield, OH 45502).

**PATTERNS**

| | |
|---|---|
| Aero Optic, 1929 | Gloria, c.1930 |
| Alpine Caprice, 1936 | Imperial Hunt, 1932 |
| Apple Blossom, 1930s | Lorna, 1930 |
| Caprice, 1936–1953 | Martha Washington, 1932 |
| Cleo, 1930 | Mt. Vernon, 1920s–1940s |
| Decagon, 1930s | Nautilus, 1933–1934 |
| Diane, 1934–1950s | Portia, 1932–1950s |
| Elaine, 1934–1950s | Rosalie, 1920s–1930s |
| Everglades, 1933–1934 | Rose Point, 1936–1953 |
| | Weatherford, 1926 |

## Consolidated Lamp & Glass Company, Coraopolis, Pennsylvania, 1894–1933; 1936–1967

**PATTERNS**

Catalonian, 1927–1936                                Dance of the Nudes, 1920s

## Dell Glass Company, Millville, New Jersey, 1930s

**PATTERNS**

Tulip, 1930s

# Diamond Glass-Ware Company, Indiana, Pennsylvania, 1891–1931

**PATTERNS**

Victory, 1929–1932

# Dunbar Flint Glass Corporation (Dunbar Glass Corporation), Dunbar, West Virginia, 1913–1953

**PATTERNS**

Aramis, 1936

Athos, 1936

Barbra, 1928

D'Artagnan, 1936

# Duncan & Miller Glass Company, Washington, Pennsylvania, 1893–1955

**PATTERNS**

Caribbean, 1936–1955

Early American Lace, 1932

Early American Sandwich, 1925–1949

Full Sail, 1925

Georgian, 1928

Kimberly, 1931

Punties, 1931

Puritan, 1929

Sandwich Duncan & Miller, 1924–1955

Spiral Flutes, 1924–early 1930s

Tear Drop, 1934–1955

Terrace, 1935

# Federal Glass Company, Columbus, Ohio, 1900–1971

**PATTERNS**

Colonial Fluted, 1928–1933

Columbia, 1938–1942

Corded Optic, 1928

Crossbar, mid-1930s

Daisy Spray & Lattice, 1928

Diamond Arch, 1938–1940

Diamond Squat, 1928

Diana, 1937–1941

Georgian, 1931–1935

Grand Slam, 1930

Heritage, late 1930s–1960s

Indian, c.1930

Jack Frost, 1928

John, mid-1930s

Lido, mid-1930s

Madrid, 1932–1939

Mary, mid-1930s

Mayfair Federal, 1934

Mutt 'N Jeff, 1928

Normandie, 1933–1940

Patrician, 1933–1937

Pear Optic, 1929–1930

Pioneer, 1930s–1970s

Raindrops, 1929–1933

Rosemary, 1935–1937

Sharon, 1935–1939

Squat Optic, 1928

Sylvan, 1931–1932

Tall Boy, 1928

Trump Bridge, 1928

Tudor Ring, 1928

Wheat, early 1930s

# Fenton Glass Company, Williamstown, West Virginia, 1906–present

## REFERENCE BOOKS

Heacock, William. *Fenton Glass: The First Twenty-five Years.* Privately printed, 1978 (Antique Publications, P.O. Box 553, Marietta, OH 45750).

———. *Fenton Glass: The Second Twenty-five Years.* Privately printed, 1980 (Antique Publications, P.O. Box 553, Marietta, OH 45750).

## PATTERNS

Franklin, 1934

Georgian Fenton, c.1930

Lincoln Inn, 1928

Plymouth, 1933

# Fostoria Glass Company, Fostoria, Ohio; Moundsville, West Virginia, 1887–1986

## REFERENCE BOOKS

Kerr, Ann. *Fostoria: An Identification and Value Guide of Pressed, Blown & Hand Molded Shapes.* Paducah, Kentucky: Collector Books, 1994.

McGrain, Patrick, ed. *Fostoria: The Popular Years.* Privately printed, 1982 (P.O. Box 219, Frederick, MD 21701).

Piña, Leslie. *Fostoria Designer George Sakier, With Values.* Atglen, Pennsylvania: Schiffer Publishing Ltd., 1996.

———. *Fostoria: Serving the American Table 1887–1986, With Price Guide.* Atglen, Pennsylvania: Schiffer Publishing Ltd., 1995.

Weatherman, Hazel Marie. *Fostoria: Its First Fifty Years.* Privately printed, 1972 (P.O. Box 280, Springfield, MO 65721).

## PATTERNS

| | |
|---|---|
| American, 1915–1986 | Legion, 1931–1940 |
| Baroque, 1936–1966 | Manor, 1931–1944 |
| Century, 1926–1986 | Midnight Rose, 1933–1957 |
| Chantilly, late 1940s–early 1950s | Morning Glory, 1931–1944 |
| Chateau, 1933–1940 | Navarre, 1937–1980 |
| Chintz, 1940–1972 | Nectar, 1934–1943 |
| Colony, 1920s–1970s | New Garland, 1930–1934 |
| Fairfax, 1927–1960 | Rambler, 1935–1958 |
| Florentine, 1931–1944 | Royal, 1925–1934 |
| Fuchsia, 1931–1944 | Springtime, 1933–1944 |
| Hermitage, 1932–1945 | Sunray, 1935–1944 |
| June, 1928–1952 | Trojan, 1929–1944 |
| Kashmir, 1930–1934 | Versailles, 1928–1944 |
| Lafayette, 1931–1960 | Vesper, 1926–1934 |

# Hazel Atlas Glass Company, Washington, Pennsylvania; Zanesville, Ohio; Clarksburg, West Virginia; Wheeling, West Virginia, 1902–1956

## REFERENCE BOOKS

Warner, Ian. *Swankyswigs: A Pattern Guide and Check List.* Privately printed, 1982 (P.O. Box 57, Otisville, MI 48463).

Weatherman, Hazel Marie. *Decorated Tumbler.* Privately printed, 1978 (P.O. Box 280, Springfield, MO 65721).

Weatherman, Hazel Marie. *Price Guide to the Decorated Tumbler.* Privately printed, 1979 (P.O. Box 280, Springfield, MO 65721).

## PATTERNS

Afghan & Scottie Dog, 1938
Aurora, late 1930s
Cloverleaf, 1930–1936
Colonial Block, early 1930s and 1950s
Colony, 1930s
Diamond Point Columns, late
    1920s–1930s
Floral Sterling, early 1930s
Florentine No. 1, 1932–1935
Florentine No. 2, 1932–1935
Fruits, 1931–1933
Hazel Atlas Quilt, 1937–1940
Homespun (Fine Rib), 1938–1940s
Moderntone, 1935–1942
Moderntone Little Hostess, 1940s
Moderntone Platonite, 1940–1950s

New Century, 1930–1935
Newport, 1936–1940
Ovide, 1929–1935
Polo, 1938
Ribbon, 1930s
Roxana, 1932
Royal Lace, 1934–1941
Shirley Temple, 1934–1942
Sportsman Series, 1940s
Starlight, 1930s
Swankyswigs, 1933–1940; 1947–1956
Tom & Jerry, 1930s
Twentieth Century, 1928–1931
White Ship, 1938
Windmill, 1938
X Design, 1928–1932

# A. H. Heisey & Company, Newark, Ohio, 1896–1957

## PATTERNS

Chintz, 1931–1938
Crystolite, 1938–1956
Empress, 1930–1938
Greek Key (Grecian Border),
    1912–1938
Ipswich (Early American Scroll),
    1931–1946; 1951–1953
Lariat, 1946–1956
Minuet, 1939–1950s
Octagon, 1925–1937

Old Sandwich (Early American
    Thumbprint), 1931–1956
Orchid, 1940–1957
Plantation, 1950–1956
Provincial, 1938–1956
Ribbed Octagon, 1925–1936
Ridgeleigh, 1935–1957
Saturn, 1937–1957
Twist, 1928–1937
Victorian, 1933–1953

# Imperial Glass Company, Bellaire, Ohio, 1904–1982

## REFERENCE BOOKS
Scott, Virginia R. *The Collector's Guide to Imperial Candlewick.* Privately printed, 1990 (275 Milledge Terr., Athens, Georgia 30606).

## PATTERNS

Beaded Block, 1927–1930s
Blaise, c.1930
Block with Rose
Candlewick, 1937–1982
Cape Cod, 1932–1980s
Chesterfield, c.1930
Diamond Quilted, 1920s–1930s
Early American Hobnail, 1930s
Flora, c.1925
Fountain Swirl, 1928–1930
Hazen, c.1930
Hobstars Intaglio, c.1930
Huckabee, c.1930
Ida, c.1930
Imperial Optic Rib, 1927
Imperial Plain Octagon, 1927

Laced Edge, early 1930s
Lindburgh, c.1930
Little Jewel, late 1920s–1930
Monticello
Mt. Vernon, c.1930
New Jewel, 1931
Pillar Flute, c.1930
Scroll Fluted, c.1930
Shaffer, c.1930
Spring Flowers, 1920s
Spun, 1935
Strawflower, c.1930
Tradition, 1930s
Twisted Optic, 1927–1930
Viking, 1929
Woodbury, c.1930

# Indiana Glass Company, Dunkirk, Indiana, 1907–present

## PATTERNS

Avocado, 1923–1933
Artura, c.1930
Bananas, c.1930
Christmas Candy, 1937; 1950s
Cracked Ice, 1930s
Indiana Custard, 1930s–1950s
King Arthur, c.1930
Lily Pons, c.1930
Loganberry, c.1930
No. 610, 1926–1932
No. 612, 1930–1933

No. 615, 1929–1932
No. 616, 1930–1932
No. 618, 1932–1937; 1960s
No. 620, 1933–1970s
Old English, late 1920s–early 1930s
Orange Blossom, 1957
Pretzel, 1930s–1970s
Sandwich Indiana, 1920s–1980s
Soda Fountain, c.1930
Tea Room, 1926–1931

## Jeannette Glass Company, Jeannette, Pennsylvania, c.1900–present

**PATTERNS**

Adam, 1932–1934
Anniversary, 1947–1949; 1970s
Bridget, 1925
Camellia, 1947–1951
Chantilly, 1960s
Cherry Blossom, 1930–1939
Cosmos, 1950s
Cubist, 1929–1933
Daisy J, 1926
Dewdrop, 1954–1955
Doric, 1935–1938
Doric & Pansy, 1937–1938
Floragold, 1950s
Floral, 1931–1935

Harp, 1954–1957
Hexagon Optic, 1928–1932; c.1960
Holiday, 1947–1949
Homespun, 1939–1940
Iris, 1928–1932; 1950s
Jadite, 1936–1938
Lombardi, 1938
Pretty Polly Party Dishes, 1937–1938
Sierra, 1931–1933
Sunburst, 1938–1941
Sunflower, late 1920s–early 1930s
Swirl, 1937–1938
Windsor, 1936–1946

## Jenkins Glass Company, Kokomo, Indiana; Arcadia, Indiana, 1901–1932

**PATTERNS**

Arcadia Lace, 1901–1932
Blossoms & Band, 1927
Fieldcrest
Hob, 1927–1931
Huck Finn, c.1930
Jenkins' Basket

Ocean Wave, c.1930
Sea-Side
Twin Dolphin
Yoo-Hoo, c.1930
Yo-Yo, c.1930

## Lancaster Glass Company, Lancaster, Ohio, 1908–1937

**PATTERNS**

Centaur, 1930s
Jane, c.1930
Jubilee, early 1930s

Patrick, c.1930
Yvonne, mid-1930s

## Libbey Glass Company, Toledo, Ohio, 1892–present

**PATTERNS**

Shirley Temple, 1972

## Liberty Works, Egg Harbor, New Jersey, 1903–1934

**PATTERNS**

American Pioneer, 1931–1934
Bamboo Optic, 1929
Egg Harbor, 1929

Octagon Bamboo Optic, 1929
Truman, 1930

## Louie Glass Company, Weston, West Virginia, 1926–1995

**PATTERNS**

Chico, 1936
Groucho, 1936
Harpo, 1936

Semper, 1931
Zeppo, 1936

## Macbeth-Evans Glass Company, Indiana (several factories); Toledo, Ohio; Charleroi, Pennsylvania; Corning, New York, 1899–1936 (acquired by Corning)

**PATTERNS**

American Sweetheart, 1930–1936
April, c.1930s
Bordette, 1930–1940
Chinex Classic, c.1938–1942
Cremax, 1930s–1940s
Crystal Leaf, 1928
Diamond Dart, 1928
Dixie, 1931
Dogwood, 1929–1934
Fanfare, c.1930s
Ivex, 1930–1940
Leaf, early 1930s

MacHOB, 1928
Oxford, 1930–1940
Petalware, 1930–1940
Pie-Crust, 1930–1940
Ringed Target, 1931
S Pattern, 1930–1935
Scrabble, 1931
Sheffield, 1930–1940
Squirt, 1931
Thistle, 1929–1930
Yankee, 1931

## McKee Glass Company, Jeannette, Pennsylvania, 1853–1961

**REFERENCE BOOKS**

McPhee Stout, Sandra. *The Complete Book of McKee Glass.* North Kansas City, Missouri: Trojan Press, Inc., 1972.

**PATTERNS**

Autumn, 1934
Clico, 1930
Flower Band, 1934

Laurel, 1930s
Lenox, 1930s
Octagon Edge, 1920s–1930s

Rock Crystal, 1920s–1930s
Scallop Edge, 1920s–1930s
Scottie Dog, 1930s

Tom & Jerry, 1940s
Wiggle, 1925

## Morgantown Glass Works, Morgantown, West Virginia, late 1800s–1972

**PATTERNS**

Art Moderne, 1929
Dancing Girl, 1920s–1930s
Hughes, 1932
Krinkle, 1924
Langston, 1932
Marilyn, 1929
Melon, 1932
Millay, 1932

Palm Optic, 1929
Peacock Optic, 1929–1930
Pineapple Optic, 1929
Primrose Lane, 1929
Simplicity, 1920s–early 1930s
Sommerset, 1932
Square, 1928

## New Martinsville Glass Manufacturing Company, New Martinsville, West Virginia, 1901–1944

**REFERENCE BOOKS**

Measell, James. *New Martinsville Glass, 1900–1944*. Privately printed, 1994 (Antique Publications, P.O. Box 553, Marietta, OH 45750).

**PATTERNS**

Moondrops, 1932–1940s

Radiance, 1936–1939

## Paden City Glass Manufacturing Company, Paden City, West Virginia, 1916–1951

**REFERENCE BOOKS**

Barnett, Jerry. *Paden City: The Color Company*. Astoria, Illinois: Stevens Publishing, 1978.

**PATTERNS**

Cupid, 1930s
Line 191, 1928
Nora Bird, 1929–1930s
Orchid, early 1930s
Peacock & Wild Rose, 1930s

Peacock Reverse, 1930s
Penny Line, 1932
Popeye & Olive, early 1930s
Wotta Line, 1933

## L. E. Smith Glass Company, Mt. Pleasant, Pennsylvania, 1907–present

**PATTERNS**

By Cracky, late 1920s

Do-Si-Do, 1930s

Gothic Arches, 1920s

Hammered Band, early 1930s

Homestead, 1930s

Mt. Pleasant, mid-1920s–1934

Soda Shop, mid-1920s

## Standard Glass Manufacturing Company, Lancaster, Ohio, 1924–c.1984
(became subsidiary of Hocking/Anchor Hocking in 1940)

**PATTERNS**

Blanche, c.1930

Grape, l930s

Rose, c.1930

Trudy, c.1930

## Tiffin Glass Company, Tiffin, Ohio, 1888–1980 (Factory R of U.S. Glass Company)

**REFERENCE BOOKS**

Bickenheuser, Fred. *Tiffin Glassmasters.* Privately printed, 1979 (Glassmasters Publications, P.O. Box 524, Grove City, OH 43123).

**PATTERNS**

Cadena, early 1930s

Cherokee Rose, 1940s–1950s

Classic, 1913–1930s

Flanders, mid-1910s–mid-1930s

Fuchsia, 1937–1940

June Night, 1940s–1950s

Velva, late 1930s

## U.S. Glass Company (United States Glass Company), Pennsylvania (several factories); Tiffin, Ohio; Gas City, Indiana; West Virginia, 1891–1963

**PATTERNS**

Aunt Polly, late 1920s–1935

Bee Hive, 1926

Cherry-Berry, early 1930s

Comet, mid-1920s

Craquel, 1924

Deerwood, 1920s–1930s

Diner, 1927

Flanders, 1914–1935

Floral & Diamond Band, 1920s

Flower Garden with Butterflies,
   late 1920s

Fuchsia, 1930s–1940s

Lariette, 1931

Octagon, 1927–1929

Primo, 1932

Shirley Temple, 1934–1942

Strawberry, 1930s

Thorn, 1930s

U.S. Swirl, late 1920s

## Westmoreland Glass Company, Grapeville, Pennsylvania, 1890–1985

### REFERENCE BOOKS

Grisel, Ruth Ann. *Westmoreland Glass: Our Children's Heirlooms.* Privately printed, 1993 (FSJ Publishing Co., P.O. Box 122, Iowa City, IA 52244).

Kovar, Lorraine. *Westmoreland Glass, 1950–1984.* Privately printed, 1991 (Antique Publications, P.O. Box 553, Marietta, OH 45750).

————. *Westmoreland Glass, 1950–1984.* Volume II. Privately printed, 1991 (Antique Publications, P.O. Box 553, Marietta, OH 45750).

Newbound, Betty and Bill. *Collector's Encyclopedia of Milk Glass Identification & Values.* Paducah, Kentucky: Collector Books, 1995.

Wilson, Chas West. *Westmoreland Glass Identification & Value Guide.* Paducah, Kentucky: Collector Books, 1996.

### PATTERNS

Della Robbia, 1920s–1930s

Doreen, 1924

English Hobnail, 1920–1970s

Lotus, 1920s–1930s

Marguerite, 1924

Orphan Annie, 1925

Princess Feather, 1939–1948; 1960s

Scramble, 1924

Wagner, 1924

Wakefield, 1933–1960s

Woolworth, early 1930s

# General Reference Books

Florence, Gene. *Collectible Glassware from the 40s, 50s, 60s: An Illustrated Value Guide.* 4th edition. Paducah, Kentucky: Collector Books, 1998.

———. *Collector's Encyclopedia of Depression Glass.* 13th edition. Paducah, Kentucky: Collector Books, 1998.

———. *Elegant Glassware of the Depression Era.* 7th edition. Paducah, Kentucky: Collector Books, 1998.

———. *Kitchen Glassware of the Depression Years.* 5th edition. Paducah, Kentucky: Collector Books, 1995.

———. *Very Rare Glassware of the Depression Years.* 5th series. Paducah, Kentucky: Collector Books, 1995.

**Kovel, Ralph and Terry. *Kovels' Antiques & Collectibles Price List.* 30th edition. New York: Crown Publishers, 1998.**

**———. *Kovels' Guide to Selling, Buying, and Fixing Your Antiques and Collectibles.* New York: Crown Publishers, 1995.**

**———. *Kovels' Know Your Collectibles.* New York: Crown Publishers, 1981, updated 1992.**

Luckey, Carl F., with Mary Burris. *Identification & Value Guide to Depression Era Glassware.* 3rd edition. Iola, Wisconsin: Books Americana/Krause, 1994.

Rogove, Susan Tobier, and Marcia Buan Steinhauer. *Pyrex by Corning.* Privately printed, 1993 (Antique Publications, P.O. Box 553, Marietta, OH 45750).

Washburn, Kent G. *Price Survey.* 4th edition. Privately printed, 1994 (8048 Midcrown, Suite 26, San Antonio, TX 78218-2334).

Weatherman, Hazel Marie. *Colored Glassware of the Depression Era 1.* Privately printed, 1970 (Weatherman Glassbooks, P.O. Box 280, Ozark, MO 65721).

———. *Colored Glassware of the Depression Era 2.* Privately printed, 1974 (Weatherman Glassbooks, P.O. Box 280, Ozark, MO 65721).

———. *Price Trends to Colored Glassware of the Depression Era 1.* Privately printed. (Weatherman Glassbooks, P.O. Box 280, Ozark, MO 65721).

———. *Supplement & Price Trends for Colored Glassware of the Depression Era Book 2.* Privately printed. (Weatherman Glassbooks, P.O. Box 280, Ozark, MO 65721).

Whitmyer, Margaret and Kenn. *Bedroom & Bathroom Glassware of the Depression Years.* Paducah, Kentucky: Collector Books, 1990.

Yeske, Doris. *Depression Glass: A Collector's Guide.* Atglen, Pennsylvania: Schiffer Publishing Ltd., 1997.

# DINNERWARE

# DINNERWARE

# Introduction

This book has changed to reflect the collecting trends of the late 1990s. The inexpensive dinnerware sets made in America are the main focus of this section. We also included sets made in other countries, but sold in quantity in America. Azalea pattern, made in Japan, and Liberty Blue, made in England, are two of these new entries. We list the prices for the most popular everyday sets being collected today. Formal dinnerwares made by firms like Lenox or Royal Worcester are not included.

Because dishes were made by so many manufacturers, there is a problem with variations in vocabulary. Most sugar bowls made for these dinnerware sets had covers. Today many have lost their original covers and are sold as open sugars. We do not include the word *open* in the description, but we do indicate if there is a cover. A gravy boat with a liner is a gravy boat with the oval tray that it rests on. Sometimes the liner is permanently attached to the gravy boat. A mayonnaise bowl may also have a liner.

A lug soup is a bowl with a flat handle called a lug. Other soup bowls may have pierced handles or no handles. Oatmeal bowl and cereal bowl are both names for a bowl about 6 inches in diameter. We use the name cereal bowl. We list both a pickle dish and a pickle tray. The tray is flat. An after-dinner coffee cup is larger than a demitasse but smaller than a coffee cup. A few mixing bowls have covers. The covers are very rare and sell for high prices. We list the bowls with and without the covers. A French baker or fluted baker is a bowl with straight sides.

One strange size indication is often used by dealers. A piece is "36s." When the dinnerware was made it was packed in barrels. The words 30s or 36s refers to the number of pieces that would fit in a barrel. The larger the number, the smaller the size of the piece. If that is the common way the piece is described today, we have included it in the listing. The height of a pitcher or jug is one indication of size; the number of liquid ounces it holds is also important. We have tried to list both. Wherever possible, we have used both the name of the piece and the size, so the listing is "plate, dinner, 10 in." Although most dinner plates are 10 inches in diameter, a few are smaller and we have listed the actual size in each case.

The terms "kitchenware" and "dinnerware" are used in the original sense. A dinnerware set includes all the pieces that might have been used on a dinner table, including dishes, bowls, platters, tumblers, cups, pitchers, and serving bowls. A kitchenware set has bowls and storage dishes of the type used in a kitchen and does not include dinner plates or cups. Kitchenware includes rolling pins, pie servers, and other kitchen utensils. A few kitchenware bowls are listed, but other pieces are not.

Colors often were given romantic names, and, whenever possible, we have used these original factory names. Some colors, such as Camellia (rose), Cadet (light blue), Indian Red (orange), or Dresden (deep blue), are explained in the paragraph descriptions.

It is important to remember that the descriptions of dinnerware may include many strange names. Some are the factory names, some refer to the pattern (decorations applied to the piece), and many were used by the factory to describe the shape. For example, Taverne is a pattern; Laurel is the shape of the dish used to make that pattern; and Taylor, Smith, and Taylor is the name of the company that made the dinnerware. Sometimes a name refers to both a pattern and a shape.

Pieces of American dinnerware are constantly being discovered in attics, basements, garage sales, flea markets, and antiques shops. The publications that offer them through the mail use descriptions that often include both the pattern and the shape name. Learn to recognize the shapes that were used by each maker. Authors of some of the other books about dinnerwares have arbitrarily named the pieces. Sometimes these names, although referring to the same piece, are different in different books. We have tried to cross-reference these names so you can locate them in any of the books.

This year we have included the bibliography of dinnerware books in a new form. It is not a traditional bibliography. Instead we have made it more "user friendly." Look up the factory that made your dinnerware pattern. (If you don't know the factory name, you will find it in the paragraph listing prices in the main section of the book.) Under the factory name is a list of the most collectible patterns made by that factory. We have changed to this form because so many dinnerware pieces are marked with the name of the maker, not the name of the pattern. Some of the patterns are priced in this book, some are not. The listing also includes the books that picture or discuss your pattern. General books about pottery marks and dinnerware are listed separately. Some companies have changed their names during the years of dinnerware production. Gladding, McBean & Company became Franciscan Ceramics, Inc., and eventually was purchased by the Water-

# The Changing Styles and Colors
## of
# DEPRESSION GLASS
# AND DINNERWARE

## DEPRESSION GLASS

This Waterford, or Waffle, 2-handled plate is an example of a popular clear glass pattern.

Clear and pastel-colored glassware in matching sets became popular about 1925. The Fostoria Glass Company of Fostoria, Ohio, made the first of these glass sets, which included dinner plates, coffee cups, and other pieces to be used at a dinner table. The glassware was expensive and its popularity led to similar pieces being made by other companies that were able to produce a less expensive glass.

Inexpensive glass was made by a method called tank molding. Silica sand, soda ash, and limestone were heated, and the molten glass mixture was passed through pipes to the automated pressing mold. Patterns were acid-etched or tooled into the mold so the finished glassware had a design. Because the pressing process made a glass that often had flaws or bubbles, patterns used as decoration

This Princess cookie jar was made in light green, a common pastel color.

The Floral pattern features a lacy-type design of poinsettias. This is a pink sugar bowl that was originallly sold with a cover.

This pink Hobnail cup gets its name from the bumpy 19th-century glassware of the same name.

Indiana Glass Company's Sandwich pattern is similar to glass made in the 19th century by the Sandwich Glass Works of Sandwich, Massachusetts; hence the name.

were often lacy in appearance to help hide the flaws.

During the late 1960s, interest in the inexpensive pastel glass led to several books, and the term "Depression glass" came into general use, even though the glassware was made before, during, and after the Depression. The name has gradually come to include other glassware made from 1925 through the 1970s: lacy types, pseudo-Sandwich glass patterns, hobnail variations, solid-colored wares of ruby, cobalt, or green, and many opaque-glass patterns. In the past few years another term, "elegant glassware of the Depression era," has come into use. This refers to the better-quality glass made at the same time. There is much overlap between these types of glass, and even the exact name to use for a pattern may be in doubt.

Depression glass designs can be divided into groups. The pseudo-etched designs, like Adam or Cherry Blossom, were made first, from about 1925 to 1935, in pastel colors.

Pseudo-etched designs, like the one on this green Adam bowl, were made in the mold. They hid the flaws in inexpensive molded glass.

Raised designs, often with fruit and flower patterns, such as Open Rose and Sharon, were made in the mid-1930s. At the same time other patterns were made of deep colors like cobalt blue or Royal Ruby or Forest Green. Opaque glass, pastels, and clear glass were also popular.

Geometric wares, such as Hobnail and Ribbon, were made during the late 1920s, and again in the late 1930s and early 1940s. Simple outlines and bold colors predominated. Art Deco–influenced geometric designs included Cubist, Imperial Octagon, and U.S. Octagon.

Enameled or silk-screened patterns were developed during the 1940s. White-enameled designs were added to cobalt blue, Royal Ruby, Forest Green, and clear glass. Shirley Temple pieces, originally given away with cereal, and Windmill are among the most popular with collectors today.

A few patterns, Windsor Diamond and Floral & Diamond Band, for example, were designed to resemble the cut glass of the 19th century or the Lacy Sandwich patterns made by the Sandwich, Massachusetts, glass-works. About ten pseudo-Sandwich patterns were sold, most of which were referred to as Sandwich in the manufacturers' catalogs.

Opaque glass was popular in the 1930s. Each of the colors was given a special name by the

Anchor Hocking made glassware in strong, solid colors like these Royal Ruby cups and this Forest Green pitcher.

This Iris pattern covered butter features a raised design.

The Art Deco era is characterized by geometric designs, like this Cubist bowl.

company that produced it. Monax or Ivrene are opaque white glasswares. So are Azurite, Chinex, Clambroth, and Cremax. Opaque green glass was known by a variety of names, including Jade-ite by Anchor Hocking and Jadite by Jeannette Glass Company. Jade green is a generic name used by many companies. Delphite is an opaque blue glass.

The famous Swankyswigs, glasses that held cheese spread, first made in 1933, were made with enamel decorations of many colors. But the 1940s and after was the the time of color-added decoration on other glasswares. Bands or stripes were used on some patterns; colorful stylized flowers were added to opaque white wares. Some pieces were even colored to look like solid-color pottery.

This Windmill sugar bowl, made in the 1940s, features a white enamel design on cobalt blue glass. White Ship and the Sportsman Series are related patterns made by the Hazel Atlas Company.

The Windsor Diamond pattern provides an inexpensive alternative to cut glass. This salt and pepper set was made by the Jeanette Glass Company.

Some pieces, like Cherry Blossom, were made in clear pastel colors or of opaque glass. This plate is Delphite, an opaque blue. Other colors include green, jadite (opaque green), pink, and red.

Depression glass dinner sets are popular with collectors, but so are the utility wares that date from the same period. Utility dishes were meant to be used in the kitchen and not on the table, and included leftover dishes, lemon reamers, cookie jars, and canister sets.

Swankyswigs, small glasses that were made to hold cheese spread, are decorated with colorful enamel designs.

The Ring pattern features multicolored enameled stripes.

A word of warning about the use of these dishes. Most can be used in a microwave and dishwasher with no problem. But patterns with designs that change the thickness of the glass may have stress points that will pop in a microwave. And dishes with decals like White Sails or with an iridescent finish will be harmed by the high temperatures of a dishwasher. Ceramic dinnerware and the prices for these pieces can be found in the second half of this book.

Fire King used several decorations on its opaque white lines. This cup and saucer feature the Bachelor Button design.

These mugs by Fire-King are colored to look like solid-color pottery.

# DINNERWARE

The first ceramic pots made in the American colonies were redware. In the 1600s local red clay was dug, worked, and fired to make utilitarian pots and dishes. Salt-glazed pottery, a ware that did not chip as easily, was developed by the 1700s. Transfer-printed wares made in England were popular in America in the 19th century, and American factories, many near clay beds in Ohio and New Jersey, began to make inexpensive pottery dishes. Other popular dishes of the 19th century included iron-

Noritake's Azalea-pattern cake plate competed with similar American wares.

stone china, luster-decorated pieces, and colorful majolica. But it was not until the late 1920s that the "modern" dish styles evolved. Expensive and inexpensive dishes were made in thousands of different designs.

Many dinnerware sets were made in America from the 1930s through the 1960s. Some collectors refer to these sets as "Depression dinnerware," but the name used by manufacturers was "American dinnerware," which is

Friendly Village dinnerware, first made in 1953, is still made by the English company Johnson Brothers.

Colorful Fiesta is probably the most popular Homer Laughlin pattern.

the name still used by most collectors and dealers. Not all dishes were American made, however. There were also some popular dinnerware patterns marketed like the American pieces, such as Azalea, made by the Japanese company Noritake, and Friendly Village, made by Johnson Brothers in England.

Pottery, porcelain, semi-porcelain, ironstone, and other ceramic wares are included in the category of dinnerware. Most were made in potteries located in southern Ohio and in West Virginia near the Ohio River. Each

Riviera is another Homer Laughlin line.

Color is again the main focus of Homer Laughlin's Harlequin line.

El Patio pattern, produced from 1936 to 1956 by Franciscan Ceramics of California, was made in twenty solid colors.

Here are a sugar and creamer in the traditional Willow pattern by the Buffalo China Company of Buffalo, New York.

factory made many patterns for sale to gift shops and department stores. The potteries also made special patterns for use as premiums and free giveaways or to sell for low prices as store promotions. Dishes were given away at movies, stuffed into soap and cereal boxes and bags of flour, or sold for very low prices at grocery stores.

Dinnerware patterns fall into many categories. The first patterns to be rediscovered by collectors of the 1980s and 1990s were the solid-colored pottery lines such as Fiesta, Riviera, and Harlequin. Some colorful dinnerware was also made in California potteries before 1960. One

Liberty pattern made by an English company in the Staffordshire district of England features historical scenes, such as this plate picturing Washington at Valley Forge.

BELOW: Colonial Homestead,
also by Royal China, was inspired
by traditional transfer wares.

ABOVE: Currier & Ives,
by Royal China Company,
shows 19th-century scenes.

of these is El Patio by Franciscan. El Patio dishes are heavy and have a handcrafted look. Sets were sold in mix-and-match colors. These dishes have remained popular, and pieces were made in the 1990s in new colors.

Traditional-looking pieces reminiscent of the 19th century, including Willow and Liberty, have also remained popular. Some traditional patterns, like Currier & Ives and Colonial Homestead, are modern interpretations of older transfer patterns.

Nocturne was made by Southern Potteries, also called Blue Ridge by collectors.

ABOVE: Blueberry was one of many fruit designs made by Stangl Pottery.

Many manufacturers in the 1930s preferred hand-painted, peasantlike decorations on their dinnerware. Included in this group are the pieces made by Southern Potteries under the name Blue Ridge; the pottery by Stangl of New Jersey picturing fruit, flowers, or birds; and the pieces by Gladding McBean (Franciscan), Metlox, and Red Wing.

Cameo Ware is an unusual type of dinnerware made about 1935 by Harker and others. To make Cameo Ware, a solid-colored plate was embel-

California Provincial is a pattern in the Poppy Trail line by Metlox.

Franciscan's Desert Rose
pattern is still popular.

This Bob White pitcher by
Red Wing Potteries, made from
1956 to 1967, incorporates
modern shapes with
hand-painted bird decorations.

Harker's Ivy Wreath plate
is part of the Cameo Ware line.

lished with a white decoration that in the finished product appears to be cut into the colored glaze. Cameo dinnerware pieces usually picture flowers and leaves, and some special children's wares have nursery rhyme animals or birds.

Realistically shaped pieces resembling corn were produced by several makers about 1955. The most important are Corn King and Corn Queen by the Shawnee Pottery Company. Green and yellow dishes were made in full sets. Other dishes were made in three-dimensional shapes. Most famous is

Hull made this figural
Red Riding Hood
salt and pepper set.

Ears of corn inspired many glass and
dinnerware lines, illustrated by this Corn King
large covered casserole, surrounded by
corn-shaped pieces made by other factories.

the Red Riding Hood line first manufactured by Hull in 1943. Figural
cookie jars, a few figural teapots, and
salt and pepper shakers were made by
both dinnerware firms and those who
specialized in kitchen wares.

Most of the dinnerware made after
the 1930s was decorated with decal
designs. These colored, printed patterns were applied to the dishes, and
often the same decal was used on several differently shaped plates or
bowls. The most famous of these
designs, Autumn Leaf, was made for
and sold by the Jewel Tea Company
after 1936. Reproductions of Autumn
Leaf are being made today.

Mexican-inspired designs such as
Mexicana by Homer Laughlin and
Patio by Paden City were popular during the late 1930s. At least twenty different sets were made that picture
cacti, haciendas, or sleeping Mexicans.

An Autumn Leaf
ball pitcher made by Hall for
the Jewel Tea Company.

Patio is a Mexican-inspired
decoration on Paden City's
Shell-Crest shape.

Red Poppy is one
of Hall's floral lines.

Hall also made Crocus,
another flower-inspired pattern.

The Hall China Company made many decal-decorated wares, including Poppy, Red Poppy, and Crocus. These dishes were often made with matching kitchen pieces, including coffeepots, stove-top salt and pepper shakers, cookie jars, leftover jars, and mixing bowls. Black silhouette designs on light-colored dishes were popular in the 1930s. Silhouette pictures to hang on the wall were very much in style. Silhouette pattern dishes by the Crooksville China Company and Taverne by the Hall China Company are the best known.

This is a Silhouette teapot made by Crooksville China Company.

American Modern is Russel Wright's most famous dinnerware.

Some dishes with innovative shapes and subtle earth-tone colors became favorites in the 1940s and 1950s. Important industrial designers, such as Russel Wright, who created American Modern and Iroquois; Walter Dorwin, who designed Conversation for Taylor, Smith, and Taylor; and Ben Seibel, who designed Raymor for Roseville, made these dishes. American Modern, the most famous dinnerware by Russel Wright, is said to be the best-selling dinnerware of all time.

Even more modern-looking dinnerware was made by Eva Zeisel (Hallcraft, Century, and Tomorrow's Classic for Hall) and other industrial designers and company art directors in the 1950s and 1960s. These include Starburst by Franciscan and California Contempora by Metlox. Many of the modern shapes and decorations used in this dinnerware were copied by other factories.

This Iroquois syrup with the Improptu design is another line by Russel Wright.

Starburst is one of Franciscan's modern lines.

Metlox's California Contempora pattern has a free-form design.

The 1950s saw another trend: casual entertaining and outdoor living became popular. The dishes designed for these pastimes were often made in realistic forms of leaves and flowers or were colored in the subdued tones of nature. Woodfield by Steubenville was typical.

Because plastic dinnerware like Melmac didn't break easily, its popularity grew in the 1960s. However, plastic dinnerware did scratch, and it eventually lost favor to Pyroceram, a ceramiclike glass substance made by Corning for its baking dishes and Corelle dinnerware. Even though Corelle dinnerware is still popular today, the American dinnerware era was over by the 1970s. Unable to compete with cheaper wares made in Asia, most American potteries closed in the 1960s and 1970s. Today most of our dishes are made in England or in countries such as Sri Lanka or Thailand.

This Woodfield bowl by Steubenville Pottery has a natural color and a leaf design.

Eva Zeisel created the Hallcraft line for Hall. This serving bowl features the Dawn design on a Hallcraft shape.

ford Wedgwood Group. We use the name that was in use most of the time the pattern was made.

Although hundreds of patterns are included in this book, many patterns were not seen at sales this year and are not included. Prices listed in this book are actual prices asked by dealers at shows, shops, and through national advertising. It is not the price you would pay at a garage sale or church bazaar. Prices are not estimates. If a high and low are given, we have recorded several sales. There is a regional variation in the prices, especially for the solid-colored wares. In general, these pieces are high priced in the East and West, lower in the center of the country.

There have been a few reissues of dinnerware. Harlequin was put back into production in 1979 for the Woolworth Company, the sole distributor. Complete dinner sets were made in the original colors, except that the salmon is a deeper color than the original. The sugar bowls were made with closed handles. Fiesta was reissued by Homer Laughlin China Company in 1986. The original molds and marks were used. The new Fiesta has a china body that shrinks a little more than the semivitreous clay body used before. This means that most new pieces are slightly smaller than the old ones. Dinner plates, soup bowls, and cereal bowls were made slightly larger to accommodate modern tastes. New molds were made for these pieces. The dinner plates are 10 1/2 inches. The new dishes were first made in cobalt blue (darker than the original), black, white, apricot, and rose. Other colors have been added. A few of the pieces have been slightly redesigned since 1986, with variations in handles and bases. A special line was added with cartoon decorations. A Fiesta lookalike has been made by Franciscan since 1978 under the name Kaleidoscope and a line called Cantinaware has been sold by Target stores. We have tried to indicate in the paragraphs in the main section if any reproductions of a pattern have been made.

This book is a report of prices for pieces offered for sale during the past year. Most of the patterns included in earlier books are found here because the collectors still buy these patterns. Many newly popular patterns are also included.

Depression glass and prices for these pieces can be found in the first half of this book.

Particular patterns can be found by using either the Depression Glass or Dinnerware main listings, both of which are arranged alphabetically. Depression Glass begins on page 11 and Dinnerware on page 121.

# Clubs and Publications

## CLUBS

**Abingdon Pottery Collectors Club,** *Abingdon Pottery Collectors Newsletter* (newsletter), R.R. 1, Box 145, Abingdon, IL 61410.

**Blue & White Pottery Club,** *Blue & White Pottery Club* (newsletter), 224 12th Street NW, Center Point, IA 52405.

**Currier & Ives Dinnerware Collectors,** *Collectors' Newsletter* (newsletter), 29470 Saxon Rd., Toulon, IL 61483.

**Fiesta Collector's Club,** *Fiesta Collector's Quarterly* (newsletter), P.O. Box 471, Valley City, OH 44280.

**Fiesta Club of America, Inc.,** *Fiesta Club of America Newsletter* (newsletter), P.O. Box 15383, Loves Park, IL 61132-5383.

**Franciscan Collectors Club,** *Franciscan Newsletter* (newsletter), 8412 5th Ave. NE, Seattle, WA 98115, e-mail: gmcb1@aol.com

**Frankoma Family Collectors Association,** *Pot & Puma* (newsletter); *Prairie Green Sheet* (newsletter), 5632 NW 58th Terr., Oklahoma City, OK 73122-7329.

**Hall China Collector Club,** *Hall China Collector Club Newsletter* (newsletter), P.O. Box 360488, Cleveland, OH 44136.

**Homer Laughlin Collectors Club,** *The Homer Laughlin Glaze* (newsletter), P. O. Box 16174, Loves Park, IL 61132-6174.

**National Autumn Leaf Collectors Club,** *Autumn Leaf Newsletter* (newsletter), P.O. Box 1, Mira Loma, CA 91752-0001.

**Novelty Salt & Pepper Shakers Club,** *Novelty Salt & Pepper Shakers Club Newsletter* (newsletter), 581 Joy Road, Battle Creek, MI 49017.

**Red Wing Collectors Society,** *Red Wing Collectors Newsletter* (newsletter), P.O. Box 50, Red Wing, MN 55066.

**Shawnee Pottery Collector's Club,** *Exclusively Shawnee* (newsletter), P.O. Box 713, New Smyrna Beach, FL 32170-0713.

**Stangl/Fulper Collectors Club,** *Stangl/Fulper Times* (newsletter), P.O. Box 538, Flemington, NJ 08822.

**Watt Collectors Association,** *Watt's News* (newsletter), P.O. Box 184, Galesburg, IL 61402-0184.

**Watt Pottery Collectors USA,** *Spoutings* (newsletter), P.O. Box 26067, Fairview Park, OH 44126.

**Wedgwood Society of New York,** *Ars Ceramica* (magazine), 5 Dogwood Ct., Glen Head, NY 11545.

## PUBLICATIONS

*Antique Trader Weekly* (newspaper), P.O. Box 1050, Dubuque, IA 52004-1050.

*Bauer Quarterly* (newsletter), P.O. Box 2524, Berkeley, CA 94702, e-mail: bauerpot@ix.netcom.com

*California Pottery Trader* (newsletter), P.O. Box 844, Cambria, CA 93428.

*Currier & Ives Quarterly* (newsletter), P.O. Box 504, Riverton, KS 66770 (Currier & Ives dinnerware by Royal China Company).

*Daze* (newsletter), P.O. Box 57, Otisville, MI 48463.

*Fiesta Collector's Quarterly* (newsletter), P.O. Box 471, Valley City, OH 44280.

*Hull Pottery News* (newsletter), 15-H Fiedler Ct., Fenton, MO 63026.

***Kovels on Antiques and Collectibles* (newsletter), P.O. Box 22200, Beachwood, OH 44122.**

*Laughlin Eagle* (newsletter), 1270 63rd Terr. S., St. Petersburg, FL 33705.

*Lu-Ray Relay* (newsletter), 204 S. Veitch, #3, Arlington, VA 22204, e-mail: mforbes@lewin.com (Taylor, Smith and Taylor's Lu-Ray Pastels and other dinnerware lines).

***Matching Services: China, Silver, Crystal* (leaflet), Ralph and Terry Kovel (P.O. Box 22900, Beachwood, OH 44122).**

*National Blue Ridge Newsletter* (newsletter), 144 Highland Dr., Blountville, TN 37617-5404.

*Pottery Collectors Express* (newsletter), P.O. Box 221, Mayview, MO 64071-0221.

*Purinton Pastimes* (newsletter), P.O. Box 9394, Arlington, VA 22219, e-mail: lhinterl@aol.com

*Vernon Views* (newsletter), P.O. Box 945, Scottsdale, AZ 85252.

*Willow Word* (magazine), P.O. Box 13382, Arlington, TX 76094-0382.

# ·A·

## AMBERSTONE

Fiesta is a popular dinnerware pattern found in solid colors. In 1967, Amberstone was made by the Homer Laughlin China Company of Newell, West Virginia, using the Fiesta shapes. The pieces were glazed a rich brown. Some pieces had black machine-stamped underglaze patterns. The pieces were used for supermarket promotions and were called Genuine Sheffield dinnerware. Full sets of dishes were made.

| | |
|---|---|
| Creamer | 10.00 |
| Cup & Saucer | 5.00 to 8.00 |
| Pie Plate | 85.00 |
| Plate, Dessert, 6 In. | 2.00 |
| Plate, Dinner, 10 In. | 7.00 |
| Plate, Luncheon, 8 In. | 4.00 |
| Sugar | 16.00 |

## AMERICAN MODERN

Russel Wright was a designer who made dinnerware in modern shapes for many companies, including Iroquois China Company, Harker Pottery Company, Steubenville Pottery, Paden City Pottery (Justin Tharaud and Sons), Sterling China Company, Edwin M. Knowles China Company, and J.A. Bauer Pottery Company. American Modern was made by the Steubenville Pottery Company,

Steubenville, Ohio, from 1939 to 1959. The original dishes were made in Bean Brown (a shaded brown), Chartreuse, Coral, Granite Gray, Seafoam (blue-green), and White. The brown was replaced with Black Chutney (dark brown) during World War II. Cantaloupe, Cedar Green, and Glacier Blue were added in the 1950s. Matching linens and glassware were made.

*Russel Wright*
MFG. BY
STEUBENVILLE

### BEAN BROWN

| | |
|---|---|
| Bowl, Fruit, 1 Lug, 6 1/4 In. | 18.00 to 20.00 |
| Bowl, Salad | 50.00 |
| Casserole, Cover | 45.00 to 55.00 |
| Celery Dish | 40.00 to 45.00 |
| Cup & Saucer, After Dinner | 50.00 |
| Plate, Dinner, 10 In. | 14.00 |
| Plate, Salad, 8 In. | 18.00 to 20.00 |
| Platter, 13 3/4 In. | 32.00 to 38.00 |
| Refrigerator Jar | 200.00 |

### BLACK CHUTNEY

| | |
|---|---|
| Bowl, Vegetable, Cover, 10 In. | 70.00 |

| | |
|---|---|
| Casserole, Cover | 55.00 |
| Coffeepot | 225.00 to 245.00 |
| Cup | 5.00 |
| Pitcher, Water | 100.00 to 125.00 |
| Platter, Square, 13 In. | 32.50 |
| Soup, Dish, Lug | 20.00 |
| Sugar & Creamer | 42.00 |
| Teapot | 145.00 |

### CANTALOUPE

| | |
|---|---|
| Pitcher | 275.00 |
| Plate, Dinner, 10 In. | 22.00 |

### CEDAR GREEN

| | |
|---|---|
| Bowl, Vegetable, Divided, 10 In. | 100.00 |
| Carafe, Jug | 135.00 |
| Celery Dish | 16.00 to 20.00 |
| Chop Plate | 47.00 |
| Cup | 5.00 |
| Cup, Coffee, Cover | 22.00 |
| Pitcher, Cover | 700.00 |
| Plate, Dinner, 10 In. | 6.00 to 12.00 |
| Relish | 225.00 |
| Teapot | 145.00 to 175.00 |
| Tumbler, Child's | 55.00 |

### CHARTREUSE

| | |
|---|---|
| Bowl, Vegetable, 10 In. | 8.00 |
| Butter | 150.00 |
| Carafe | 85.00 |
| Celery Dish | 20.00 |
| Chop Plate, 13 In. | 20.00 to 30.00 |
| Coffeepot | 125.00 |
| Coffeepot, After Dinner | 68.00 |
| Creamer | 7.50 to 15.00 |
| Cup | 2.50 |
| Cup & Saucer | 9.00 to 18.00 |
| Goblet, 4 In. | 36.00 |
| Gravy Boat | 20.00 |
| Pepper Shaker | 12.00 |
| Pitcher, Cover | 350.00 |
| Pitcher, Water | 70.00 |
| Plate, Bread & Butter, 6 In. | 5.00 |
| Plate, Dinner, 10 In. | 9.00 |
| Plate, Salad, 8 1/2 In. | 7.00 |
| Platter, 13 1/2 In. | 20.00 |
| Relish, Divided | 22.00 |
| Salt Shaker | 10.00 |

Saucer . . . . . . . . . . . . . . .3.00
Sherbet, 2 1/2 In. . . . . . .22.00
Sugar, Cover . . . . . . . . . .10.00
Teapot . . . . . . . . . . . . . .85.00

### CORAL
Bowl, Fruit, Lug . . . . . . . .12.00
Bowl, Salad, Serving . . . .85.00
Bowl, Vegetable, 10 In. . .18.00
Carafe . . . . . .135.00 to 145.00
Casserole, Cover, 12 In. . .75.00
Celery Dish . . . .15.00 to 30.00
Cup, After Dinner . . . . . . .17.00
Cup, Child's . . . . . . . . . .20.00
Cup & Saucer . . . .6.00 to 8.00
Cup & Saucer, After
Dinner . . . . . .20.00 to 24.00
Dish, Pickle . . . . . . . . . .20.00
Gravy Boat . . . . . . . . . .22.00
Pitcher,
7 1/2 In. . . . . . .65.00 to 75.00
Pitcher, Water . . . . . . . .110.00
Plate, Bread & Butter,
6 1/4 In. . . . . . . . .2.50 to 5.00
Platter,
13 3/4 In. . . . . .18.50 to 20.00
Relish, Divided, Reed-Wrapped
Handle . . . . . . . . . . . .275.00
Relish, Rosette . . . . . . .225.00
Salt & Pepper . . . . . . . .20.00
Saucer . . . . . . . . . . . . . . .3.00
Soup, Dish, Child's . . . . .45.00
Soup, Dish, Lug . . . . . . . .7.50
Stack Set . . . . . . . . . . .275.00
Sugar, Cover . . . . . . . . . .16.00
Sugar & Creamer,
Cover . . . . . . .24.00 to 30.00
Teapot . . . . . . . . . . . . . .75.00
Tumbler, Iced Tea . . . . .35.00

### GRANITE GRAY
Bowl, Vegetable,
Divided . . . . . . . . . . . . .58.00
Bowl, Vegetable, Open . . .22.00
Butter, Cover . . . . . . . .175.00
Casserole,
Cover . . . . . . .45.00 to 55.00
Coaster, Pair . . . . . . . . . .18.00
Coffeepot, After Dinner . .85.00
Creamer . . . . . . .9.00 to 12.00
Cup, After Dinner . . . . . . .17.00
Cup, Coffee, Cover . . . . . .22.00
Cup & Saucer . . .6.00 to 12.00

Cup & Saucer, After
Dinner . . . . . .28.00 to 30.00
Gravy Boat . . . . . . . . . .25.00
Plate, Bread & Butter,
6 1/4 In. . . . . . . . .2.50 to 5.00
Plate, Dinner, 10 In. . . . .10.00
Plate, Salad, 8 In. . . . . . .12.00
Platter, 13 3/4 In. . . . . . .20.00
Relish, Divided, Rattan
Handle . . . . . . . . . . . .275.00
Salt & Pepper . . . . . . . .16.00
Soup, Dish, Lug . . . . . . .15.00
Sugar, Cover . . . . . . . . . .20.00

### SEAFOAM
Bowl, Salad . . . . . . . . .100.00
Bowl, Vegetable,
Cover, 12 In. . . . . . . . .50.00
Coffeepot, After
Dinner . . . . . . . . . . . .120.00
Cup . . . . . . . . . .8.00 to 12.00
Cup, After
Dinner . . . . . .12.00 to 18.00
Cup & Saucer . . . . . . . .24.00
Cup & Saucer, After
Dinner . . . . . . . . . . . . .6.00
Plate, Bread & Butter,
6 In. . . . . . . . . .3.00 to 6.00
Plate, Dinner, 10 In. . . . . .8.00
Relish, Divided, Rattan
Handle . . . . . . . . . . . .185.00
Salt & Pepper . . . . . . . .10.00
Saucer . . . . . . . . . . . . . . .3.00
Sherbet . . . . . . . . . . . . .15.00
Soup, Dish, Lug . . . . . . .10.00
Sugar, Cover . . . .12.00 to 14.00
Teapot . . . . . . . . . . . . .135.00

### WHITE
Bowl, Salad . . . . . . . . .140.00
Chop Plate . . . . . . . . . . .75.00
Coffeepot, Cover . . . . . . .65.00
Cup & Saucer . . . . . . . .48.00
Pitcher, Ice Lip . . . . . . .195.00
Teapot . . . . . . . . . . . . .145.00

## ANTIQUE GRAPE
Antique Grape is a pattern
introduced by Metlox Potteries
in 1964. The firm had been
making a pattern called Sculptured Grape with a raised
grapevine border in natural col-

ors. Antique Grape is the same
shape but according to the
brochure has carved grapes and
leaves raised on a soft beige
antique finish against a warm
white background. It was made
until at least 1975.

Bowl, Divided, 8 1/2 In. . .35.00
Creamer . . . . . . . . . . . . .18.00
Gravy Boat, 1 Pt. . . . . . .32.00
Platter, 9 In. . . . . . . . . .32.00
Salt & Pepper . . . . . . . .20.00
Sugar, Cover . . . . . . . . . .20.00
Teapot . . . . . . . . . . . . . .95.00

## ANYTIME
Anytime is the name of both a
shape and pattern made by
Vernon Kilns from 1956 to
1958. It has abstract streaks of
gray, green, mocha, and yellow. The pattern and name
rights were purchased by Metlox Potteries in 1958 and Anytime continued to be produced.

Chowder . . . . . . . . . . . . .8.00
Pitcher, 2 Qt. . . . . . . . . .35.00
Relish . . . . . . . . . . . . . .25.00
Tumbler . . . . . . . . . . . . .28.00

## APPLE BLOSSOM

Two companies made patterns called Apple Blossom. Crooksville China Company of Crooksville, Ohio, made a pink flowered pattern. The pattern listed here was made by Homer Laughlin China Company of Newell, West Virginia, from 1935 to 1955. It has a flowered border and gold trim.

Bowl, 13 In. . . . . . . . . . .95.00
Compote, 7 In. . . . . . . . .85.00
Grill Plate, 10 In. . . . . . .55.00
Pitcher . . . . . . . . . . . . .395.00
Plate, 11 1/2 In. . . . . . . .65.00
Relish, 4 Sections . . . . .135.00
Sandwich Server,
    2 Handles . . . . . . . . . .45.00

## APPLE FRANCISCAN

Gladding, McBean & Company made Apple pattern dishes, one of its Franciscan Ceramics "Classics" designs, beginning in 1940. The pattern is still being made, but Franciscan Ceramics is now part of Waterford Wedgwood USA. Several other factories also made patterns called Apple.

Ashtray . . . . . .18.00 to 20.00
Berry Bowl . . . . . . . . . . .3.00
Bowl, Cereal,
    6 In. . . . . . . . .10.00 to 15.00
Bowl, Fruit,
    5 1/4 In. . . . . . .8.00 to 13.00
Bowl, Salad,
    10 In. . . . . .115.00 to 145.00
Bowl, Salad, Crescent . . . .30.00
Bowl, Vegetable,
    8 1/2 In. . . . . . .15.00 to 25.00

Bowl, Vegetable, 9 In. . . .50.00
Bowl, Vegetable, Oval,
    Divided, 10 1/2 In. . . . . .45.00
Bowl, Vegetable, Scalloped,
    8 1/4 In. . . . . . .25.00 to 32.00
Butter, Cover, 1/4 Lb. . . . .40.00
Cake Plate, 12 1/2 In. . . . .35.00
Casserole,
    Cover . . . . . . .65.00 to 95.00
Chop Plate,
    12 In. . . . . . . . .38.00 to 60.00
Chop Plate, 14 In. . . . . . .100.00
Cigar Box, Cover . . . . . . .95.00
Cigarette Box . .95.00 to 125.00
Coaster . . . . . . . . . . . . .50.00
Compote, Footed,
    8 In. . . . . . . . .60.00 to 85.00
Cookie Jar,
    Cover . . . . .280.00 to 300.00
Creamer, Individual . . . . .30.00
Cup . . . . . . . . . . . . . . . . .5.00
Cup, After Dinner . . . . . .40.00
Cup & Saucer . . .8.00 to 18.50
Cup & Saucer, After
    Dinner . . . . . . .35.00 to 60.00
Eggcup . . . . . . . .20.00 to 35.00
Gravy Boat . . . .35.00 to 45.00
Gravy Boat, Underplate . .50.00
Grill Plate . . . . . . . . . . .90.00
Mixing Bowl, Medium . .165.00
Mixing Bowl, Small . . . .115.00
Mixing Bowl Set,
    3 Piece . . . . . . . . . . .500.00
Mug, 7 Oz. . . . . . . . . . . .25.00
Mug, 10 Oz. . . . . . . . . . .65.00
Pitcher, Iced Tea,
    5 1/4 In. . . . . . . . . . . .30.00
Pitcher, Milk,
    6 1/4 In. . . . . .60.00 to 95.00
Pitcher, Syrup . . .75.00 to 90.00
Pitcher, Water . . . . . . . . .80.00
Plate, 12 In. . . . . . . . . . .76.00
Plate, Bread & Butter,
    6 1/2 In. . . . . . . .4.00 to 8.00
Plate, Breakfast,
    9 1/2 In. . . . . .10.00 to 16.00
Plate, Child's,
    Sections . . . .125.00 to 195.00
Plate, Dinner,
    10 1/2 In. . . . . .16.00 to 25.00
Plate, Salad,
    8 1/2 In. . . . . . .9.00 to 14.00

Plate, Salad, Crescent . . . .25.00
Plate, Steak . . . . . . . . . .150.00
Platter,
    12 1/2 In. . . . . .48.00 to 50.00
Platter, 14 In. . . .33.00 to 75.00
Platter, 19 In. . . . . . . . .245.00
Relish,
    3 Sections . . . .55.00 to 70.00
Relish, Oval . . . .23.00 to 25.00
Salt & Pepper . . .20.00 to 25.00
Salt & Pepper, Tall . . . . .60.00
Saucer . . . . . . . . . . . . . . .2.00
Sherbet, Footed . . . . . . . .24.00
Soup, Dish . . . .20.00 to 28.00
Sugar, Cover . . . . . . . . . .40.00
Sugar, Cover, Small . . . .20.00
Sugar & Creamer,
    Cover . . . . . . .35.00 to 38.00
Sugar & Creamer, Cover,
    Large . . . . . . . . . . . . . .60.00
Teapot, Cover . . . . . . . . .70.00
Tumbler . . . . . .25.00 to 28.00
Tureen, Soup, Large . . . .375.00

## APPLE PURINTON

Apple pattern was also made by Purinton Pottery of Shippenville, Pennsylvania. The hand-decorated dinnerware was made in the early 1940s. It was designed by William Blair. The apple was colored red with yellow and brown highlights, the stems and leaves were green, blue, and dark brown. The trim colors were red, cobalt blue, or blue-green.

Bean Pot, Cover, Individual,
    3 3/4 In. . . . . . .50.00 to 75.00
Bowl, Fruit,
    12 In. . . . . . . . .35.00 to 45.00
Canister, Coffee, Blue . . .65.00

Canister, Coffee, Red . . . .55.00

Canister, Flour . . . . . . . .35.00

Canister Set, Cobalt Trim,
4 Piece . . . . . . . . . . . .475.00

Casserole, Cover . . . . . . .65.00

Chop Plate,
12 In. . . . . . . .35.00 to 40.00

Chop Plate, Scalloped
Border, 12 In. . . . . . . .58.00

Coffeepot, 8 Cup . . . . . .90.00

Cookie Jar, Red Trim . . . .64.00

Creamer . . . . . . . . . . . . .15.00

Ginger Jar, Cover, Paper
Label . . . . . . . . . . . . . .45.00

Grill Plate . . . . . . . . . . .60.00

Jug, Dutch, 5 Pt. . . . . . . .75.00

Jug, Petals, Honey . . . . .45.00

Lazy Susan Set,
7 Piece . . . . . .85.00 to 130.00

Mug . . . . . . . . . . . . . . .20.00

Oil & Vinegar,
Cobalt Trim . . . . . . . .275.00

Oil & Vinegar,
Red Trim . . . .75.00 to 125.00

Plate, Dinner, 10 In. . . . .20.00

Plate, Salad, 7 1/2 In. . . . .8.00

Platter, 2 Sections,
12 1/4 In. . . . . .35.00 to 55.00

Platter, Meat, 12 In. . . . .40.00

Relish, 3 Sections . . . . . .50.00

Salt & Pepper . . . . . . . .25.00

Saucer . . . . . . . . .3.00 to 5.00

Sugar, Cover . . . . . . . . . .25.00

Sugar, Open . . . . . . . . . .10.00

Sugar & Creamer . . . . . .40.00

Sugar & Creamer,
Miniature . . . . . . . . . . .25.00

Tea & Toast Set, Snack . .25.00

Tumbler, Iced Tea, 12 Oz. 28.00

## APPLE WATT

The Watt Pottery Company was incorporated in Crooksville, Ohio, in 1922. They made a variety of hand-decorated potteries. The most popular is Apple pattern, sometimes called Red Apple. Dinnerware sets and kitchenware were made beginning in 1952. The company burned to the ground in 1965.

Baker, Cover, No. 67 . . .140.00

Baker, Cover, No. 96 . . .125.00

Baker, No. 85, 3-Leaf,
Rectangular . . . . . . . .1000.00

Bean Pot, 2 Handles,
No. 76 . . . . . . . . . . . .200.00

Bowl, Cover, No. 601,
Ribbed, 8 3/4 In. . . . . . .80.00

Bowl, Salad, No. 73 . . . . .95.00

Bowl, Salad, No. 74,
2-Leaf . . . . . . .30.00 to 40.00

Bowl, Spaghetti, No. 24,
3-Leaf . . . . . .85.00 to 175.00

Canister, No. 72 . . . . . .600.00

Canister, Sugar, No. 81 . .650.00

Casserole, Cover, No. 5,
2-Leaf . . . . . . . . . . . . .60.00

Casserole, Stick Handle,
No. 18, Individual . . . .150.00

Chop Plate,
No. 49 . . . .300.00 to 350.00

Coffee Server, Cover,
No. 115 . .2350.00 to 3000.00

Cookie Jar, No. 503 . . . .495.00

Creamer, No. 62,
2-Leaf . . . . .115.00 to 130.00

Ice Bucket, No. 59 . . . . .325.00

Mixing Bowl, No. 5,
2-Leaf . . . . . . . . . . . . .45.00

Mixing Bowl, No. 5,
Ribbed . . . . . . . . . . . . .60.00

Mixing Bowl, No. 6,
Ribbed . . . . . . . . . . . . .55.00

Mixing Bowl, No. 7,
Ribbed . . . . . . . . . . . . .55.00

Mixing Bowl Set, No. 63,
No. 64, No. 65,
Nested . . . . . . . . . . . . .185.00

Mug,
No. 121 . . . .175.00 to 200.00

Mug, No. 501 . . . . . . . .265.00

Mug, No. 701 . . . . . . . .475.00

Nappy, No. 04 . . .60.00 to 70.00

Pie Plate, No. 33 . . . . . .100.00

Pitcher, No. 16, 2-Leaf . . .60.00

Pitcher, No. 17, Ice Lip,
8 In. . . . . . . . . . . . . . .175.00

Plate, Dinner, No. 29,
10 In. . . . . . . . . . . . . .250.00

Salad, Cover, No. 73 . . . .190.00

Salad, No. 73, Green
Band . . . . . . . . . . . . .100.00

Salt & Pepper, Barrel . . .425.00

Salt & Pepper,
Hourglass . . .150.00 to 225.00

Sugar, Cover, No. 98 . . .400.00

Sugar & Creamer, No.
98, No. 62, 3-Leaf . . . .595.00

Teapot, No. 505 . . . . . .4000.00

## ARCADIA

Arcadia has a hand-painted brown and mustard laurel leaf border and was made by Vernon Kilns of Los Angeles, California, from 1942 to 1955.

Cup & Saucer, After
    Dinner . . . . . . . . . . . . . .16.00
Gravy Boat  . . . . . . . . . .22.00
Plate, Breakfast, 9 1/2 In.  .12.00

## AUTUMN FOLIAGE

Autumn Foliage was made by
the Watt Pottery Company
from 1959 to 1965. It has
brown leaves on brown stems.
It is also called Brown Leaves.

Bean Pot, No. 76  . . . . . .145.00
Cookie Jar, No. 76  . . . . . .80.00
Creamer, No. 62 . . . . . . .195.00
Cruet Set, No. 126  . . . . .625.00
Sugar, Cover, No. 98  . . .140.00
Teapot, No. 505  . . . . . . .980.00

## AUTUMN LEAF

One of the most popular
American dinnerware patterns,
Autumn Leaf was made for the
Jewel Tea Company, a grocery
chain, beginning in 1936. Hall
China Company of East
Liverpool, Ohio; Crooksville
China Company of Crooks-
ville, Ohio; Harker Pottery
Company of Chester, West
Virginia; and Paden City Pot-
tery of Paden City, West

Virginia, made dishes with this
design. The Autumn Leaf pattern always has the same
shades of dark yellow and rust
leaves. The shape of the dish
varies with the manufacturer.
Several special terms are used
to describe these shapes, such
as "bud-ray," which describes a
bowl lid with a knob sur-
rounded by raised rays. Collectors can find Autumn Leaf
pattern tinware, plastic table-
cloths, glassware, clocks, even
painted furniture. There are
several books about Autumn
Leaf and a collectors club listed
at the back of this book. The
Jewel Tea pattern is listed here.
Reproductions using the
Autumn Leaf decoration have
been made since 1990. These,
unlike the originals, are marked
"Limited Edition."

❖

**It is easy to glue pieces
of broken china. Use a
new, fast-setting but
not instant glue.
Position the pieces cor-
rectly, then use tape to
hold the parts together.
If the piece needs spe-
cial support, lean it in a
suitable position in a
box filled with sand.**

❖

Baker, French, 4 1/2 In.  . .70.00
Baker, Oval, 7 x 5 x
    1 1/2 In. . . . . . . . . . . .270.00
Bean Pot, 2 Handles  . . . .150.00
Bean Pot, Cover,
    2 Handles  . . . . . . . . .360.00
Bean Pot, Cover,
    Handle  . . .995.00 to 1100.00
Bowl, 2 Sections, Oval  . .170.00
Bowl, 9 In.  . . . . .25.00 to 30.00
Bowl, Fruit, 5 In.   . .4.00 to 8.00
Bowl, Salad  . . . . . . . . . .36.00
Bowl, Vegetable,
    2 Sections, 10 1/2 In. . .175.00
Bowl, Vegetable, Cover, Oval,
    10 1/2 In.  . . . . .69.00 to 80.00
Bowl, Vegetable, Round,
    9 In. . . . . . . . . . . . . . . .75.00
Butter, Square,
    1/4 Lb. . . . . . . . . . . . .500.00
Cake Plate,
    9 1/2 In. . . . . . .18.50 to 35.00
Cake Plate, Metal Base . .265.00
Candy Dish, Gold
    Trim . . . . . . .525.00 to 545.00
Casserole, Cover,
    10 Oz. . . . . . . . . . . . . .35.00
Casserole, Cover, 2 Qt. . . .22.00
Coaster, 3 1/4 In.  . . . . . . .12.00
Coffeepot,
    Electric . . . . .395.00 to 435.00
Coffeepot, Metal Drip,
    8 Cup . . . . . . .85.00 to 120.00
Cookie Jar, Big Ear  . . . .275.00
Cookie Jar,
    Tootsie      285.00 to 350.00

Creamer, Rayed . . . . . . . .36.00
Cup, Ruffled . . . . . . . . . .30.00
Cup & Saucer, After
    Dinner . . . . . . . . . . . . .50.00
Custard Cup . . . . . . . . .12.00
Drip Jar, Cover . . . . . . . .36.00
French Baker, 10 Oz.,
    4 1/2 In. . . . . . .50.00 to 70.00
French Baker, Flute,
    3 Pt. . . . . . . . . . . . . . .30.00
Gravy Boat . . . .25.00 to 50.00
Jam Jar . . . . . . . . . . . . .40.00
Jug, Ball . . . . . . .40.00 to 50.00
Mixing Bowl,
    3 Piece . . . . . .55.00 to 110.00
Mug, Irish Coffee . . . . .200.00
Pie Baker . . . . . . . . . . . .55.00
Plate, Dinner, 10 In. . . . . .17.00
Platter, Oval, 11 3/8 In. . . .8.50
Platter, Oval, 13 1/2 In. . .29.00

❖

Protect your home and antiques from theft. Use a timer on your lights even when you are at home. This will set a pattern of certain lights going on and off each day. When you are away, the house will appear to have normal activity. Also park a car near the front of the house. The car will block the driveway so a burglar cannot load up through the garage. Have someone keep your trash cans filled. This will make the house look occupied. Keep the grass mowed and the snow shoveled. Stop your mail and news-paper deliveries.

❖

Salt & Pepper, Left Hand
    Salt . . . . . . . . . . . . . . .44.00
Salt & Pepper,
    Range . . . . . . .25.00 to 35.00
Salt & Pepper,
    Ruffled . . . . . . .26.00 to 28.00
Soup, Cream . . . .36.00 to 45.00
Stack Set, 4 Piece . . . . .200.00
Sugar, Cover, Rayed . . . . .50.00
Teapot, Aladdin . . . . . . .65.00
Teapot, Aladdin,
    Insert . . . . . . .98.00 to 120.00
Teapot, Donut . . . . . . . . .110.00
Teapot, Long Spout,
    Sunshine . . . . .90.00 to 120.00
Teapot, New York . . . .1000.00
Teapot, Newport . . . . . . .350.00
Tidbit, 3 Tiers . . . . . . . . .200.00
Warmer, Oval . . . . . . . . .150.00
Warmer, Round . . . . . . .240.00

## AZALEA

Azalea pattern was made for Larkin Company customers from 1918 to 1941. Larkin, the soap company, was in Buffalo, New York. The dishes were made by Noritake China Company of Japan. Each piece of the white china was decorated with pink azaleas.

Ashtray . . . . . . . . . . . . .32.00
Berry Bowl, 5 1/2 In. . . . .25.00
Bowl, 4 3/4 In. . .18.00 to 24.00
Bowl, Fruit, 11 3/4 In. . .155.00
Cup & Saucer . . . . . . . . .14.00
Plate, Dessert, 6 In. . . . . . .6.00
Plate, Dinner,
    10 In. . . . . . . . .18.00 to 37.00
Sauce Bowl, 5 1/4 In. . . . . .8.00
Saucer . . . . . . . . . . . . . . .5.00
Saucer, After Dinner . . . . .12.00

Sugar & Creamer, Cover  .30.00
Trivet . . . . . . . . . . . . . .40.00

## BALLERINA

Solid-colored pottery was popular in the 1950s. Universal Potteries of Cambridge, Ohio, made Ballerina from 1947 to 1956. Ballerina was very modern in shape and had solid-colored glazes. A later line was decorated with abstract designs. The original solid-colored Ballerina dinnerware was offered in Dove Gray, Jade Green, Jonquil Yellow, and Periwinkle Blue. In 1949 Chartreuse and Forest Green were added. By 1955 Burgundy, Charcoal, and Pink were added, while some other colors had been discontinued. There was also a line called Ballerina Mist, which was a pale blue-green with decal decorations.

**DOVE GRAY**
Bowl, Vegetable, Round,
    7 In. . . . . . . . . . . . . . . .12.00

Plate, Dinner, 10 In. . . . . .12.50
Relish . . . . . . . . . . . . . . .5.00

#### JADE GREEN
Bowl, 36s . . . . . . . . . . . . . 8.00
Eggcup . . . . . . .10.00 to 12.00
Plate, 6 In. . . . . . . . . . . . .3.00
Platter, Round, Lug,
   10 In. . . . . . . . . . . . . . .14.00

#### PINK
Cup . . . . . . . . . . . . . . . . .6.00
Plate, Dinner, 10 In. . . . . .12.00

---

## BALLERINA MIST
The shapes of Ballerina Mist
are those used for the Ballerina
pattern also made by Universal
Potteries of Cambridge, Ohio.
This 1950s pattern was pale
blue-green with decal decorations.

Pitcher, Ice Lip          15.00
Pitcher, Juice . . . . . . . . . .12.50
Stack Set, Cover .40.00 to 45.00

**BEEHIVE,** see Ring

---

## BLUE BOUQUET
Standard Coffee of New
Orleans, Louisiana, gave Blue
Bouquet pattern dinnerware
and kitchenware as a premium
from the early 1950s to the
early 1960s. Although it was
made by the Hall China Company, East Liverpool, Ohio, it
is most easily found in the
South. The pattern is very plain
with a thin blue border inter-
rupted by roses. Blue Ridge
also made a pattern called Blue
Bouquet, but the pattern listed
here is by Hall China Company.

Bean Pot . . . . . . . . . . .175.00
Bowl, Fruit, 5 1/2 In. . . . .12.00
Bowl, Radiance, 6 In. . . . .25.00
Bowl, Radiance, 7 In. . . . .30.00
Bowl, Radiance, 9 In. . . . .45.00
Bowl, Salad, 9 In. . . . . . .30.00
Bowl, Vegetable, 9 In. . . .30.00
Casserole . . . . . . . . . . . .75.00
Coffeepot . . . . . . . . . . .100.00
Creamer, Boston . . . . . . .20.00
Cup . . . . . . . . . . . . . . . .18.00
French Baker . . . . . . . . .25.00
Pie Baker . . . . . . . . . . . .30.00
Plate, Bread & Butter,
   7 In. . . . . . . . . . . . . . .12.00
Plate, Breakfast, 9 In. . . . .18.00
Plate, Dessert, 6 In. . . . . . .8.00
Platter, Oval, 11 In. . . . . .30.00
Saucer . . . . . . . . . . . . . . .4.00
Soup, Dish . . . . . . . . . . .20.00
Teapot, Aladdin . . . . . . . .80.00

**BLUE WILLOW,** see Willow

---

## BLUEBERRY
Stangl Pottery of Trenton, New
Jersey, made Blueberry (pattern No. 3770) before 1942.
The heavy red pottery dishes
were glazed with a yellow border and a sgraffito decoration
of blueberries in the center.

Cup & Saucer . . . . . . . .16.00
Plate, Bread & Butter, 6 In. 2.50

---

## BOB WHITE
Bob White was made by Red
Wing Potteries from 1956 to
1967. It was one of the most
popular dinnerware patterns
made by the factory. The pattern, a modern hand-painted
design, shows a stylized bird
and background.

Bowl, Cereal, 6 In. . . . . . .25.00
Bowl, Salad, 12 In. . . . . . .50.00
Bread Tray, 24 In. . . . . . .100.00
Butter Warmer, Cover,
   1/4 Lb. . . . . . . .75.00 to 95.00
Carafe . . . . . . . . . . . . .195.00
Casserole, Cover,
   2 Qt. . . . . . . . . .40.00 to 45.00
Casserole, Cover,
   4 Qt. . . . . . . . . .50.00 to 52.00
Creamer . . . . . . . . . . . . .20.00
Cruet . . . . . . . . . . . . . . .30.00
Cup & Saucer . .10.00 to 25.00
Gravy Boat,
   Cover . . . . . . .47.50 to 55.00
Jug, 60 Oz. . . . . . . . . . . .45.00
Lazy Susan, 5 Piece . . . .125.00
Mug . . . . . . . . . . . . . . .80.00
Pitcher, Water, 60 Oz.,
   6 3/4 In. . . . . . .25.00 to 38.00

Pitcher, Water, 112 Oz.,
  12 In. . . . . . . . . . . . . .60.00
Plate, Bread & Butter,
  6 1/2 In. . . . . . . . . . . . .9.50
Plate, Dinner,
  10 1/2 In. . . . . .10.00 to 17.50
Plate, Salad,
  6 1/2 In. . . . . . . .6.00 to 8.00
Platter, 13 In. . . . . . . . . .90.00
Platter, 20 In. . . . . . . . .100.00
Relish,
  3 Sections . . . .47.50 to 55.00
Salt & Pepper,
  Bird Shape . . . .32.00 to 50.00
Salt & Pepper, Hourglass
  Shape, 6 In. . . . . . . . . .25.00
Sugar & Creamer,
  Cover . . . . . . . . . . . . .40.00
Teapot . . . . . . . . . . . . . .75.00
Teapot, Stand . .95.00 to 120.00
Tray, Cocktail . . . . . . . . .40.00

## BOW KNOT

Bow Knot is a variation of the Whirligig pattern. It has a piecrust rim on a Colonial shape. It was made by Blue Ridge in the 1950s. Bow Knot is colored chartreuse and brown, Whirligig is red and light blue.

Cornucopia, 7 1/2 In. . . .125.00
Cup . . . . . . . . . . . . . . .14.00
Flowerpot, 6 1/2 In. . . . .160.00
Plate, Salad, 7 In. . . . . . . .15.00
Tumbler . . . . . . . . . . . . .25.00
Wall Pocket, 8 In. . . . . . .175.00

## CALICO

Calico is one of the plaid designs made by Vernon Kilns of Vernon, California. The design was pink and blue with a blue border. Other related plaids are Coronation Organdy (gray and rose), Gingham (green and yellow), Homespun (cinnamon, yellow, and green), Organdie (brown and yellow), Tam O'Shanter (rust, chartreuse, and dark green), and Tweed (yellow and gray-blue).

Berry Bowl . . . . . . . . . . .9.00
Creamer . . . . . . . . . . . . .20.00
Cup & Saucer . . . . . . . .42.00
Plate, Bread & Butter,
  6 In. . . . . . . . . . . . . . . .9.00
Salt & Pepper . . . . . . . .35.00

## CALIFORNIA IVY

California Ivy was one of the most popular patterns made by the Metlox Potteries of Manhattan Beach, California. It was introduced in 1946. The pattern was named for its ivy vine border.

Berry Bowl, 5 1/2 In. . . . . .9.00
Bowl, 2 Sections, 11 In. . .45.00
Bowl, Round, 9 In. . . . . .40.00
Bowl, Salad, 11 1/4 In. . . .50.00
Bowl, Vegetable, Round,
  10 In. . . . . . . . . . . . . .25.00
Coaster . . . . . . . . . . . . .16.00
Creamer . . . . . . . . . . . . .14.00
Cup . . . . . . . . . .6.00 to 12.00
Cup & Saucer . . . . . . . .12.00
Plate, 9 1/4 In. . . . . . . . .11.00
Plate, Dinner,
  10 In. . . . . . . . .9.00 to 12.00
Plate, Luncheon,
  9 1/4 In. . . . . . . . . . . . .12.00
Plate, Salad, 6 In. . .5.00 to 7.00

❖

**Don't store dishes for long periods of time in old newspaper wrappings. The ink can make indelible stains on the china.**

❖

Platter, Oval,
13 In. . . . . . . .36.00 to 50.00
Relish . . . . . . . . . . . . . .25.00
Saucer . . . . . . . . . . . . . . .3.00
Sugar & Creamer . . . . . . .35.00

## CALIFORNIA PROVINCIAL

California Provincial dinner-ware pictures a rooster in the center. The rooster is maroon, green, and yellow. The border is green and coffee brown. It was made by Metlox Potteries beginning in 1950. A similar design, in different colors, was called Red Rooster.

Basket, Vegetable, Round,
8 1/2 In. . . . . . . . . . . . .50.00
Bowl, 10 In. . . . . . . . . . .80.00
Bowl, Vegetable,
2 Sections, 10 In. . . . . . .48.00
Bread Basket . . .55.00 to 68.00
Butter, Cover . . . . . . . . .55.00
Canister, Coffee . . . . . . .55.00
Canister, Sugar . . . . . . . .70.00
Canister, Tea . . . . . . . . .70.00
Casserole, Individual . . . .22.00
Chop Plate, 12 In. . . . . . .75.00
Coaster . . . . . . . . . . . . .20.00
Coffee Carafe &
Warmer . . . . . . . . . .275.00
Coffeepot . . . . . . . . . . .115.00
Condiment Set, Cover . . . .65.00
Cup, 6 Oz. . . . . . . . . . . .12.00
Cup & Saucer . . . . . . . . .16.00
Dish, Hen On Nest . . . . .95.00
Jam Jar . . . . . . . . . . . . .55.00
Mug, Cocoa . . . .35.00 to 38.00
Mug, Cover, Large . . . . .65.00

Pitcher, Figural,
Rooster . . . . . . . . . . .275.00
Plate, Dinner, 10 In. . . . . .16.00
Plate, Luncheon, 9 In. . . . .32.00
Platter, 12 In. . . . . . . . . .28.00
Platter, Oval, 13 1/2 In. . .55.00
Salt & Pepper . . . . . . . .27.00

## CALIFORNIA STRAWBERRY

California Strawberry dinner-ware pictures a red strawberry on an avocado green vine. It is one of the Poppytrail lines made by Metlox Potteries from 1961 to 1980.

Bowl, Divided, Round,
9 In. . . . . . . . . . . . . . . .40.00
Bowl, Fruit, 5 1/2 In. . . . .10.00
Bowl, Salad, 11 In. . . . . . .50.00
Bowl, Vegetable,
Cover, 11 1/4 In. . . . . . .35.00
Butter, Cover . . . . . . . . .45.00
Casserole, 7 In. . . . . . . . .55.00
Coffeepot . . . . . . . . . . .75.00
Creamer . . . . . . . . . . . . .15.00
Cup & Saucer . . . . . . . . .10.00
Fork & Spoon Set . . . . . .55.00
Gravy Boat, Fast Stand . . .30.00
Plate, Bread & Butter,
6 In. . . . . . . . . . . . . . . . .6.00
Plate, Dinner,
10 In. . . . . . . . .10.00 to 15.00
Plate, Salad,
8 In. . . . . . . . . .8.00 to 10.00
Platter, Oval, 13 In. . . . . .30.00
Salt & Pepper . . . . . . . .20.00
Soup, Dish, 6 3/4 In. . . . . .15.00
Sugar, Cover . . . . . . . . . .18.00
Sugar & Creamer,
Cover . . . . . . . . . . . . .40.00

Teapot . . . . . . . . . . . . . .80.00
Vegetable, Cover, 2 Qt. . .25.00

## CAMEO ROSE HALL

Cameo Rose made by Hall China Company has gray and white decal decorations and a gold trim. It was not made by the cameo process used for cameo shellware and other de-signs. Reproductions using the Cameo Rose decoration have been made since 1997. These, unlike the originals, are marked "Limited Edition."

Butter . . . . . . . . . . . . . .50.00
Plate, Dinner, 10 In. . . . . .12.00
Plate, Salad, 8 In. . . . . . . .10.00
Teapot . . . . . . . . . . . . . .50.00

**CAMEO ROSE HARKER,** see also
Cameo Shellware

## CAMEO SHELLWARE

Another cameo pattern, Cameo Shellware, has the same design as Cameo Rose, but the dishes are fluted.

Creamer . . . . . . . .8.00 to 10.00
Cup & Saucer . . . . . . . . .10.00
Plate, Dinner, 9 1/2 In. . . .10.00
Plate, Square, 7 1/2 In. . . . .6.00

## CARNIVAL

One pattern named Carnival was made by Stangl Pottery, Trenton, New Jersey, from 1954 to 1957. It is decorated with abstract star patterns.

Bowl, Salad, 10 In. . . . . . .32.00
Creamer . . . . . . . . . . . . .18.00

❖

Be careful loading the dishwasher. Metal utensils that touch ceramic dishes may leave marks on china. Dishes can also show black marks if rubbed against a stainless steel sink. The marks can be removed with a wet sponge and a bit of silver polish or other mild abrasive.

❖

Plate, Dinner, 10 In. . . . . .10.00
Platter, 12 1/2 In. . . . . . .25.00
Platter, 14 1/2 In. . . . . . .35.00

## CASUAL CALIFORNIA
Vernon Kilns made Casual California, a very popular solid-color dinnerware, from 1947 to 1956. It was made in Acacia Yellow, Dawn Pink, Dusk Gray, Lime Green, Mahogany Brown, Mocha Brown, Pine Green, Sno-white, and Turquoise Blue.

**MOCHA BROWN**
Platter, 13 In. . . . . . . . . .60.00

**PINE GREEN**
Plate, Dinner, 10 In. . . . . .22.00

## CAT-TAIL
Cat-Tail pattern dishes must have been found in most homes in America in the 1940s. Sears, Roebuck and Company fea-

tured the pattern from 1934 to 1956. It was made by the Universal Potteries of Cambridge, Ohio. The red and black cattail design was used for dinnerware and matching tinware, kitchenware, glassware, furniture, and table linens.

Cake Plate, Handle,
    12 1/2 . . . . . .15.00 to 20.00
Cup & Saucer . . . . . . . . . .14.00
Grill Plate . . . . . . . . . . .18.00
Sugar . . . . . . . . . . . . . . .17.00
Plate, Dinner,
    10 In. . . . . . . . . . . . . .12.00

## CENTURY
Century pattern was made by the Homer Laughlin China Company. The ivory dinnerware had floral decals.

Batter Set, Marked Wells,
    18K Gold Banding . . . .350.00

Casserole . . . . . . . . . . . .75.00
Jug, Gold Trim,
    2 1/2 Pt. . . . . . . . . . . . .65.00

## CHATELAINE
Vernon Kilns of Los Angeles and Vernon, California, introduced the solid-colored Chatelaine pattern in 1953. Pieces were square with leaf handles. It was made in Bronze, Topaz, Jade with a leaf decoration, and Platinum with a leaf decoration.

**JADE**
Cup & Saucer . .20.00 to 22.00
Plate, Dinner,
    10 In. . . . . . . . . . . . . .20.00
**TOPAZ**
Plate, Salad,
    7 1/2 In. . . . . . .10.00 to 12.00

## CHESTERTON
Chesterton was a pattern produced by Harker Pottery Company of Chester, West Virginia, from 1945 to 1965. The pieces had a gadroon border. They were made in Blue, Gray, Green, Pink, or Yellow.

**GRAY**

Cup & Saucer .........5.00
Plate, Breakfast, 9 In. .....8.00

## CHINTZ

Chintz is a floral decorated pattern made by Vernon Kilns in about 1942 and again in 1950. The pattern in red, blue, yellow, green, and maroon resembled the English dinnerware patterns of the early nineteenth century. Another pattern named Chintz was made by Blue Ridge. Many English manufacturers made overall patterns now called Chintz by collectors. Only the Vernon Kilns chintz pattern is listed here.

Bowl, Chowder .........13.00
Cup & Saucer ........25.00
Plate, Bread & Butter,
    6 In. ...............10.00
Plate, Dinner, 9 1/2 In. ...50.00
Plate, Salad, 7 1/2 In. ....14.00
Sugar & Creamer ......26.00

---

❖

**Don't keep a house key
in an obvious spot in
the garage or yard.**

❖

## COLONIAL HOMESTEAD

Colonial Homestead was one of many patterns made by Royal China Company of Sebring, Ohio. The dinnerware was made from about 1951 and was offered by Sears, Roebuck and Company all through the 1960s. It was designed by Gordon Parker. The Royal China Company closed in 1986. A different pattern by the same name was made by Metlox Potteries.

Bowl, 5 1/2 In. ..........3.00
Canister, Cookie, Cover ..40.00
Canister, Flour, Cover ...32.00
Casserole, Cover .......15.00
Cup & Saucer .........4.00
Gravy Boat, Underplate ..21.00
Plate, Bread & Butter,
    6 In. ...............1.50
Plate, Dinner, 10 In. ......8.50
Plate, Salad, 7 In. ........2.50
Plate, Sherbet, 6 1/2 In. ...1.25
Salt & Pepper ........10.00
Soup, Dish, 8 1/2 In. .....11.00
Teapot, Cover ...23.50 to 60.00

**COORS,** see Rosebud

## CORAL REEF

Coral Reef was designed by Don Blanding for Vernon Kilns in 1938. The tropical fish in the design were colored blue, mustard, and maroon on a cream background.

**MAROON**
Cup ................45.00
**MUSTARD**
Cup & Saucer ........60.00
Plate, Dinner, 9 In. ......55.00

## CORN KING

Dishes shaped like ears of corn? This novel idea became a popular reality when Corn King pattern was sold by Shawnee Pottery Company, Zanesville, Ohio, before 1954. The green and yellow pieces, three-dimensional representations of ears of corn, ranged from dinner plates to small salt and pepper shakers. Corn King has darker yellow corn kernels and lighter green leaves than a later pattern called Corn Queen.

Bowl, Cereal,
    No. 94 ......45.00 to 55.00

Bowl, No. 92, 5 In. . . . . . .37.00
Butter, Cover,
   No. 72 . . . . . .65.00 to 75.00
Casserole, Cover,
   No. 74, 11 In. . .60.00 to 85.00
Casserole, Individual, No. 73,
   9 Oz. . . . . . . .15.00 to 125.00
Creamer,
   No. 70 . . . . . .24.00 to 40.00
Cup & Saucer, No. 90,
   No. 91 . . . . . . .55.00 to 65.00
Mixing Bowl, No. 5,
   5 In. . . . . . . . .25.00 to 40.00
Mixing Bowl, No. 6,
   6 1/2 In. . . . . . .35.00 to 50.00
Mixing Bowl, No. 8,
   8 In. . . . . . . . . . . . . . .65.00
Mug, No. 69,
   8 Oz. . . . . . . .45.00 to 55.00
Pitcher, No. 71,
   40 Oz. . . . . . .85.00 to 95.00
Plate, No. 68,
   10 In. . . . . . . .32.00 to 45.00
Plate, No. 93, 8 In. . . . . . .40.00
Platter, No. 96,
   11 3/4 In. . . . . . . . . . . .41.00
Relish, No. 79 . . .25.00 to 40.00
Salt & Pepper,
   No. 76 . . . . . .20.00 to 34.00
Salt & Pepper,
   No. 77 . . . . . .32.00 to 35.00
Sugar, Cover,
   No. 78 . . . . . .30.00 to 45.00
Sugar & Creamer, No. 78,
   No. 70 . . . . . .65.00 to 75.00
Teapot, Cover, No. 75,
   30 Oz. . . . . . .97.00 to 125.00

---

**Use half the amount of detergent the manufacturer recommends. Most dishwashing products contain trisodium phosphate, which may dull the glaze on some dishes.**

---

Teapot, No. 65,
   10 Oz., Individual  . .250.00 to
325.00

## CORN QUEEN

Corn King was redesigned slightly by Shawnee Pottery Company, Zanesville, Ohio, and continued to be marketed from 1954 to 1961. The kernels of the new line were lighter yellow and the foliage was a deeper green. It was called Corn Queen.

Bowl, Fruit, No. 92,
   6 In. . . . . . . . . . . . . . .35.00
Bowl, Vegetable, No. 95,
   9 In. . . . . . . . . . . . . . .52.00
Butter, Cover,
   No. 72 . . . . . .48.00 to 55.00
Cookie Jar, No. 66 . . . . .198.00
Creamer, No. 70,
   15 Oz. . . . . . .14.00 to 30.00
Mixing Bowl, No. 5,
   5 In. . . . . . . . . . . . . . .35.00
Mixing Bowl, No. 6,
   6 1/2 In. . . . . . . . . . . . .40.00
Mixing Bowl, No. 8,
   8 In. . . . . . . . . . . . . . .45.00
Mug, No. 69, 8 Oz. . . . . . .45.00
Pitcher, Coffee,
   No. 71, Qt. . . . . . . . . .80.00
Plate, No. 68, 10 In. . . . . .19.00
Plate, No. 91, 8 In. . . . . . .11.00

Platter, No. 96, 12 In. . . . .49.00
Relish, No. 79 . . . . . . . . .32.00
Salt & Pepper, No. 76,
   3 1/4 In. . . . . . .19.00 to 20.00
Salt & Pepper, No. 77,
   5 1/4 In. . . . . . .35.00 to 48.00
Saucer, No. 91,
   5 1/2 In. . . . . . . . . . . .20.00
Sugar, Cover, No. 78 . . . .24.00
Teapot, Cover,
   No. 75 . . . . .125.00 to 180.00

## CORONADO

Franciscan dinnerware was made by Gladding, McBean in Los Angeles, California. Coronado, also called Swirl, was a popular plain-colored art ware made from 1935 to 1942. At least fifty different shapes and fifteen different glossy and matte colors were made. Another pattern called Coronado was made by Vernon Kilns. The Franciscan pieces are listed in this book.

**AQUA**
Plate, Bread & Butter,
   6 1/2 In. . . . . . . . . . . . . .4.00
Plate, Breakfast, 9 In. . . . . .6.50
Plate, Salad, 7 In. . . . . . . . .4.50

**CORAL**
Cereal, 2 Handles . . . . . . .10.00

**WHITE**
Butter Dish, Cover . . . . . .30.00
Cup & Saucer . . . . . . . . . .5.00
Plate, 6 1/2 In. . . . . . . . . .3.50
Soup, Dish . . . . . . . . . . . .6.00

**COTTAGE,** see Petit Point House

## COUNTRY GARDEN

Three raised flowers are pictured on the Country Garden dinnerware. The pattern was made by Stangl Pottery of Trenton, New Jersey, from 1956 to 1974. Country Garden was also made by Blue Ridge and Red Wing Potteries, but only the Stangl pattern is listed here.

| | |
|---|---|
| Bowl, Salad, 12 In. | 40.00 to 45.00 |
| Bread Tray | 40.00 |
| Cruet, Stopper | 35.00 |
| Cup | 5.00 |
| Plate, Luncheon, 8 In. | 10.00 |
| Salt & Pepper | 20.00 |
| Saucer | 13.00 |
| Server | 10.00 |

## CRAZY RHYTHM

Crazy Rhythm was a hand-painted abstract pattern made by Red Wing Potteries on the Futura shape in 1960.

| | |
|---|---|
| Bowl, Vegetable, Divided | 25.00 to 40.00 |
| Creamer | 20.00 |

| | |
|---|---|
| Platter, 13 In. | 30.00 |
| Sugar | 20.00 |

## CROCUS

Crocus was a popular name for dinnerware patterns. Prices listed are for the Crocus pattern by Hall China Company of East Liverpool, Ohio, in the 1930s. The decal-decorated dinnerware was sometimes called Holland. The design was a border of oddly shaped crocuses in black, lavender, red, green, and pink. Most pieces have platinum trim. Other firms, including Stangl Pottery and Blue Ridge, had very different-looking dinnerwares called Crocus. Reproductions using the Crocus decoration have been made since 1993. These, unlike the originals, are marked "Limited Edition."

| | |
|---|---|
| Bowl, Radiance, 7 In. | 30.00 |
| Bowl, Radiance, 9 In. | 45.00 |
| Coffee Dispenser, Metal | 25.00 |
| Coffeepot, Terrace | 100.00 |
| Jug, Ball | 195.00 |
| Teapot, Banded | 175.00 |

| | |
|---|---|
| Tureen, Soup | 395.00 |

**CURIOSITY SHOP,** see Old Curiosity Shop

## CURRIER & IVES

Currier & Ives was made by the Royal China Company of Sebring, Ohio, from 1949 until about 1983. It was designed by Gordon Parker and is based on the old Currier & Ives prints. Early pieces were date coded. It is a blue and white or pink and white pattern that was popular as a store premium. The Royal China Company closed in 1986. Currier & Ives patterns were also made by Homer Laughlin and Scio. Some serving pieces were made by Harker Pottery Company. Only the Royal China pattern is listed here.

| | |
|---|---|
| Ashtray | 8.00 to 10.00 |
| Bowl, Cereal, 6 In. | 8.50 |
| Bowl, Fruit, 5 1/2 In. | 3.00 to 8.00 |
| Bowl, Vegetable, Round, 9 In. | 18.00 to 20.00 |
| Bread Tray, Round | 5.00 |
| Cake Plate, Tab Handle, 10 In. | 20.00 to 28.00 |

Casserole,
   Cover . . . . . . .75.00 to 85.00
Chop Plate, 12 In. . . . . . .25.00
Coffee Mug . . . . . . . . . .23.00
Creamer . . . . . . . . . . . . .7.50
Cup . . . . . . . . . . .2.50 to 3.00
Cup & Saucer . . . . . . . . .4.00
Gravy Boat . . . . . . . . . .20.00
Gravy Boat,
   Underplate . . . .24.00 to 28.00
Hostess Set, 9 Piece . . . .100.00
Pie Plate . . . . . . . . . . . .20.00
Plate, 12 In. . . . . . . . . . .24.00
Plate, Bread & Butter,
   6 In. . . . . . . . . . .2.25 to 5.00
Plate, Calendar, 1983 . . . .22.00
Plate, Dinner,
   10 In. . . . . . . . . .4.00 to 5.00
Plate, Luncheon,
   8 In. . . . . . . . .12.00 to 25.00
Plate, Salad,
   7 In. . . . . . . . . .6.00 to 10.00
Platter, 13 In. . . . . . . . . .28.00
Platter, Oval,
   13 x 10 In. . . . .33.00 to 37.00
Salt & Pepper . . .15.00 to 20.00
Saucer . . . . . . . . . . . . . .1.00
Soup, Dish . . . . .10.00 to 12.00
Sugar, Cover . . . . . . . . . .12.00
Sugar & Creamer . . . . . . .2.50
Sugar & Creamer,
   Cover . . . . . . . . . . . . .24.00
Teapot . . . . . . . . . . . . .125.00

## ·D·

## DAISY

Daisy, or Hawaiian 12-point Daisy, is a Fiesta Casual pattern made by the Homer Laughlin China Company of Newell, West Virginia. It was first made in 1962 and discontinued in 1968. Daisy pattern, on the familiar Fiesta shape, has a turquoise rim and turquoise and brown daisies in the center. Patterns named Daisy were also made by Red Wing, Stangl, and Taylor, Smith, and Taylor. Only the Homer Laughlin pattern is listed here.

Cup & Saucer . . . . . . . . .15.00
Plate, Dinner, 10 In. . . . .20.00

## DESERT ROSE

Desert Rose by Franciscan is a popular pattern with today's collectors. It was introduced in 1942 by Gladding, McBean's Franciscan Ceramics. Franciscan Ceramics was purchased by Waterford Wedgwood USA in 1979, and the pattern is still being made. The flowers on the dishes are a soft pink.

Ashtray, Individual . . . . .20.00
Ashtray, Oval,
   9 In. . . . . . . . .65.00 to 85.00
Berry Bowl,
   5 1/4 In. . . . . . .8.00 to 10.00
Bowl, Cereal,
   6 In. . . . . . . . .12.00 to 13.00
Bowl, Footed, 10 In. . . . .90.00
Bowl, Microwave,
   Square . . . . . . . . . . . .245.00
Bowl, Salad, 10 In. . . . .110.00
Bowl, Vegetable,
   8 In. . . . . . . . .37.00 to 38.00
Bowl, Vegetable,
   10 1/2 In. . . . . . . . . . .85.00
Bowl, Vegetable, 12 In. . .70.00
Bowl, Vegetable,
   2 Sections, 10 In. . . . .35.00 to
45.00
Bowl, Vegetable, Cover,
   8 x 4 1/2 In. . . .45.00 to 50.00
Bowl, Vegetable, Round,
   9 In. . . . . . . . .32.00 to 40.00
Box, Heart Shape . . . . . .165.00
Butter, Cover,
   1/4 Lb. . . . . . .45.00 to 50.00
Candleholder, 3 In.,
   Pair . . . . . . . .75.00 to 95.00
Candy Dish . . . . . . . . . .100.00
Casserole, Cover,
   1 1/2 Qt. . . . . . .90.00 to 95.00
Celery Dish . . . . . . . . . .35.00
Chop Plate,
   14 In. . . . . . . .82.00 to 95.00
Cigarette Box . . . . . . .125.00
Coffeepot,
   Cover . . . . . .95.00 to 150.00
Compote, Footed,
   8 In. . . . . . . . .65.00 to 75.00
Cookie Jar, Cover,
   10 1/2 In. . . . . . . . . . .295.00
Creamer, Individual . . . . .45.00
Cup & Saucer . . .8.00 to 10.00
Cup & Saucer, After
   Dinner . . . . . .50.00 to 65.00
Cup & Saucer, Tea, Low . .8.50
Eggcup . . . . . . . .26.00 to 35.00
Goblet, 6 1/2 In. . . . . . . .15.00
Gravy Boat, 2 Spout . . . .50.00
Gravy Boat,
   Underplate . . . .30.00 to 35.00
Grill Plate . . . .90.00 to 125.00
Jam Jar, Cover . . . . . . . .90.00

Mixing Bowl,
9 In. . . . . . .175.00 to 195.00
Mug, 10 Oz. . . . . . . . . . .35.00
Mug, 12 Oz. . . . .40.00 to 45.00
Mug, 16 Oz., 4 1/2 In. . . .50.00
Pitcher, Milk, 1 Qt. . . . . .90.00
Pitcher, Syrup, 1 Pt.,
6 1/4 In. . . . . .65.00 to 75.00
Pitcher, Water,
2 1/2 Qt. . . . .100.00 to 125.00
Plate, Bread & Butter,
6 1/2 In. . . . . . . .6.00 to 8.00
Plate, Breakfast,
9 1/2 In. . . . . .10.00 to 12.00
Plate, Crescent Shape,
8 1/2 In. . . . . .27.50 to 30.00
Plate, Dinner,
10 1/2 In. . . . .12.00 to 19.00
Plate, Divided, Child,
Square . . . . . . . . . . . .190.00
Plate, Luncheon,
8 In. . . . . . . . . .7.00 to 10.00
Plate, Sandwich,
11 1/2 In. . . . . . . . . . . .50.00
Platter, Oval,
12 1/2 In. . . . .32.00 to 45.00
Platter, Oval,
14 In. . . . . . . .35.00 to 65.00
Platter, Sandwich,
11 1/2 In. . . . . . . . . . . .75.00
Platter, Turkey, 19 In. . . .300.00
Relish, 11 In. . . . . . . . . .40.00
Relish, 3 Sections,
12 In. . . . . . . .65.00 to 70.00
Salad, Footed, 10 In. . . . .90.00
Salt & Pepper, 6 In.,
Pair . . . . . . . .50.00 to 65.00
Salt & Pepper
Mill . . . . . . .250.00 to 295.00
Sherbet, Footed . .20.00 to 30.00
Soup, Dish, Flat
Rim . . . . . . . .16.00 to 26.00
Soup, Dish, Footed,
5 1/2 In. . . . . . . . . . . . .32.00
Sugar, Individual . . . . . . .75.00

---

❖

**Glue broken china
with invisible mending
cement that is
waterproof.**

❖

---

Sugar & Creamer,
Cover . . . . . . .35.00 to 50.00
Teapot, Cover . .95.00 to 120.00
Tile, Square, 6 In. . . . . . .65.00
Tureen, Soup, Large . . . .500.00
Vase, Bud, 6 In. . . . . . . .55.00

## EARLY CALIFORNIA

In the late 1930s, Vernon Kilns of Vernon, California, made a solid-color line of dinnerware called Early California. The dishes, in Blue, Brown, Green, Orange, Pink, Turquoise, or Yellow, were made to be used as mix-and-match sets. The dishes are marked with the name of the pattern.

**BLUE**
Cup & Saucer . . . . . . . .13.00
Tumbler . . . . . . . . . . . . .20.00

**BROWN**
Creamer . . . . . .10.00 to 12.00
Plate, Dinner, 10 1/2 In. . .10.00

**TURQUOISE**
Egg Cup . . . . . . . . . . . .16.00
Plate, Salad, 6 1/2 In. . . . . .5.00

**BLUE**
Plate, Dinner, 10 1/2 In. . .11.00

## EGGSHELL NAUTILUS

Eggshell Nautilus is a shape that was made by Homer Laughlin China Company from 1937 to the 1950s. The nautilus shell motif can been seen in the handles. The shape was decorated in many different ways.

Bowl, Gold Rim,
5 1/4 In. . . . . . . .1.00 to 3.00
Bowl, Gold Rim,
8 1/4 In. . . . . . . . . . . . .10.00
Creamer . . . . . . . . . . . . .10.00
Cup . . . . . . . . . . . . . . . .1.00
Plate, Breakfast, 9 In. . . . .9.50
Plate, Luncheon, 8 In. . . . .6.00
Plate, Salad, 6 In. . . . . . . .5.00
Sugar & Creamer,
Cover . . . . . . . . . . . . .18.50

---

## EL PATIO

El Patio is one of many solid-color dinnerware patterns made by Franciscan Ceramics from 1936 to 1956. It comes in twenty colors.

**CORAL**
Bowl, Round, 8 1/2 In. . . .30.00
Cup & Saucer . . . . . . . .10.00
Plate, Dinner, 10 1/2 In. . .12.00
Plate, Luncheon,
9 1/4 In. . . . . . . . . . . . .10.00
Sugar & Creamer . . . . . . .22.00
Teapot . . . . . . . . . . . . . .75.00

**IVORY**
Plate, Breakfast, 9 1/4 In. .10.00
Plate, Dessert, 6 1/4 In. . . . .5.00

### TURQUOISE
Plate, Dessert, 6 1/4 In. . . . .5.00
Plate, Dinner, 10 1/2 In. . .12.00
Plate, Luncheon,
   9 1/4 In. . . . . . . . . . . . .10.00

### YELLOW
Plate, Luncheon, 8 1/4 In. . .9.00
Platter, 13 In. . . . . . . . . .45.00

## ✦F✦

**FESTIVE FRUIT,** see Fruit Stangl

## FIESTA

Fiesta ware was introduced in 1936 by the Homer Laughlin China Company, Newell, West Virginia. It was originally designed by Frederick Hurten Rhead. The line was redesigned in 1969 and withdrawn in 1973. The design was characterized by a band of concentric circles, beginning at the rim. The complete Fiesta line in 1937 had 54 different pieces. Rarities include the covered onion bowl, the green disk water jug, the 10-inch cake plate, and the syrup pitcher. Cups had full-circle handles until 1969, when partial-circle handles were made. The original Fiesta colors were Dark Blue, Fiesta Red, Light Green, Old Ivory, and Yellow. Later, Chartreuse, Forest Green, Gray, Medium Green, Rose, and Turquoise were added. From 1970 to 1972 the redesigned Fiesta Ironstone was made only in Antique Gold, Mango Red, and Turf Green. Homer Laughlin reissued Fiesta in 1986 using new colors but the original marks and molds. The new colors were Apricot, Black, Cobalt Blue, Rose (pink), and White. In 1989 the company added three other colors—Periwinkle Blue, Turquoise, and Yellow. See American Dinnerware In-

troduction for more information. Most Fiesta ware was marked with the incised word Fiesta. Some pieces were hand-stamped before glazing. The word genuine was added to the mark in the 1940s. The Fiesta shape was also made with decal decorations, but these are not considered Fiesta by collectors; instead, they are collected by the pattern names. There is also a Fiesta Kitchen Kraft line, a group of kitchenware pieces made in the early 1940s in Blue, Green, Red, or Yellow. These were bake-and-serve wares. Glassware and linens were made to match the Fiesta colors.

### CHARTREUSE
Ashtray  . . . . . .65.00 to 95.00
Bowl, Cereal,
  5 1/2 In. . . . . .30.00 to 31.00
Bowl, Dessert,
  6 In. . . . . . . . .40.00 to 42.00
Bowl, Fruit, 4 3/4 In. . . . .30.00

Casserole, Cover, 2 Handles,
  10 In. . . . . . .225.00 to 300.00
Chop Plate, 13 In. . . . . . .56.00
Coffeepot  . . . .585.00 to 785.00
Cup & Saucer, After
  Dinner . . . . . . . . . . . .625.00
Mug,
  Tom & Jerry  . .75.00 to 95.00
Pitcher, Water, Disk  . . . .275.00
Plate, Bread & Butter,
  7 In. . . . . . . . . . . . . . .13.00
Plate, Dessert,
  6 In. . . . . . . . . .9.00 to 12.00
Plate, Dinner,
  10 In. . . . . . . .32.00 to 36.00
Plate, Luncheon,
  9 In. . . . . . . . .16.00 to 19.00
Platter, Oval,
  12 In. . . . . . . .40.00 to 50.00
Sauceboat  . . . . . . . . . . .55.00
Saucer  . . . . . . . . .7.00 to 8.00
Soup, Cream . . . . . . . . . .75.00
Sugar, Cover . . . . . . . . . .65.00
Sugar & Creamer, Tray,
  3 Piece  . . . . .275.00 to 280.00
Teapot, Medium, 6 Cup  .100.00

### COBALT BLUE
Chop Plate, 13 In. . . . . . .35.00
Marmalade, Cover  . . . .268.00
Plate, Dinner, 10 In. . . . .38.00
Saucer . . . . . . . . . . . . . .4.00
Sugar . . . . . . . . . . . . . .20.00

### DARK BLUE
Ashtray  . . . . . . . . . . . .95.00
Bowl, Dessert,
  6 In. . . . . . . . .35.00 to 37.00
Bowl, Fruit, 4 3/4 In. . . . .25.00
Bowl, Fruit, 11 3/4 In. . .485.00
Bowl, Salad, Footed . . . .625.00
Candleholder, Bulb,
  Pair . . . . . . . . . . . . . .100.00
Candleholder, Tripod,
  Pair  . . . . . .400.00 to 950.00
Carafe  . . . . . .125.00 to 375.00
Casserole, Cover . . . . . .295.00
Chop Plate, 13 In. . . . . . .45.00
Chop Plate, 15 In. . . . . . .50.00
Coffeepot . . . . . . . . . . .200.00
Coffeepot, After
  Dinner . . . . . . . . . . . .550.00
Compote, Footed, Low,
  12 In. . . . . . .115.00 to 120.00

Compote,
Sweets . . . . . .80.00 to 150.00
Cover, Mixing Bowl,
No. 1, 5 In. . . . . . . . . .575.00
Creamer . . . . . . . . . . . . . .20.00
Creamer, Stick Handle . . .55.00
Cup . . . . . . . . . . . . . . . .20.00
Cup & Saucer . . . . . . . . .85.00
Cup & Saucer, After
Dinner . . . . . . . . . . . . .68.00
Eggcup . . . . . . . 56.00 to 58.00
Grill Plate, 10 1/2 In. . . . .42.00
Grill Plate, 12 In. . . . . . . .65.00
Marmalade, Cover . . . . .265.00
Mixing Bowl, No. 1,
5 In. . . . . . . . . . . . . . .95.00
Mixing Bowl, No. 2,
6 In. . . . . . . . . . . . . . .195.00
Mixing Bowl, No. 3,
7 In. . . . . . . . . . . . . . .120.00
Mixing Bowl, No. 4,
8 In. . . . . . . .115.00 to 125.00
Mixing Bowl, No. 6,
10 In. . . . . . . . . . . . . .215.00
Mug . . . . . . . . . . . . . . .60.00
Mug,
Tom & Jerry . .50.00 to 55.00
Mustard . . . . .190.00 to 325.00
Nappy,
8 1/2 In. . . . . . .35.00 to 50.00
Pitcher, 2 Pt. . . . . . . . . . .120.00
Pitcher, Ice Lip . . . . . . . .155.00
Pitcher, Juice, Disk,
30 Oz. . . . . . .135.00 to 165.00
Pitcher, Water, Disk . . . .150.00
Plate, Dessert, 6 In. . . . . . .9.00
Plate, Dinner, 10 In. . . . . .38.00
Platter, Oval, 12 In. . . . . .30.00
Relish Tray . . . . . . . . . .300.00
Sauceboat . . . . . . . . . . . .65.00
Saucer . . . . . . . . . . . . . . .4.00
Soup, Cream . . . .50.00 to 55.00
Soup, Onion,
Cover . . . . . .450.00 to 550.00
Sugar & Creamer, Cover,
Individual . . . . . . . . . .350.00
Sugar & Creamer,
Pair . . . . . . . . .50.00 to 75.00
Syrup . . . . . . . . . . . . . .300.00
Teapot, Large,
8 Cup . . . . . .225.00 to 335.00
Tray, Utility . . . . . . . . . . .30.00

Tumbler, Juice,
5 Oz. . . . . . . . .35.00 to 45.00
Tumbler, Water,
10 Oz. . . . . . . .55.00 to 60.00
Vase, 8 In. . . . .550.00 to 820.00
Vase, 10 In. . .525.00 to 1150.00
Vase,
12 In. . . . .1150.00 to 1600.00
Vase, Bud,
6 1/2 In. . . . . .90.00 to 125.00

**FIESTA RED**
Ashtray . . . . . . .45.00 to 65.00
Bowl, Cereal,
5 1/2 In. . . . . . .25.00 to 28.00
Bowl, Dessert, 6 In. . . . . .38.00
Bowl, Fruit, 4 3/4 In. . . . .35.00
Bowl, Fruit,
11 3/4 In. . . .155.00 to 175.00
Bowl, Salad, Footed . . . .625.00
Bowl, Salad, Individual,
7 1/2 In. . . . . . . . . . . . .48.00
Cake Plate, 10 In. . . . . . .50.00
Candleholder, Bulb,
Pair . . . . . . . .85.00 to 120.00
Candleholder, Tripod . . .950.00
Carafe . . . . . .190.00 to 325.00
Casserole . . . . . . . . . . .295.00
Casserole, Cover,
2 Handles, 10 In. . . . . .200.00
Chop Plate,
15 In. . . . . . . .40.00 to 57.00
Coffeepot . . . .195.00 to 225.00
Coffeepot, After
Dinner . . . . . . . . . . . .360.00
Compote, Footed, Low,
12 In. . . . . . . .90.00 to 100.00
Compote,
Sweets . . . . . .60.00 to 70.00
Cover, Mixing Bowl,
No. 1 . . . .1000.00 to 1400.00
Cover, Mixing Bowl,
No. 4 . . . . . . . . . . . . .850.00
Creamer,
Individual . . .185.00 to 350.00

❖

**Some tea and coffee
stains can be removed
by rubbing dishes with
damp baking soda.**

❖

Creamer, Stick
Handle . . . . . .48.00 to 65.00
Cup & Saucer . .25.00 to 75.00
Cup & Saucer, After
Dinner . . . . .85.00 to 130.00
Marmalade . . . . . . . . . .235.00
Mixing Bowl, No. 1,
5 In. . . . . . . .260.00 to 275.00
Mixing Bowl, No. 2,
6 In. . . . . . . . . . . . . . .75.00
Mixing Bowl, No. 3,
7 In. . . . . . . . . . . . . . .55.00
Mixing Bowl, No. 5,
9 In. . . . . . . . . . . . . . .120.00
Mixing Bowl, No. 6,
10 In. . . . . . . . . . . . . .150.00
Mug . . . . . . . . . .65.00 to 70.00
Mug, Tom & Jerry . . . . . .70.00
Mustard . . . . . . . . . . . .365.00
Nappy, 8 1/2 In. . . . . . . .35.00
Pitcher, Juice, Disk,
30 Oz. . . . . . .340.00 to 410.00
Pitcher, Water,
Disk . . . . . . .158.00 to 175.00
Plate, Bread & Butter,
7 In. . . . . . . . . . .6.00 to 10.00
Plate, Deep,
8 In. . . . . . . . . .30.00 to 42.00
Plate, Dessert, 6 In. . . . . . .4.00
Plate, Dinner,
10 In. . . . . . . .40.00 to 60.00
Plate, Luncheon, 9 In. . . . .20.00
Platter, Oval,
12 In. . . . . . . .40.00 to 46.00
Relish . . . . . . . . . . . . .425.00
Salt & Pepper . . . . . . . .26.00
Sauceboat . . . . . .50.00 to 60.00
Saucer . . . . . . . . . .2.00 to 4.00
Saucer, After Dinner . . . . .12.00
Soup, Cream . . . .58.00 to 75.00
Soup, Onion,
Cover . . . . . .460.00 to 690.00
Sugar & Creamer . . . . . . .35.00
Syrup . . . . . . .300.00 to 450.00
Teapot, Large,
8 Cup . . . . . .165.00 to 285.00
Teapot, Medium,
6 Cup . . . . . . . . . . . . .160.00
Tray, Utility . . . . . . . . . . .48.00
Tumbler, Juice,
5 Oz. . . . . . . . .40.00 to 50.00
Tumbler, Water,
10 Oz. . . . . . . .60.00 to 75.00

Vase, 8 In. . . . .925.00 to 985.00
Vase, 10 In. . . .799.00 to 895.00
Vase, 12 In. . . . . . . . .1700.00
Vase, Bud,
6 1/2 In. . . . .100.00 to 125.00

### FOREST GREEN
Ashtray . . . . . .72.00 to 90.00
Bowl, Cereal,
5 1/2 In. . . . . .27.00 to 32.00
Bowl, Dessert,
6 In. . . . . . . . .40.00 to 42.00
Bowl, Fruit, 4 3/4 In. . . . .30.00
Casserole,
Cover . . . . . .300.00 to 435.00
Chop Plate, 13 In. . . . . . .75.00
Chop Plate, 15 In. . . . . .125.00
Coffeepot . . . .228.00 to 230.00
Creamer . . . . . . . . . . . . .30.00
Cup & Saucer, After
Dinner . . . . . . . . . . . .625.00
Cup & Saucer, Tea . . . . .40.00
Mixing Bowl, No. 3,
7 In. . . . . . . . . . . . . .120.00
Mixing Bowl, No. 4,
8 In. . . . . . . . . . . . . .100.00
Mug . . . . . . . . .50.00 to 85.00
Mug,
Tom & Jerry . .65.00 to 85.00
Nappy, 8 1/2 In. . . . . . . .65.00
Nut Dish . . . . . . . . . . .125.00
Pitcher, Juice, Disk,
30 Oz. . . . .265.00 to 365.00
Plate, Deep, 8 In. . . . . . .45.00
Plate, Dessert, 6 In. . . . . . .9.00
Plate, Luncheon, 9 In. . . . .11.00
Saltshaker . . . . . . . . . . . .10.00
Sauceboat . . . . .35.00 to 90.00
Saucer . . . . . . . . . . . . . . .3.00
Soup, Cream . . . .40.00 to 55.00
Teacup . . . . . . . . . . . . . .20.00
Teapot, Medium,
6 Cup . . . . .395.00 to 475.00
Tumbler, Water, 10 Oz. . .50.00

### GRAY
Ashtray . . . . . . . . . . . . .95.00
Bowl, Cereal, 5 1/2 In. . . .24.00
Bowl, Dessert,
6 In. . . . . . . . . .28.00 to 40.00
Bowl, Fruit,
4 3/4 In. . . . . . .24.00 to 30.00
Bowl, Salad, 7 1/2 In. . . . .43.00

Casserole,
Cover . . . . . .195.00 to 375.00
Chop Plate,
13 In. . . . . . . .60.00 to 95.00
Chop Plate, 15 In. . . . . . .70.00
Coffeepot . . . . . . . . . . .540.00
Creamer . . . . . .25.00 to 35.00
Cup & Saucer, After
Dinner . . . . . . . . . . . .625.00
Eggcup . . . . . . . . . . . .135.00
Mug . . . . . . . . .80.00 to 85.00
Mug,
Tom & Jerry . .80.00 to 95.00
Nappy, 8 1/2 In. .45.00 to 60.00
Pitcher, Juice, Disk,
30 Oz. . . . . . . . . . . . .145.00
Pitcher, Water, Disk,
2 Qt. . . . . . .250.00 to 370.00
Plate, Deep,
8 In. . . . . . . .48.00 to 50.00
Plate, Dessert, 6 In. . . . . . .6.00
Plate, Dinner, 10 In. . . . . .37.00
Plate, Luncheon,
9 In. . . . . . . . .17.00 to 19.00
Platter, Oval, 12 In. . . . .52.00
Salt & Pepper . . . . . . . .41.00
Saltshaker . . . . . . . . . . .25.00
Sauceboat . . . . . . . . . . .75.00
Soup, Cream . . . .65.00 to 95.00
Sugar, Cover . . . . . . . . . .75.00
Teapot, Medium,
6 Cup . . . . . . . . . . . .325.00
Tumbler, Juice, 5 Oz. . . . .30.00

### LIGHT GREEN
Ashtray . . . . . .32.00 to 65.00
Bowl, Cereal,
5 1/2 In. . . . . .20.00 to 26.00
Bowl, Fruit, 4 3/4 In. . . . .18.00
Bowl, Salad, Footed . . .575.00
Candleholder, Bulb, Pair . .88.00

❖

**Stains on porcelain
can be removed by
soaking in a mixture
of two tablespoons of
Polident denture
cleaner in a quart of
tepid water.**

❖

Candleholder, Tripod,
Pair . . . . . . . . . . . . . .300.00
Carafe . . . . . .265.00 to 330.00
Casserole, Cover . . . . . .130.00
Chop Plate,
13 In. . . . . . . .30.00 to 38.00
Coffeepot, After
Dinner . . . . . . . . . . . .175.00
Coffeepot, Cover, Stick
Handle, After
Dinner . . . .275.00 to 475.00
Compote, 12 In. . . . . . . .68.00
Creamer, Stick Handle . . .50.00
Cup . . . . . . . . . . . . . . .20.00
Cup & Saucer . .50.00 to 62.00
Eggcup . . . . . . .35.00 to 50.00
Jug, 2 Pt. . . . . . . . . . . .150.00
Marmalade . . . . . . . . .300.00
Mixing Bowl, Cover,
No. 1 . . . . . . . . . . . .1150.00
Mixing Bowl, No. 1,
5 In. . . . . . . . . . . . . .230.00
Mixing Bowl, No. 3,
7 In. . . . . . . .95.00 to 120.00
Mixing Bowl, No. 4,
8 In. . . . . . . .75.00 to 155.00
Mixing Bowl, No. 5,
9 In. . . . . . .115.00 to 175.00
Mixing Bowl, No. 7,
11 In. . . . . . . . . . . . . .215.00
Mustard . . . . .150.00 to 250.00
Nappy, 8 1/2 In. . . . . . . .54.00
Plate, Bread & Butter,
7 In. . . . . . . . . . .9.00 to 12.00
Plate, Deep, 8 In. . . . . . .35.00
Plate, Dinner,
10 In. . . . . . . .22.00 to 34.00
Plate, Luncheon,
9 In. . . . . . . . . .8.00 to 12.00
Platter, Oval, 12 In. . . . .22.00
Platter, Oval, 13 In. . . . .75.00
Relish . . . . . . . . . . . . .225.00
Salt & Pepper . . . . . . . .20.00
Saltshaker . . . . . . . . . . .16.00
Sauceboat . . . . . . . . . . .35.00
Soup, Onion . . . . . . . . .950.00
Sugar . . . . . . . . . . . . . . .45.00
Syrup . . . . . .225.00 to 375.00
Teapot, Medium,
6 Cup . . . . .120.00 to 145.00
Tray, Utility . . . . . . . . . . .30.00
Tumbler, Water,
10 Oz. . . . . . . .50.00 to 55.00

Vase, 8 In. . . . .475.00 to 675.00
Vase, 10 In. . . .500.00 to 700.00
Vase,
12 In. . . . .1250.00 to 1400.00
Vase, Bud, 6 1/2 In. . . . . .50.00

**MEDIUM GREEN**
Ashtray . . . . .175.00 to 260.00
Bowl, Cereal,
5 1/2 In. . . . . .45.00 to 75.00
Casserole, Cover,
2 Handles, 10 In. . . . . .560.00
Chop Plate, Metal & Rattan
Handle, 13 In. . . . . . .220.00
Cup, Tea . . . . . . . . . . . . .195.00
Cup & Saucer . .58.00 to 95.00
Mug . . . . . . . .95.00 to 145.00
Plate, Bread & Butter,
7 In. . . . . . . . .30.00 to 45.00
Plate, Deep,
8 In. . . . . . .110.00 to 135.00
Plate, Dessert,
6 In. . . . . . . . .13.00 to 35.00
Plate, Dinner,
10 In. . . . . . .80.00 to 150.00
Plate, Luncheon,
9 In. . . . . . . .36.00 to 65.00
Platter, Oval,
12 In. . . . . . .170.00 to 175.00
Salt &
Pepper . . . . .110.00 to 270.00
Sauceboat . . . .220.00 to 250.00
Sugar & Creamer . . . . . . .95.00
Teapot, Large,
8 Cup . . . . . . . . . . . . .1650.00
Teapot, Medium,
6 Cup . . . . .950.00 to 1000.00

**OLD IVORY**
Ashtray . . . . . . . . . . . . . .75.00
Bowl, Cereal,
5 1/2 In. . . . . . .25.00 to 28.00
Bowl, Dessert,
6 In. . . . . . . .35.00 to 45.00
Bowl, Fruit,
4 3/4 In. . . . . . .20.00 to 22.00
Bowl, Fruit, 11 3/4 In. . .165.00
Bowl, Salad, 9 1/2 In. . . . .30.00
Bowl, Salad, Footed . . . .625.00
Candleholder, Bulb,
Pair . . . . . . . . . . . . . .100.00
Candleholder, Tripod,
Pair . . . . . . . . . . . . . .950.00
Carafe . . . . . .225.00 to 375.00
Chop Plate, 13 In. . . . . . .30.00

Chop Plate,
15 In. . . . . . . . .60.00 to 70.00
Coffeepot . . . . . . . . . . . .135.00
Coffeepot, Cover, After
Dinner . . . .432.00 to 440.00
Compote, 12 In. . . . . . .225.00
Cover, Mixing Bowl,
No. 3, 7 In. . . . . . . . .612.00
Creamer . . . . . . .18.00 to 20.00
Creamer, Stick
Handle . . . . . . .38.00 to 55.00
Cup & Saucer, After
Dinner . . . . . . .60.00 to 90.00
Eggcup . . . . . . . .48.00 to 90.00
Marmalade . . .175.00 to 325.00
Mixing Bowl, No. 1,
5 In. . . . . . . . . . . . . . .350.00
Mixing Bowl, No. 2,
6 In. . . . . . .100.00 to 230.00
Mixing Bowl, No. 4,
8 In. . . . . . . . . . . . . . .225.00
Mixing Bowl, No. 5,
9 In. . . . . . . . . . . . . . .275.00
Mixing Bowl, No. 6,
10 In. . . . . . . . . . . . . . .360.00
Mug, Tom & Jerry,
Gold Trim . . . .45.00 to 65.00
Mustard, Cover . . . . . . . .155.00
Nappy, 8 1/2 In. . . . . . . .45.00
Pitcher, Ice Lip,
2 Qt. . . . . . . .120.00 to 125.00
Plate, Bread & Butter,
7 In. . . . . . . . . . . . . . . .9.00
Plate, Calendar, 1954,
10 In. . . . . . . . .42.00 to 45.00
Plate, Deep, 8 In. . . . . . .40.00
Plate, Dessert,
6 In. . . . . . . . . .10.00 to 12.00
Plate, Dinner,
10 In. . . . . . . . .29.00 to 40.00
Plate, Luncheon,
9 In. . . . . . . . . .9.00 to 12.00
Relish . . . . . . . . . . . . . .175.00
Relish, Cobalt Blue
Center . . . . . . . . . . . .350.00
Relish, Red Center . . . .350.00
Salt & Pepper . . . . . . . .26.00
Sauceboat . . . . . . . . . . .48.00
Saucer . . . . . . . . . . . . . . .2.00
Soup, Cream . . . . . . . . . .60.00
Soup, Onion,
Cover . . . . .510.00 to 950.00
Sugar & Creamer . . . . . . .80.00

Syrup . . . . . . .600.00 to 650.00
Teapot, Medium,
6 Cup . . . . . . . . . . . . .140.00
Tumbler, Juice,
5 Oz. . . . . . . . .42.00 to 45.00
Tumbler, Water,
10 Oz. . . . . . . .48.00 to 60.00
Vase, 8 In. . . . .435.00 to 895.00
Vase, 10 In. . .895.00 to 1185.00
Vase,
12 In. . . . .1400.00 to 1500.00
Vase, Bud, 6 1/2 In. . . . . .65.00

**ROSE**
Ashtray . . . . . . . . . . . . . .95.00
Bowl, Fruit,
4 3/4 In. . . . . . .25.00 to 28.00
Casserole . . . .135.00 to 375.00
Chop Plate,
15 In. . . . . . . .95.00 to 150.00
Coffeepot . . . . . . . . . . . .450.00
Creamer . . . . . . . . . . . . .38.00
Creamer, Stick Handle . . .28.00
Cup & Saucer, After
Dinner . . . . . . . . . . . .625.00
Eggcup . . . . . . . . . . . . .135.00
Mug . . . . . . . . . .80.00 to 95.00
Nappy, 8 1/2 In. . . . . . . .40.00
Pitcher, Water, Disk . . . .310.00
Plate, Bread & Butter,
7 In. . . . . . . . . . . . . . . .15.00
Plate, Deep, 8 In. . . . . . .55.00
Plate, Luncheon,
9 In. . . . . . . . . .19.00 to 23.00
Saucer . . . . . . . . . .4.00 to 8.00
Soup, Cream . . . .60.00 to 95.00
Teapot, Medium,
6 Cup . . . . . .350.00 to 450.00

**TURQUOISE**
Ashtray . . . . . . .34.00 to 50.00
Bowl, Cereal, 5 1/2 In. . . .22.00
Bowl, Fruit,
4 3/4 In. . . . . . .18.00 to 20.00
Bowl, Fruit, 11 3/4 In. . .200.00
Bowl, Salad, 7 1/2 In. . . . .72.00
Bowl, Salad, Footed . . . .575.00
Cake Plate,
10 In. . . . . . .600.00 to 605.00
Candleholder, Bulb,
Pair . . . . . . .100.00 to 110.00
Candleholder, Tripod,
Pair . . . . . . . . . . . . . .890.00
Carafe . . . . . .215.00 to 380.00

Casserole . . . . .75.00 to 135.00

Casserole, Cover,
2 Handles, 10 In. . . . . .110.00

Chop Plate, 13 In. . . . . . .35.00

Chop Plate, 15 In. . . . . . .40.00

Coffeepot . . . . . . . . . . .225.00

Creamer . . . . . .21.00 to 25.00

Creamer, Stick
Handle . . . . . .55.00 to 115.00

Cup . . . . . . . . . . . . . . .16.00

Cup & Saucer . . . . . . . .29.00

Cup & Saucer, After
Dinner . . . . . .62.00 to 115.00

Eggcup . . . . . . . . . . . . .55.00

Marmalade . . .178.00 to 325.00

Mixing Bowl, No. 1,
5 In. . . . . . . . . . . . . . .275.00

Mixing Bowl, No. 2,
6 In. . . . . . .115.00 to 210.00

Mixing Bowl, No. 3,
7 In. . . . . . . . . . . . . . .225.00

Mixing Bowl, No. 4,
8 In. . . . . . .120.00 to 225.00

Mixing Bowl, No. 5,
9 In. . . . . . .120.00 to 250.00

Mixing Bowl, No. 7,
11 1/2 In. . . . . . . . . . . .200.00

Mug . . . . . . . . . . . . . .46.00

Mug, Tom &
Jerry . . . . . . . .45.00 to 52.00

Mustard . . . . . . . . . . . .275.00

Nappy, 8 1/2 In. . . . . . . .24.00

Nappy, 9 1/2 In. . . . . . . .60.00

Pitcher, Ice Lip,
2 Qt. . . . . . . .132.00 to 195.00

Pitcher, Syrup . . . . . . . .275.00

Pitcher, Water,
Disk . . . . . . .85.00 to 100.00

Plate, Bread & Butter,
7 In. . . . . . . . . . . . . . .12.00

Plate, Dessert, 6 In. . . . . . .8.00

Plate, Dinner,
10 In. . . . . . . .22.00 to 60.00

Plate, Luncheon, 9 In. . . . .14.00

Platter, Oval, 12 In. . . . . .40.00

Relish, 5 Multicolored
Sections . . . . . . . . . . . .200.00

Salad, 7 1/2 In. . . . . . . . .70.00

Salt & Pepper . . . . . . . .16.00

Saltshaker . . . . . . . . . . .12.00

Sauceboat . . . . . . . . . . .30.00

Saucer . . . . . . . . . . . . . .8.00

---

❖

**Put foam or paper plates between the china plates stacked for storage.**

❖

---

Soup, Cream . . . . . . . . . .45.00

Soup, Onion, Cover . . . .900.00

Sugar, Cover . . . .35.00 to 36.00

Syrup . . . . . .500.00 to 585.00

Teapot, Large,
8 Cup . . . . .140.00 to 280.00

Teapot, Medium,
6 Cup . . . . . .45.00 to 110.00

Tray,
Figure 8 . . . .240.00 to 245.00

Tray, Utility . . . . . . . . . .30.00

Tumbler, Juice, 5 Oz. . . . .50.00

Tumbler, Water,
10 Oz. . . . . . .50.00 to 75.00

Vase, 8 In. . . . . . . . . . .595.00

Vase, 10 In. . .600.00 to 1000.00

Vase, 12 In. . . . . . . . . .1400.00

### YELLOW

Ashtray . . . . . . . . . . . . .50.00

Bowl, Cereal, 5 1/2 In. . . .20.00

Bowl, Dessert, 6 In. . . . . .26.00

Bowl, Fruit,
4 3/4 In. . . . . . .18.00 to 20.00

Bowl, Fruit, 5 1/2 In. . . . .20.00

Bowl, Fruit, 11 3/4 In. . .350.00

Bowl, Salad, 7 1/2 In. . . . .69.00

Bowl, Salad, Footed . . . .575.00

Cake Plate,
10 In. . . . . . .490.00 to 500.00

Candleholder, Bulb,
Pair . . . . . . . .98.00 to 100.00

Candleholder, Tripod . . .215.00

Carafe . . . . .190.00 to 330.00

Casserole . . . . .65.00 to 125.00

Casserole, French, Cover, Stick
Handle . . . .215.00 to 225.00

Chop Plate,
13 In. . . . . . . .17.50 to 35.00

Chop Plate, 15 In. . . . . . .70.00

Coffeepot . . . .135.00 to 175.00

Compote, Footed, Low,
12 In. . . . . . . . . . . . . . .50.00

Creamer . . . . . . . . . . . . .18.00

---

Creamer,
Individual . . . . .45.00 to 75.00

Creamer, Stick
Handle . . . . . . .30.00 to 45.00

Cup . . . . . . . . . . . . . . .18.00

Cup & Saucer . .20.00 to 26.00

Cup & Saucer, After
Dinner . . . . . . .55.00 to 85.00

Eggcup . . . . . . . .43.00 to 50.00

Mixing Bowl, Cover,
No. 4 . . . .1300.00 to 1400.00

Mixing Bowl, No. 1,
5 In. . . . . . . .250.00 to 325.00

Mixing Bowl, No. 2,
6 In. . . . . . . .62.00 to 80.00

Mixing Bowl, No. 4,
8 In. . . . . . . . . . . . . . .145.00

Mixing Bowl, No. 5,
9 In. . . . . . . . . . . . . . .165.00

Mixing Bowl, No. 6,
10 In. . . . . . . . . . . . . . .285.00

Mug . . . . . . . . .45.00 to 50.00

Mug, Tom & Jerry . . . . . .60.00

Mustard . . . . . . . . . . . .200.00

Nappy,
8 1/2 In. . . . . . .37.50 to 40.00

Pitcher, Ice Lip,
2 Qt. . . . . . . . . . . . . . .85.00

Pitcher, Juice, Disk,
30 Oz. . . . . . . .40.00 to 50.00

Pitcher, Water, Disk . . . . .75.00

Pitcher Set, Juice,
7 Piece . . . . . . . . . . . . .350.00

Plate, Bread & Butter,
7 In. . . . . . . . . . .6.00 to 12.00

Plate, Calendar, 1954,
10 In. . . . . . . . . . . . . . .30.00

Plate, Deep,
8 In. . . . . . . .35.00 to 40.00

Plate, Dessert, 6 In. . . . . . .5.00

Plate, Dinner,
10 In. . . . . . . .18.50 to 25.00

Plate, Luncheon,
9 In. . . . . . . . . .8.00 to 14.00

Platter, Oval, 12 In. . . . . .25.00

Salt & Pepper . . .10.00 to 18.00

Saltshaker . . . . . . . . . . .12.00

Saucer . . . . . . . . . . . . . .3.00

Soup, Cream . . . .35.00 to 40.00

Soup, Onion . . . . . . . . . .950.00

Syrup . . . . . . .425.00 to 565.00

Teapot, Large, 8 Cup . . .155.00

Teapot, Medium, 6 Cup . .95.00

Tray, Relish . . . . . . . . .160.00
Tray, Utility . . . . . . . . . . .25.00
Tumbler, Juice,
   5 Oz. . . . . . . . .30.00 to 45.00
Tumbler, Water,
   10 Oz. . . . . . .50.00 to 60.00
Vase, 8 In. . . . . . . . . . .400.00
Vase, 10 In. . . .795.00 to 860.00
Vase, 12 In. . . . . . . . . .1250.00
Vase, Bud, 6 1/2 In. . . . . .60.00

**FIESTA,** see also Amberstone;
   Fiesta Kitchen Kraft

**FIESTA CASUAL,** see Daisy

## FIESTA KITCHEN KRAFT

Fiesta Kitchen Kraft was a
bake-and-serve line made in the
early 1940s by Homer Laughlin
China Company, Newell, West
Virginia. It was made in Red,
Yellow, Green, and Blue.

### BLUE
Cake Server . . . . . . . . .275.00
Casserole, Cover,
   Individual . . . . . . . . . .75.00
Fork . . . . . . . . . . . . . .150.00
Jar, Cover,
   Medium . . . .175.00 to 250.00

---

❖

**Pack plates to be moved
vertically with a pad
under and between the
plates. The weight of a
stack of plates can crack
the bottom plates.**

❖

---

Jar, Cover, Small . . . . .200.00
Mixing Bowl, 6 In. . . . . .100.00
Mixing Bowl, 8 In. . . . . .100.00
Pie Plate, 9 In. . . . . . . . .65.00
Platter, Frame . . . . . . . . .60.00
Spoon . . . . . .130.00 to 170.00

### GREEN
Cake Plate, 11 In. . . . . . .50.00
Cake Server, Original
   Label . . . . .150.00 to 250.00
Casserole, Cover,
   Individual . . .145.00 to 185.00
Fork . . . . . . . .100.00 to 130.00
Jar, Cover, Large . . . . . .325.00
Jar, Cover, Medium . . . .325.00
Jar, Cover, Small,
   Sticker . . . . . . . . . . .375.00
Leftover, Cover,
   Stacking . . . . . . . . . .225.00
Pie Plate, 10 In. . . . . . . .50.00
Platter, 13 In. . . . . . . . . .70.00
Salt & Pepper . . . . . . . .90.00

### IVORY
Stack Unit . . . . . . . . . .175.00

### RED
Cake Plate . . . . . . . . . . .70.00
Cake Server . . . . . . . . .180.00
Carafe . . . . . . . . . . . . .299.00
Casserole, 8 1/2 In. . . . . .135.00
Fork . . . . . . . . . . . . . .180.00
Jar, Cover, Large . . . . . .325.00
Jar, Cover,
   Small . . . . .200.00 to 325.00
Jug, Cover . . . . . . . . . .385.00
Pie Plate, 9 In. . . . . . . . .60.00
Salt & Pepper . . . . . . . .90.00
Spoon . . . . . .110.00 to 180.00

### YELLOW
Cake Plate, 11 In. . . . . . .50.00
Cake Server . .150.00 to 190.00
Casserole, Cover . . . . . .225.00
Casserole, Cover,
   Individual . . .115.00 to 185.00
Fork . . . . . . . . . . . . . .210.00
Jar, Cover,
   Medium . . . .325.00 to 360.00
Jar, Cover, Small . . . . . .325.00
Jug, Cover . . . . . . . . . . .75.00
Pie Plate, 9 In. . . .25.00 to 35.00
Pie Plate, 10 In. . .35.00 to 50.00
Platter, 13 In. . . . .    70.00

## FRIENDLY VILLAGE

Friendly Village is made by
Johnson Brothers, Ltd. of Han-
ley, England, now part of the
Waterford Wedgwood Group.
The pattern has been made
since 1953 and is still being
made. It is decorated with a
black transfer design tinted in
pastel colors and features
scenes of rural life.

Plate, Bread & Butter . . . . .4.00
Plate, Dinner, 10 In. . . . . .8.00
Platter, 11 3/4 In. . . . . . .18.00
Platter, Turkey, 20 In. . . .125.00
Sugar & Creamer,
   Cover . . . . . . .45.00 to 50.00

## FRUIT & FLOWERS

Fruit & Flowers pattern, No.
4030, was made by Stangl
Pottery, Trenton, New Jersey,
from 1957 to 1974. The design
shows a mixed grouping of
flowers, leaves, grapes, and
fanciful shapes. Pieces have a
colored border. Universal Potteries also made a pattern called
Fruit & Flowers, but only the
Stangl pattern is listed here.

Bowl, Vegetable, 8 In. . . .35.00
Cup . . . . . . . . . . . . . . .15.00

Gravy Boat, Liner . . . . . . .45.00
Pitcher, 12 Oz. . . . . . . . .20.00
Pitcher, Pt. . . . . . . . . . . .35.00
Pitcher, Qt. . . . . . . . . . . .18.00
Plate, Luncheon, 8 In. . . . .18.00
Salt & Pepper  . . . . . . . .24.00
Vegetable, 8 In.  . . . . . . . .35.00

## FRUIT PURINTON

Fruit patterns were very popular in the 1940s and sets of dishes called Fruit were made by Franciscan Ceramics, Purinton Pottery, Red Wing Potteries, and Stangl Pottery. The Fruit pattern listed here was made by Purinton from 1936 to about 1950. It pictures large fruits.

Canister Set, Revolving  . .78.00
Lazy Susan  . . . . . . . . . .125.00
Salt & Pepper, Jug  . . . . . .16.00
Teapot, 4 Cup . . . . . . . . . .45.00
Teapot, 6 Cup . . . . . . . . . .45.00

## FRUIT STANGL

Stangl Pottery, Trenton, New Jersey, made Fruit pattern from 1942 to 1974. The dishes had center designs that were different fruits. Some pictured apples, some pears, grapes, or

other fruit. This pattern, No. 3697, was sometimes called Festive Fruit. It was marked Terra Rose.

Bowl, 5 In. . . . . . . . . . . .15.00
Bowl, Vegetable,
   Divided . . . . . . . . . . . .40.00
Gravy Boat . . . . . . . . . . .25.00
Plate, Luncheon, 8 In. . . . .15.00
Sugar & Creamer  . . . . . .25.00

## ·G·

## GINGHAM

Vernon Kilns, Vernon, California, made six different plaid patterns. Each plaid was given a special name. Gingham is the pattern with a dark green border and green and yellow plaid. Other related plaids are Calico (pink and blue), Coronation Organdy (gray and rose), Homespun (cinnamon, yellow, and green), Organdie (brown and yellow), Tam O'Shanter (rust, chartreuse, and dark green), and Tweed (yellow and gray-blue).

Bowl, Deep, 5 In. . . . . . . .14.00
Casserole, Cover,
   Individual  . . . . . . . . . .28.00
Chop Plate,
   12 In. . . . . . . . .20.00 to 40.00
Creamer  . . . . . . . . . . . . .9.00
Eggcup  . . . . . . . . . . . . .18.00
Pitcher, 2 Pt. . . . . . . . . . .36.00
Plate, Luncheon, 9 1/2 In. . .5.00
Plate, Sherbet, 6 In.  . . . . . .9.00
Saucer . . . . . . . . . . . . . . .4.00
Sugar & Creamer  . . . . . . .8.00
Tumbler, 5 1/2 In. . . . . . . .20.00

## GOLDEN HARVEST

Golden Harvest was made by Stangl Pottery from 1953 to 1973. The pattern pictured yellow flowers on a gray background.

Chop Plate, 14 1/2 In. . . . .25.00
Cup . . . . . . . . . . . . . . . . .4.00
Cup & Saucer  . . .6.00 to 12.00
Plate, 14 1/2 In.  . . . . . . . .35.00
Shaker  . . . . . . . . . . . . . . .4.00

**The best defense against a burglary is a nosy neighbor.**

## GRASS

Grass is a pattern designed by Russel Wright for E. M. Knowles from 1957 to 1962. The gray dinnerware has a few abstract lines of gold and dark gray strewn across the pieces. It is one of the few pieces by Wright that is not just a solid color.

**BOWL**

Salad, 5 In. . . . . .10.00 to 15.00
Vegetable, 8 In. . . . . . . . .17.00
Plate, 6 In. . . . . . . . . . . . .6.00

## HACIENDA

A Mexican-inspired pattern, Hacienda was made by Homer Laughlin China Company, Newell, West Virginia, in 1938. The dinnerware was made on the Century shape. A decal showed a bench, cactus, and a portion of the side of a Mexican home. Most pieces have red trim at the handles and at the edge of the plate. After 1936, Franciscan Ceramics also made a dinnerware pattern called Hacienda, but only Hacienda by Homer Laughlin is listed here.

Bowl, Oval, Red Trim,
9 In. . . . . . . . . . . . . . . .15.00
Bowl, Square, Red Trim . .15.00
Cup & Saucer . . . . . . . . .24.00
Nappy . . . . . . . . . . . . . .40.00
Platter, Red Trim . . . . . . .15.00

## HALL TEAPOT

Teapots of all sizes and shapes were made by the Hall China Company of East Liverpool, Ohio, starting in the 1920s. Each pot had a special design name such as Airflow or Boston. Each shape could be made in one of several colors, often with names like Cadet (light blue), Camellia (rose), Canary (yellow), Dresden (deep blue), Delphinium (medium purple-blue), Green Lustre (dark green), Indian Red (orange), Mahogany (dark brown), and Marine (dark purple-blue). An infuser is an optional piece that was usually sold separately. It held the tea leaves while the water was poured through them. Coffeepots were also made by Hall. Reproduction teapots have been made since 1992. These, unlike the originals, are marked "Limited Edition."

**AIRFLOW**
Canary, Gold, 6 Cup . . . . .55.00
Chinese Red, 8 Cup . . . .120.00
Cobalt . . . . . . . . . . . . . .50.00
Cobalt, Gold . . .95.00 to 100.00
Emerald . . . . . . . . . . . . .55.00
Indian Red . . . . . . . . . .200.00
Turquoise, Gold . . . . . . .95.00
Warm Yellow, Gold,
8 Cup . . . . . . . . . . . . .55.00

**ALADDIN**
Black, Gold, 6 Cup . . . . .60.00
Canary, Gold . . .35.00 to 45.00
Canary, Gold, Infuser . . . .58.00
Cobalt, Gold . . . . . . . . . .45.00
Cobalt, Gold, Oval
Infuser . . . . . . . . . . . .120.00
Cobalt, Oval Infuser . . . . .85.00
Emerald . . . . . . . . . . . .145.00
Maroon . . . . . . . . . . . . .18.00
Maroon, Gold . . . . . . . . .75.00
Pink, Infuser . . . . . . . . . .45.00

**ALBANY**
Emerald, Gold . . . . . . . . .35.00

**AUTOMOBILE**
Canary . . . . . . . . . . . . .675.00
Emerald, Platinum . . . . .575.00
Turquoise, 6 Cup . . . . . .600.00

**BALTIMORE**
Warm Yellow . . . . . . . . .50.00

**BASKET**
Cadet . . . . . . . . . . . . . .375.00
Canary, 6 Cup . . . . . . . .185.00
Emerald, 6 Cup . . . . . . .200.00

**BASKETBALL**
Black . . . . . . . . . . . . . .550.00
Chinese Red . . . . . . . . .950.00
Warm Yellow . . . . . . . .775.00

**BIRD CAGE**
Maroon, Gold . . . . . . . .650.00

## BOSTON
Canary . . . . . . . . . . . . . .55.00
Emerald, Gold, 2 Cup . . . .40.00
Mahogany, With Trivet  . .60.00
Pink, 2 Cup  . . . . . . . . . .40.00

## CLEVELAND
Emerald . . . . . . . . . . . . .65.00

## CUBE
Stock Brown, 1 Cup . . . .60.00
Turquoise, 1 Cup . . . . .125.00
Turquoise, 2 Cup . . . . .140.00
Warm Yellow, 1 Cup  . . .250.00

## DONUT
Maroon  . . . . . . . . . . . .425.00
Warm Yellow, Gold . . . .475.00

## FOOTBALL
Maroon  . . . .500.00 to 625.00

## FRENCH
Canary, Gold  . . . . . . . . .70.00
Ivory, Gold . . . . . . . . . . . .4.00
Rose  . . . . . . . . . . . . . . .40.00
Rose, Gold  . . . . . . . . . . .40.00

## GLOBE
Cadet, Dripless . . . . . . . .45.00
Canary  . . . . . . . . . . . . . .80.00
Emerald, 6 Cup . .90.00 to 95.00

## HOLLYWOOD
Emerald, 8 Cup  . .40.00 to 55.00
Green Lustre, 6 Cup . . . . .40.00
Ivory, Gold, 6 Cup . . . . .45.00
Maroon  . . . . . . . . . . . . .45.00
Maroon, Gold Trim  . . . .45.00

## HOOK COVER
Cadet, Gold . . . .48.00 to 55.00
Dresden, Gold  . . . . . . . .35.00
Red  . . . . . . . . . . . . . . .135.00
Silver . . . . . . . . . . . . . .250.00

—❖—

**If you discover a cache of very dirty antiques and you are not dressed in work clothes, make a temporary cover-up from a plastic garbage bag.**

—❖—

Turquoise, 6 Cup  . . . . . .40.00
Warm Yellow, Gold . . . .55.00

## KANSAS
Emerald, Gold  . . . . . . .375.00

## LOS ANGELES
Cobalt, Gold . . . . . . . . . .65.00

## MCCORMICK
Emerald, Infuser . . . . . . . .80.00
Maroon, Infuser  . . . . . . .80.00
Turquoise, 2 Cup  . . . . .110.00

## MELODY
Chinese Red  . . . . . . . .325.00
Ivory, 6 Cup . . . . . . . . .350.00
Turquoise, Gold  . . . . . .250.00
Warm Yellow, Gold,
   6 Cup  . . . . . . . . . . . .350.00

## MODERNE
Chinese Red, 6 Cup  . . .695.00

## NAUTILUS
Canary, Gold Trim . . . . .135.00
Emerald  . . . . . . . . . . . .280.00
Emerald, Gold Trim . . . .225.00
Warm Yellow, Gold . . . .280.00

## NEW YORK
Marine  . . . . . . . . . . . . .25.00
Red Poppy  . . . . . . . . . . .85.00
Turquoise, Gold Trim,
   6 Cup  . . . . . . . . . . . . .25.00

## OHIO
Mahogany  . . . . . . . . . .240.00
Warm Yellow, Gold
   Polka Dots . . . . . . . . .425.00

## PARADE
Canary, 6 Cup  . . . . . . . .40.00
Canary, Gold, 6 Cup . . . .50.00
Turquoise  . . . . . . . . . . .35.00

## PHILADELPHIA
Daffodil, Gold  . . . . . . . .75.00
Stock Green, Gold,
   6 Cup . . . . . . .60.00 to 75.00

## RONALD REAGAN
White  . . . . . . . . . . . . .120.00

## SAF-HANDLE
Canary  . . . . . . .70.00 to 75.00
Chinese Red  . . . . . . . .350.00

## STAR
Cobalt, Gold . . . . . . . . . .90.00
Delphinium, 6 Cup . . . . .75.00
Emerald, Gold  . . . . . . . .60.00

Maroon, 6 Cup . . . . . . . .35.00
Turquoise, Gold  . . . . . . .50.00

## STREAMLINE
Chinese Red  . .135.00 to 190.00
Delphinium, Gold . . . . . .70.00
Emerald  . . . . . .70.00 to 75.00

## T-BALL
Maroon, Square  . . . . . . .85.00

## TWINSPOUT
Canary, Gold  . . . . . . . . .95.00
Cobalt, Ribbed  . . . . . . .115.00
Emerald  . . . . . . . . . . . . .80.00
Ivory  . . . . . . . . . . . . . . .80.00
Warm Yellow, Gold . . . .125.00

## WINDSHIELD
Camellia, Gold  . . . . . . . .40.00
Ivory, Gold Dot  .80.00 to 85.00
Maroon, Gold Dot  . . . . .85.00
Turquoise, 6 Cup  . . . . . .55.00
White, Gold Dot . . . . . . .75.00

# HARLEQUIN

Harlequin, a solid-color dinner-ware made by Homer Laughlin China Company of Newell, West Virginia, was less expensive than Fiesta. It was made from 1938 to 1964 and sold unmarked in Woolworth stores. The rings molded into the plate were at the edge of the plate well, and the rim was plain. Dishes were made in Chartreuse, Forest Green, Gray, Green (light green), Deep Maroon (sometimes called red), Mauve (blue), Rose, Spruce Green (dark green), Tangerine (red), Turquoise, and Yellow.

## CHARTREUSE
Bowl, 10 1/2 In. . . . . . . . .45.00
Casserole, Cover . . . . . .240.00

Plate, Deep, 8 In. . . . . . . .20.00
Salad, Individual . . . . . . .25.00
Sugar . . . . . . . . . . . . . . .9.50
Teapot . . . . . . .75.00 to 165.00

### FOREST GREEN
Bowl, Deep, 5 1/2 In. . . . .25.00
Bowl, Fruit, 10 1/2 In. . . .45.00
Bowl, Oatmeal, 36s . . . . .20.00
Creamer, Individual . . . .125.00
Cup . . . . . . . . . . . . . . . .14.00
Cup & Saucer . . . . . . . .13.00
Cup & Saucer,
   After Dinner . . . . . . . .80.00
Nut Dish . . . . . . . . . . . .125.00
Pitcher . . . . . . . . . . . . . .75.00
Plate, Deep, 8 In. . . . . . .25.00
Sauceboat . . . . . .28.00 to 35.00
Saucer . . . . . . . . . . . . . . .4.00
Soup, Cream . . . . . . . . . .40.00
Sugar & Creamer . . . . . .90.00
Teapot . . . . . . . . . . . . .125.00
Tumbler, Antique Car . . . .45.00

### GRAY
Creamer, Novelty . . . . . . .95.00
Cup . . . . . . . . . . . . . . . .10.00
Eggcup, Double . . . . . . .24.50
Pitcher, Water . . . . . . . .125.00
Plate, Deep, 8 In. . . . . . .38.00
Plate, Dessert,
   6 In. . . . . . . . . .3.50 to 4.00
Plate, Dinner, 10 In. . . . .45.00
Plate, Luncheon, 9 In. . . .15.00
Sauceboat . . . . . . . . . . .45.00
Sugar, Cover . . . . . . . . . .45.00
Teapot . . . . . . . . . . . . .185.00

### GREEN
Bowl, Oatmeal . . . . . . . .15.00
Creamer . . . . . . . . . . . . .15.00
Cup . . . . . . . . . . . . . . . .15.00
Cup & Saucer . . . . . . . .24.00
Plate, Bread & Butter,
   7 In . . . . . . . . . . . . . . .18.00
Plate, Deep, 8 In. . . . . . .95.00
Plate, Dinner, 10 In. . . . .35.00
Plate, Luncheon, 9 In. . . .20.00
Salad, Individual . . . . . .175.00
Saucer . . . . . . . . . . . . . .16.00

### MAROON
Candleholder, Pair . . . . .595.00
Casserole . . . . . . . . . . .130.00

---

❖

**When stacking
dinner plates, put a
piece of felt or paper
between each plate.
Never put more than
24 in one stack.**

❖

---

Casserole, Cover . . . . . .215.00
Eggcup, Double . . . . . . .38.00
Nut Cup . . . . . . . . . . . . .22.00
Plate, Deep, 8 In. . . . . . .35.00
Plate, Dinner, 10 In. . . . .55.00
Salad, Individual . . . . . . .50.00
Sugar, Cover . . . . . . . . . .45.00
Sugar & Creamer . . . . . .110.00
Tumbler . . . . . . . . . . . . .40.00

### MAUVE
Bowl, 10 1/2 In. . . . . . . .24.00
Creamer, High
   Lip . . . . . . 275.00 to 375.00
Creamer, Individual . . . .23.00
Creamer, Novelty . . . . . .45.00
Cup & Saucer . . . . . . . .10.00
Cup & Saucer, After
   Dinner . . . . . . . . . . . .150.00
Eggcup, Double . . . . . . .25.00
Nut Cup . . . . . . . . . . . . .16.00
Pitcher, Water . . . . . . . . .45.00
Pitcher, Water,
   Ball . . . . . . .70.00 to 75.00
Pitcher, Water, With
   Decal . . . . . . . . . . . . . .95.00
Plate, Dessert, 6 In. . . . . .4.00
Platter, 11 In. . . . . . . . . .12.00
Sauceboat . . . . . . . . . . .35.00
Sugar, Cover . . . . . . . . . .25.00
Sugar & Creamer, After
   Dinner . . . . . . . . . . . .150.00
Teapot . . . . . .95.00 to 120.00
Tumbler . . . . . . . . . . . . .50.00

### ROSE
Bowl, Deep,
   8 In. . . . . . . . .30.00 to 35.00
Bowl, Fruit, 5 1/2 In. . . . .7.00
Bowl, Individual,
   7 1/4 In. . . . . . . . . . . . .27.00

Bowl, Oatmeal, 36s . . . .18.00
Candleholder, Pair . . . .600.00
Casserole . . . . . . . . . . .110.00
Cup . . . . . . . . . . .6.50 to 9.00
Cup & Saucer . .10.00 to 13.00
Cup & Saucer, After
   Dinner . . . . .80.00 to 115.00
Eggcup,
   Double . . . . . .24.50 to 45.00
Nut Dish . . . . . . . . . . . .125.00
Pitcher, Water,
   Ball . . . . . . . .46.00 to 95.00
Plate, Bread & Butter,
   7 In. . . . . . . . . . . . . . . .3.00
Plate, Dessert, 6 In. . . . . . .6.00
Plate, Dinner, 10 In. . . . .11.00
Plate, Luncheon,
   9 In. . . . . . . . .10.00 to 20.00
Plate, Salad, 7 In. . . . . . . .5.00
Platter, Oval, 13 In. . . . .13.00
Salt & Pepper . . . . . . . .15.00
Sauceboat . . . . . . . . . . .19.00
Saucer . . . . . . . . . . . . . . .6.00
Soup, Cream . . . . . . . . . .22.00
Sugar, Cover . . . . . . . . . .30.00
Sugar & Creamer,
   After Dinner . . . . . . . .115.00
Teapot . . . . . . .65.00 to 75.00

### SPRUCE GREEN
Casserole, Cover . . . . . .215.00
Creamer, Individual . . . .25.00
Cup, After Dinner . . . . . .95.00
Cup & Saucer, After
   Dinner . . . . . . . . . . . .195.00
Eggcup, Double . . . . . . .25.00
Nut Cup . . . . . . . . . . . . .22.00
Pitcher, Ball . . . . . . . . . .95.00

### TANGERINE
Ashtray . . . . . .85.00 to 90.00
Creamer, Individual . . . . .16.50
Cup . . . . . . . . . . . . . . . . .7.50
Cup & Saucer . . . . . . . . .9.50
Cup & Saucer, After
   Dinner . . . . .80.00 to 130.00
Eggcup . . . . . . . . . . . . . .20.00
Marmalade . . . . . . . . . .190.00
Pitcher, Water . . . . . . . . .70.00
Sugar & Creamer, After
   Dinner . . . . . . . . . . . .130.00
Teapot . . . . . . . . . . . . .125.00

### TURQUOISE

Bowl, 6 In. . . . . . . . . . . . .15.00
Bowl, Cereal, 5 1/2 In. . . . .7.00
Bowl, Vegetable, Round,
  8 1/2 In. . . . . . . . . . . . .18.00
Creamer . . . . . . .10.00 to 18.00
Cup & Saucer . . .7.50 to 10.00
Eggcup . . . . . . . . . . . . . .20.00
Eggcup, Double . . . . . . . .15.00
Jug, 22 Oz. . . . . . . . . . . . .25.00
Marmalade . . . . . . . . . .170.00
Nappy, 9 In. . . . . . . . . . . .18.50
Plate, Bread & Butter,
  7 In. . . . . . . . . . . . . . . . .6.00
Plate, Deep, 8 In. . . . . . . .24.00
Plate, Dessert,
  6 In. . . . . . . . . . . .3.50 to 6.00
Plate, Dinner, 10 In. . . . . .10.00
Plate, Luncheon, 9 In. . . . .12.00
Platter, 10 In. . . . . . . . . . .10.00
Platter, 13 In. . . . . . . . . . .15.00
Salad,
  Individual . . . . .12.00 to 15.00
Salt & Pepper . . . . . . . . .15.00
Saucer . . . . . . . . . . . . . . .6.00
Soup, Cream . . . . . . . . . .16.00
Spoon Rest . . .225.00 to 265.00
Sugar & Creamer,
  Cover . . . . . . . . . . . . .30.00

### YELLOW

Bowl, Cereal, 5 1/2 In. . . . .4.50
Bowl, Fruit, Footed,
  11 3/4 In. . . . . . . . . . . .155.00
Casserole . . . . . . . . . . . .80.00
Cup . . . . . . . . . .7.50 to 11.00
Cup & Saucer . . . .7.00 to 9.50
Cup & Saucer, After
  Dinner . . . . . . . . . . . . .60.00
Eggcup . . . . . . . . . . . . . .20.00
Eggcup, Double .15.00 to 20.00
Jug, 22 Oz. . . . . . . . . . . . .38.00
Marmalade . . . . . . . . . .160.00
Nappy, 9 In. . . . . . . . . . . .18.50
Pitcher, Ball . . . .48.00 to 75.00
Plate, Deep, 8 In. . . . . . . .20.00
Plate, Dessert,
  6 In. . . . . . . . . . . .3.50 to 4.00
Plate, Dinner, 10 In. . . . . .10.00
Plate, Luncheon, 9 In. . . . . .7.00
Saltshaker . . . . . . . . . . . .6.00
Sauceboat . . . . . . . . . . . .25.00

Sugar . . . . . . . . . . . . . . .30.00
Sugar, Cover, 100th
  Anniversary . . . . . . . . . .34.00
Sugar & Creamer . . . . . . . .3.00
Syrup, Cover . . . . . . . . .185.00

**HAWAIIAN DAISY,** see Daisy

## HAWAIIAN FLOWERS

Hawaiian Flowers was a well-known Vernon Kilns, Vernon, California, tableware designed by Don Blanding. It was first made in 1939.

### BLUE
Chop Plate, 14 In. . . . . . .110.00
Salt & Pepper . . . . . . . .45.00

### MAROON
Chop Plate,
  12 In. . . . . . .135.00 to 145.00
Chop Plate, 14 In. . . . . . .95.00
Salt & Pepper . . . . . . . .35.00

**HOLLAND,** see Crocus

## HOMESPUN

Homespun, a yellow, green, and reddish brown plaid pattern, was made by Vernon Kilns, Vernon, California. Other related plaids are Calico (pink and blue), Coronation Organdy (gray and rose), Gingham (green and yellow), Organdie (brown and yellow), Tam O'Shanter (rust, chartreuse, and dark green), and Tweed (yellow and gray-blue).

Bowl, Vegetable,
  9 In. . . . . . . . . .8.00 to 14.00
Bowl, Vegetable,
  Divided . . . . . . . . . . . . .20.00
Carafe . . . . . . .37.50 to 42.50
Chop Plate,
  12 In. . . . . . . . .20.00 to 30.00
Coaster . . . . . . . . . . . . .30.00
Creamer, Cover . . . . . . . .17.00
Cup & Saucer . . . .5.00 to 6.00
Flowerpot, Small . . . . . . .35.00
Gravy Boat . . . . . . . . . . .16.00
Jug, Small . . . . . . . . . . . .25.00
Mixing Bowl, 5 In. . . . . . .25.00
Mixing Bowl, 8 In. . . . . . .35.00
Pitcher, 2 Qt. . . . . . . . . . .35.00
Plate, Bread & Butter . . . . .1.25
Plate, Dessert,
  6 In. . . . . . . . . . . .1.25 to 4.00
Plate, Dinner,
  9 1/2 In. . . . . . . . .5.00 to 9.00
Platter,
  12 1/2 In. . . . . . .9.00 to 10.00

Salt & Pepper .........8.00
Salt & Pepper,
Small ......10.00 to 15.00
Saucer .........3.00 to 5.00
Soup, Dish, Rim .......10.00
Sugar & Creamer ......20.00
Tidbit, Metal Handle,
3 Tiers .............26.00
Tumbler,
5 1/2 In. ......15.00 to 18.00
Water Set, 2 Qt. Pitcher,
6 Tumblers, 14 Oz.,
5 In. ..............150.00

## HOMESTEAD PROVINCIAL

Homestead Provincial is one of the Poppytrail patterns by Metlox Potteries. The designs are based on Early American folk art themes. Homestead Provincial is dark green and burgundy. The same design was made by the factory in other colors. Colonial Homestead is red and brown, and Provincial Blue is blue.

Bowl, 6 In. ...........10.00
Box, Cigarette ........65.00
Bread Tray ..........38.00
Butter ..............60.00
Canister Set, Cover,
4 Piece ............295.00
Casserole, Cover .......75.00
Coffeepot ...........65.00
Creamer ............20.00
Cup & Saucer ..10.00 to 12.00
Gravy Boat ..........45.00
Mug, Beer ...........15.00
Mug, Cover, Spout .....95.00
Plate, Bread & Butter,
6 3/8 In. ........4.00 to 7.00
Plate, Dinner, 10 In. .....12.00

Plate, Salad,
7 1/2 In. ........8.00 to 9.00
Platter, 14 In. .........50.00
Platter, 22 1/2 In. ......140.00
Salt & Pepper ...20.00 to 30.00
Snack Plate, Cup ......85.00
Soup, Dish ...........18.00
Sugar, Cover ..........28.00
Sugar & Creamer ......30.00
Sugar & Creamer,
Cover .......42.00 to 65.00
Teapot .............115.00

**HOUSE,** see listings under Petit Point

## IROQUOIS

Russel Wright was an important industrial designer. His dinnerwares were made by at least four companies. Iroquois Casual China was a Russel Wright modern design made by Iroquois China Company, Syracuse, New York. The dinnerware was less expensive than American Modern, heavier and less breakable. It was advertised as cook-and-serve. The first pieces were marked China by Iroquois with the signature of Russel Wright. In the 1950s the ware was redesigned and the mark was changed to Iroquois Casual China by Russel Wright. The dishes were made in a number of colors, designed to be mixed and matched. Sets were often sold with pieces in several colors. The original Iroquois was glazed Avocado Yellow, Ice Blue, Lemon Yellow, Nutmeg Brown, Parsley (green), or Sugar White. In 1951 more colors were added, including Aqua, Brick Red, Cantaloupe, Charcoal, Lettuce Green, Oyster (gray), Pink Sherbet, and Ripe Apricot. In 1959 some

Iroquois pieces were decorated with patterns and sold under other names. Glass tumblers were made in matching colors.

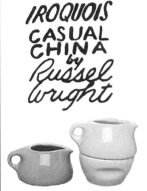

### AVOCADO YELLOW
Bowl, Vegetable,
8 In. .........22.00 to 35.00
Bowl, Vegetable,
Divided, 10 In. .......40.00
Butter ..............25.00
Carafe .....125.00 to 140.00
Gravy Boat, Fast Stand ...75.00
Sugar & Creamer,
Stacking .....25.00 to 50.00

### CANTALOUPE
Bowl, Fruit, Redesigned ..24.00
Bowl, Salad, 5 In. .......15.00
Cup & Saucer .........25.00
Plate, Dinner, 10 In. .....35.00
Plate, Salad, 7 1/2 In. ....12.00
Sugar, Cover,
Redesigned ..........50.00

### CHARCOAL
Casserole, Cover, 4 Qt.,
8 In. ...............145.00
Casserole, Divided,
10 In. ..............40.00
Cup .................8.00
Plate, Dinner, 10 In. ......8.00
Sugar & Creamer ......10.00

### ICE BLUE
Bowl, Cover, 5 In. ......15.00
Bowl, Gumbo ..........25.00
Bowl, Salad, 5 In. ........6.00
Bowl, Vegetable,
8 In. .........12.00 to 15.00

Bowl, Vegetable,
Divided, 10 In. . . . . . .20.00
Butter . . . . . . . . . . . . .95.00
Carafe . . . . . . . . . . . .110.00
Casserole, Cover, 8 In. . . .45.00
Casserole, Divided,
Round . . . . . . . . . . . . .20.00
Coffeepot, After
Dinner . . . . .75.00 to 135.00
Creamer . . . . . . . . . . . .11.00
Cup & Saucer . . . . . . . .10.00
Mug . . . . . . . . . . . . . .60.00
Plate, Bread & Butter,
6 In. . . . . . . . . . .3.00 to 4.00
Plate, Dinner, 10 In. . . . .45.00
Plate, Luncheon, 9 In. . . . .8.00
Plate, Salad,
7 1/2 In. . . . . . . .5.00 to 6.00
Platter, 12 1/2 In. . . . . . .15.00
Platter, Oval,
14 1/2 In. . . . .20.00 to 30.00
Salt & Pepper . . . . . . . .20.00
Soup, Dish, Cover,
18 Oz. . . . . . . . . . . . . .15.00
Sugar & Creamer . . . . . .25.00
Sugar & Creamer,
Stacking . . . . . . . . . . .20.00

### LEMON YELLOW
Ashtray . . . . . . . . . . . . .95.00
Bowl, Vegetable, 10 In. . .35.00
Butter . . . . . . . . . . . . .70.00
Teapot . . . . . . . . . . . . .125.00

### LETTUCE GREEN
Bowl, Vegetable, Cover,
Divided, 10 In. . . . . . .40.00
Carafe . . . . . . . . . . . . .90.00
Casserole, Cover, 6 Qt. . . .95.00
Cup . . . . . . . . . . . . . . . .3.00
Plate, Dinner, 10 In. . . . . .8.00
Plate, Salad, 7 1/2 In. . . . .4.00
Platter, 12 3/4 In. . . . . . .15.00
Sugar, Stacking . . . . . . . .20.00

### NUTMEG BROWN
Bowl, Vegetable, Divided,
10 In. . . . . . . . . . . . . .20.00
Bowl, Vegetable, Open,
10 In. . . . . . . . . . . . . .18.00
Carafe . . . . . . . . . . . . .125.00
Mug . . . . . . . . . . . . . .60.00
Plate, Salad, 7 1/2 In. . . . .8.00
Soup, Dish, 11 1/2 Oz. . . .20.00

### OYSTER
Bowl, Salad, 5 In. . . . . . . .8.00
Casserole, 10 In. . . . . . . .40.00
Cup . . . . . . . . . . . . . . . .6.00
Cup & Saucer . . . . . . . .12.00
Plate, Dinner, 10 In. . . . . .10.00
Platter, Oval, 14 1/2 In. . .45.00

### PARSLEY
Bowl, Vegetable, Open,
8 In. . . . . . . . . . . . . . .22.00
Casserole, Avocado
Yellow Cover, 2 Qt. . . .40.00
Coffeepot, After Dinner . .30.00
Creamer . . . . . . . . . . . .12.00

### PINK SHERBET
Bowl, Salad, 5 In. . . . . . . .6.00
Bowl, Vegetable,
8 In. . . . . . . . . .20.00 to 32.00
Bowl, Vegetable, Cover,
Divided . . . . . . . . . . . .40.00
Carafe . . . . .125.00 to 170.00
Casserole, 4 Qt. . . . . . . .90.00
Casserole, Cover, 2 Qt. . . .20.00
Casserole, Cover,
Redesigned, 2 Qt. . . . . .60.00
Cup & Saucer . . . . . . . .10.00
Mug . . . . . . . . . . . . . .65.00
Plate, TV . . . . . . . . . . . .48.00
Platter, 12 1/2 In. . . . . . .15.00
Saucepan,
Cover . . . . .175.00 to 195.00
Saucer, After Dinner . . . .30.00

### RIPE APRICOT
Bowl, Salad, 5 In. . . . . . . .8.00
Bowl, Vegetable, Divided,
10 In. . . . . . . . . . . . . .20.00
Bowl, Vegetable, Divided,
Cover, 10 In. . . . . . . . .40.00
Bowl, Vegetable, Open,
8 In. . . . . . . . . . . . . . .22.00
Butter . . . . . . . . . . . . .80.00
Casserole, 4 Qt. . . . . . . .85.00
Casserole, Cover,
Round . . . . . . . . . . . . .40.00
Creamer, Redesigned . . . .15.00
Pitcher, 5 1/4 In. . . . . . . .45.00
Plate, Bread & Butter,
6 In. . . . . . . . . . . . . . . .3.00
Plate, Dinner, 10 In. . . . . .9.00

### SUGAR WHITE
Bread & Butter, 6 In. . . . .4.00
Butter . . . . . . . . . . . . .125.00

Casserole, Cover, 4 Qt.,
8 In. . . . . . . . . . . . . . .145.00
Cup & Saucer . . . . . . . .12.00
Fry Pan, Cover . . . . . . .175.00
Pitcher, Cover . . . . . . . .145.00
Plate, Dinner,
10 In. . . . . . . . .9.00 to 15.00

## IVY

Ivy is a hand-painted pattern
made by Franciscan Ceramics
from 1948. Harker Pottery
Company and Paden City Pottery also made patterns called
Ivy, but only Franciscan Ivy is
listed here.

Ashtray . . . . . . . . . . . . .20.00
Bowl, 7 1/2 In. . .25.00 to 50.00
Bowl, Cereal, 6 In. . . . . .18.00
Bowl, Fruit,
5 1/4 In. . . . . . .15.00 to 18.00
Bowl, Salad, Footed,
11 In. . . . . . . . . . . . . .150.00
Bowl, Vegetable,
7 1/4 In. . . . . . . . . . . . .50.00
Bowl, Vegetable,
8 1/4 In. . . . . . . . . . . . .60.00
Bowl, Vegetable, Divided,
12 In. . . . . . . . .55.00 to 60.00
Butter, Cover . . . . . . . . .85.00
Casserole, Cover,
Handles . . . . . . . . . . .145.00
Chop Plate,
12 In. . . . . . .95.00 to 100.00
Creamer . . . . . .25.00 to 35.00
Cup & Saucer . .20.00 to 34.00
Gravy Boat, Attached
Liner . . . . . . . .75.00 to 85.00
Jar, Range, Cover . . . . . .45.00
Mixing Bowl . . . . . . . . .40.00
Pickle, Oval,
10 1/2 In. . . . . .30.00 to 65.00

Plate, Bread & Butter,
6 In. . . . . . . . . . .7.00 to 12.00
Plate, Dinner,
10 In. . . . . . . .25.00 to 27.00
Plate, Luncheon, 8 In. . . . .20.00
Platter, 11 1/2 In. . . . . . .75.00
Platter,
13 3/4 In. . . . .85.00 to 100.00
Relish, 11 In. . . . . . . . . .55.00
Salt & Pepper . . . . . . . .25.00
Saucer . . . . . . . . . . . . . . .4.00
Saucer, Jumbo . . . . . . . .10.00
Sherbet . . . . . . . . . . . . .28.00
Soup, Dish, Flat . . . . . . .30.00
Soup Dish, Footed,
5 1/2 In. . . . . . . . . . . . .18.00
Sugar & Creamer,
Cover . . . . . . .45.00 to 70.00
Tray, TV . . . . . . . . . . . .145.00
Tumbler, Water . .30.00 to 40.00

## ·L·

## LEI LANI

Lei Lani was made by Vernon Kilns from 1938 to 1942 and again from 1947 to 1955. The pattern was a maroon printed lotus flower.

Chop Plate,
14 In. . . . . . .175.00 to 195.00
Chop Plate, 17 In. . . . . .275.00
Creamer, Short . . . . . . . .35.00
Cup . . . . . . . . . . . . . . . .18.00
Cup & Saucer . . . . . . . .32.00
Plate, Breakfast,
9 1/2 In. . . . . . . . . . . . .40.00
Plate, Dinner,
10 1/4 In. . . . .55.00 to 65.00
Plate, Salad, 7 In. . . . . . .30.00
Platter, 12 In. . . . . . . . .125.00

## LIBERTY BLUE

A & P grocery commissioned the Liberty Blue dishes to tie in with the 1776-1976 bicentennial celebration of America's independence. They were made by Enoch Wedgwood in the Staffordshire district of England, in the tradition of the 19th-century Staffordshire historical blue china. They have a floral wreath border and central transfer designs of scenes from American history. The dishes were sold beginning in April 1977. There was a different center design on each plate.

Bowl, Cereal,
6 1/2 In. . . . . . .7.00 to 11.00
Bowl, Fruit, 5 In. . .5.00 to 5.50
Bowl, Vegetable,
Oval . . . . . . . .30.00 to 45.00
Butter, Cover . . . . . . . . .25.00
Casserole, Cover . . . . . . .75.00
Coaster . . . . . . . . . . . . . .8.00
Creamer . . . . . . . . . . . . .15.00
Cup & Saucer . . . .5.00 to 6.50
Gravy Boat, Underplate . .45.00
Mug . . . . . . . . . .10.00 to 15.00

Pitcher, Milk, 7 1/2 In. . .115.00
Plate, Bread & Butter,
6 In. . . . . . . . . . .2.00 to 3.50
Plate, Dinner,
10 In. . . . . . . . . .5.50 to 8.00
Plate, Luncheon,
8 1/2 In. . . . . . .11.00 to 15.00
Plate, Salad,
7 1/2 In. . . . . . . .6.00 to 9.00
Platter, 12 In. . . . . . . . . .30.00
Platter, 14 In. . . .45.00 to 65.00
Salt & Pepper . . .25.00 to 28.00
Saucer . . . . . . . . . . . . . .2.00
Soup, Dish . . . . . . . . . . .12.00
Sugar & Creamer,
Cover . . . . . . . .35.00 to 45.00
Teapot . . . . . . . . . . . . . .85.00
Tureen, Soup,
Cover . . . . .385.00 to 595.00

**LITTLE RED RIDING HOOD,** see Red Riding Hood

## LU-RAY

The characteristic slightly speckled glaze of the solid-colored Lu-Ray makes it easy to identify. Taylor, Smith, and Taylor of Chester, West Virginia, made this pattern after 1938. Pastel colors include Chatham Gray, Persian Cream, Sharon Pink, Surf Green, and Windsor Blue.

**CHATHAM GRAY**
Soup, Dish, Tab Handle . .65.00
Teapot . . . . . . . . . . . . .145.00

### PERSIAN CREAM

Bowl, 36s . . . . . . . . . . . .60.00
Bowl, 5 In. . . . . . .4.00 to 6.50
Bowl, 9 In. . . . . . . . . . . .15.00
Butter, Cover, 1/4 Lb. . . . .35.00
Cake Plate . . . . . . . . . . .110.00
Creamer . . . . . . . . . . . . .6.00
Creamer, After Dinner . . .50.00
Cup & Saucer . . . .5.00 to 8.50
Eggcup . . . . . . . .13.00 to 25.00
Grill Plate . . . . . . . . . . . .30.00
Nut Dish . . . . . . . . . . .125.00
Pitcher . . . . . . . . . . . . .135.00
Plate, Bread & Butter,
   6 In. . . . . . . . . . . . . . . .1.00
Plate, Breakfast, 9 In. . . . . .7.50
Plate, Luncheon, 8 In. . . . .20.00
Soup, Cream,
   Underplate . . . . . . . . . .110.00
Soup, Dish . . . . . . . . . . .11.00
Tumbler, Juice . . . . . . . . .70.00

### SHARON PINK

Bowl, 5 In. . . . . . .3.00 to 4.00
Bowl, 9 In. . . . . . . . . . . .12.00
Bowl, Vegetable . . . . . . .20.00
Cake Plate . . . . . . . . . . .110.00
Casserole, Cover . . . . . .140.00
Chop Plate . . . . . . . . . . .30.00
Coffeepot, After
   Dinner . . . . . . . . . . . . .135.00
Creamer . . . . . . . . . . . . .6.00
Creamer, After Dinner . . .50.00
Cup & Saucer . . . .5.00 to 8.50
Eggcup . . . . . . . . . . . . .13.00
Epergne . . . . . . . . . . . .145.00
Nappy . . . . . . . . . . . . .11.00
Nut Dish . . . . . . . . . . .125.00
Pitcher . . . . . . . . . . . . .135.00
Plate, 11 1/2 In. . . . . . . .12.00
Plate, 13 In. . . . . . . . . . .14.00

---

❖

**Cups are best stored by hanging them on cup hooks. Stacking cups inside one another can cause chipping.**

❖

---

Plate, Bread & Butter,
   6 In. . . . . . . . . . . .1.00 to 4.00
Plate, Breakfast,
   9 In. . . . . . . . . .7.50 to 18.00
Plate, Dinner,
   10 In. . . . . . . . .18.50 to 20.00
Plate, Luncheon,
   8 1/2 In. . . . . . .20.00 to 22.00
Plate, Salad, 7 1/4 In. . . . . .6.00
Platter, Oval, 14 In. . . . . .15.00
Soup, Cream . . . . . . . . . .80.00
Soup, Dish . . . . .11.00 to 14.00
Teapot, Flat Spout . . . . . .80.00
Tumbler, Juice . . .40.00 to 70.00

### SURF GREEN

Bowl . . . . . . . . . . . . . . .60.00
Cake Plate, Round,
   11 In. . . . . . . . . . . . . . .45.00
Casserole, Cover . . . . . .140.00
Chop Plate, 15 In. . . . . . .25.00
Creamer . . . . . . . .5.00 to 6.00
Cup, After Dinner . . . . . .25.00
Cup & Saucer . . . . . . . . .5.00
Cup & Saucer, After
   Dinner . . . . . . . . . . . . .45.00
Eggcup . . . . . . .13.00 to 45.00
Grill Plate . . . . . . . . . . . .30.00
Nut Dish . . . . . . . . . . .125.00
Pitcher, Footed . . . . . . .135.00
Plate, Bread & Butter,
   6 In. . . . . . . . . . .1.00 to 6.00
Plate, Luncheon,
   9 In. . . . . . . . . .7.50 to 18.00
Platter, 13 1/2 In. . . . . . . .15.00
Relish, 4 Sections . . . . .110.00
Soup, Dish . . . . . . . . . . .11.00
Tumbler, Juice . . . . . . . .70.00

### WINDSOR BLUE

Bowl, 5 In. . . . . . . . . . . . .4.00
Bowl, Vegetable, Oval,
   10 In. . . . . . . . . . . . . . .18.00
Cake Plate . . . . . . . . . .125.00
Casserole, Cover . . . . . .140.00
Creamer . . . . . . . . . . . . .6.00
Cup . . . . . . . . . . . . . . . .6.00
Cup & Saucer . . . .5.00 to 9.50
Cup & Saucer, After
   Dinner . . . . . . . . . . . . .35.00
Eggcup . . . . . . . . . . . . .13.00
Epergne . . . . . . . . . . . .145.00

Gravy Boat . . . . . . . . . .22.00
Grill Plate . . . . . . . . . . .30.00
Pitcher, Juice . .175.00 to 225.00
Pitcher, Water . . . . . . . . .75.00
Plate, Bread & Butter,
   6 In. . . . . . . . . . .2.50 to 6.00
Plate, Breakfast, 9 In. . . . .7.50
Plate, Luncheon,
   8 1/2 In. . . . . . . . . . . . .22.00
Platter, 11 1/2 In. . . . . . . .11.00
Platter, 13 1/2 In. . . . . . . .15.00
Relish, 4 Sections . . . . . .75.00
Salt & Pepper . . . . . . . .15.00
Soup, Cream,
   Underplate . . . . . . . . .110.00
Soup, Dish . . . . . . . . . . .11.00
Soup, Dish, Tab Handle . .22.00
Teapot . . . . . . . . . . . . . .98.00
Tumbler, Water . . . . . . .95.00
Underplate, For Cream
   Soup . . . . . . . . . . . . . .30.00
Vase, Bud . . . . . . . . . . .130.00

# LUTE SONG

Lute Song is a Red Wing Potteries pattern made in the 1960s. It was decorated with stylized pictures of musical instruments in pastel colors. The dishes were china, not pottery like many Red Wing patterns, and were one of the eight patterns made in 1960.

Bowl, 5 In. . . . . . . . . . . .11.00
Plate, Bread & Butter,
    7 In. . . . . . . . . . . . . . . .9.00
Saucer . . . . . . . . . . . . . . .3.00
Sugar & Creamer . . . . . . .10.00

## MAGNOLIA

A wide, bright, cranberry-red band borders Magnolia pattern by Stangl Pottery, Trenton, New Jersey. The pattern, No. 3870, was made from 1952 to 1962. Another version of Magnolia by Red Wing Potteries does not have the banded edge. It was made in 1947. Both are listed here.

Magnolia Stangl

Magnolia Red Wing

Bowl, Fruit,
    Stangl . . . . . . .9.00 to 12.00
Bowl, Vegetable, Round,
    8 In., Red Wing . . . . . .24.00
Bowl, Vegetable, Round,
    10 In., Red Wing . . . . .28.00

Chop Plate, Stangl,
    14 1/2 In. . . . . . . . . . . .40.00
Cup, Red Wing . . . . . . . . .5.00
Planter, Red Wing,
    No. 1322 . . . . . . . . . . . .40.00
Plate, Bread & Butter,
    Red Wing, 6 In. . . . . . . .6.00
Plate, Dinner, Stangl,
    10 In. . . . . . . . . . . . . . .10.00
Plate, Luncheon, Stangl,
    8 In. . . . . . . . . . . . . . . .12.00
Salt & Pepper,
    Stangl . . . . . .20.00 to 22.50
Saucer, Red Wing . .1.50 to 3.50
Sugar & Creamer, Red
    Wing . . . . . . . . . . . . . . .7.00
Sugar & Creamer,
    Stangl . . . . . . . . . . . . .45.00

## MARDI GRAS

Southern Potteries, Erwin, Tennessee, made Mardi Gras, a hand-painted dinnerware. A large blue daisy and a large pink-petaled flower are surrounded by leaves and buds. The design is placed so that only parts of the flowers are seen on the plate.

Cake Plate, 12 In. . . . . . . .35.00
Creamer . . . . . . . . . . . . . .10.00
Pie Baker . . . . . . . . . . . . .28.00
Platter, 11 1/2 In. . . . . . . .48.00

## MAYAN-AZTEC

Mayan-Aztec pattern made by Frankoma Pottery was introduced in 1948. It was made in Desert Gold, Prairie Green, White Sand, and Woodland Moss and has a Mayan geometric border. The names were simplified, and on the 1994 price list the pattern called Aztec was available in Gold, Green, and White.

**DESERT GOLD**
Creamer . . . . . . . . . . . . . .18.50
Cup . . . . . . . . . . . . . . . . .14.50
Gravy Boat . . . . . . . . . . .38.50
Shaker . . . . . . . . . . . . . . .16.50

**PRAIRIE GREEN**
Bowl, 14 Oz. . . . . . . . . . . .4.00
Mug, 8 Oz. . . . . . . . . . . . .6.00
Plate, Ada Clay, 5 In. . . . . .8.00
Plate, Ada Clay, 9 In. . . . .15.00

**WHITE SAND**
Mug, 14 Oz. . . . . . . . . . . .7.50

**WOODLAND MOSS**
Bowl, Serving, Sapulpa
    Clay . . . . . . . .10.00 to 12.00
Butter, Cover, Sapulpa
    Clay . . . . . . . . . . . . . . .30.00
Cup, Sapulpa Clay, Large . .7.00
Plate, Dinner, Sapulpa
    Clay, 10 In. . . . . . . . . . .40.00
Plate, Salad, Sapulpa
    Clay, 7 In. . . . . . . . . . . .9.00
Platter, Sapulpa Clay,
    13 In. . . . . . . . . . . . . . .12.00
Salt & Pepper, Sapulpa
    Clay . . . . . . . . . . . . . . .12.00
Saucer, Sapulpa Clay . . . . .3.00
Sugar & Creamer, Sapulpa
    Clay . . . . . . . . . . . . . . .24.00

## MAYFLOWER

Mayflower listed here is a pattern by Southern Potteries (Blue Ridge) of Erwin, Tennessee. The pattern was made in the 1950s. Another Mayflower pattern was made by Edwin M. Knowles from 1957 to 1963. May Flower is a pattern by Vernon Kilns.

| | |
|---|---|
| Bowl, 9 In. | .22.00 |
| Bowl, Tab Handle, 6 1/8 In. | .8.00 |
| Chop Plate, 12 In. | .25.00 |
| Cup & Saucer | .15.00 |
| Plate, Breakfast, 9 In. | .12.00 |
| Plate, Salad, 7 1/2 In. | .6.00 |
| Platter, 13 1/2 In. | .20.00 |
| Salt & Pepper | .15.00 |
| Sugar & Creamer, Cover | .25.00 |

## MEADOW ROSE

Meadow Rose was a pattern made by Franciscan Ceramics of Los Angeles, California, in 1977. It is a variation of the Desert Rose pattern. The flowers are colored yellow instead of pink.

| | |
|---|---|
| Bowl, Cereal | .18.00 |
| Bowl, Salad, Side | .45.00 |
| Butter, Cover | .65.00 |
| Goblet | .125.00 to 175.00 |
| Microwave Baker, Rectangular, Large | .165.00 |
| Platter, 14 In. | .38.00 |
| Saucer | .5.00 |
| Snack Plate | .165.00 |
| Teapot | .195.00 |
| Tumbler, Juice, 4 Oz., 3 3/4 In. | .40.00 |
| Tumbler, Water, 10 Oz., 5 1/2 In. | .40.00 |

## MEXICANA

The first of the Mexican-inspired patterns that became popular as a dinnerware in the 1930s was Mexicana. This decal-decorated set, designed by Frederick Hurten Rhead, was first offered in 1938. The design shows a collection of orange and yellow pots with a few cacti. The edge of the dish well is rimmed with red or occasionally yellow, green, or blue. Almost all of the pieces are Century line, a popular Homer Laughlin China Company dinnerware shape.

| | |
|---|---|
| Cup & Saucer | .28.00 |
| Jug, Cover, Kitchen Kraft | .200.00 |
| Nappy | .48.00 |
| Plate, Bread & Butter, 6 In. | .12.00 |
| Plate, Luncheon, 9 In. | .26.00 |
| Platter, 15 In. | .48.00 |

## MOBY DICK

Moby Dick was a high-priced line made by Vernon Kilns in 1939. Rockwell Kent, the famous illustrator, had illustrated Herman Melville's classic story *Moby Dick*. These illustrations were adapted for the dinnerware. Plates pictured whaling ships, other pieces showed ships and whales. The printed design was available in one of four colors: Dark Blue, Maroon, Walnut Brown, or Yellow (orange-yellow). The Ultra shape was used.

### DARK BLUE

| | |
|---|---|
| Bowl, Chowder | .30.00 to 50.00 |
| Bowl, Fruit | .25.00 |
| Chop Plate, 12 1/2 In. | .125.00 to 150.00 |
| Cup & Saucer, After Dinner | .50.00 |
| Plate, Bread & Butter, 6 1/2 In. | .35.00 to 40.00 |
| Plate, Dinner, 10 1/2 In. | .55.00 to 95.00 |
| Teapot | .175.00 |
| Tumbler | .75.00 to 115.00 |

### MAROON

| | |
|---|---|
| Jam Jar, Notched Lid | .250.00 |
| Mug | .95.00 |
| Plate, Luncheon, 9 In. | .40.00 |
| Sugar, Cover | .75.00 |

### WALNUT BROWN

| | |
|---|---|
| Pitcher, 2 Qt. | .425.00 |

## MONTEREY

J.A. Bauer Pottery Company made a solid-color pottery line from 1934 to the early 1940s. The Los Angeles, California, pottery sold full dinnerware sets with matching serving pieces. It was a mix-and-match set made in Black, Brown, Burgundy, Canary Yellow, Chartreuse, Gray, Ivory, Monterey Blue, Olive Green, Orange, Pink, Turquoise Blue, and White. A series of molded rings was used on plates, vases, cups, pitchers, and bowls.

**CANARY YELLOW**
Cake Plate   . . .185.00 to 195.00
Casserole, Individual   . . . .30.00
Chop Plate, 13 In. . . . . . . .45.00

**MONTEREY BLUE**
Chop Plate, 13 In. . . . . . . .45.00
Teapot . . . . . . . . . . . . . .95.00

**ORANGE**
Cake Plate, Pedestal   . . . .375.00
Chop Plate, 13 In. . . . . . . .45.00
Jug, Ice Lip . . . . . . . . . .125.00
Sugar & Creamer   . . . . . .40.00

**TURQUOISE BLUE**
Jug, Ice Lip . . . . . . . . . .325.00
Teapot . . . . . . . . . . . . . .60.00

## MT. VERNON

Mt. Vernon is a pattern made by the Hall China Company for Sears, Roebuck and Company in the 1940s. It has pink and green flowers in the design.

Bowl, Fruit, 5 In. . . . . . . .8.00
Creamer . . . . . .10.00 to 14.00
Cup . . . . . . . . . .8.00 to 10.00
Gravy Boat   . . . .20.00 to 25.00
Plate, Dinner, 10 In   . . . . .14.00

Saucer . . . . . . . . . . . . . .3.00
Sugar . . . . . . . . . . . . . .24.00

## ·O·

## OLD CURIOSITY SHOP

The Old Curiosity Shop is one of many patterns made by Royal China Company of Sebring, Ohio, from the late 1940s until the late 1960s. It was designed by Gordon Parker. It pictures a view of the shop and an elaborate border. The design comes in green or pink. The Royal China Company closed in 1986.

**GREEN**
Berry Bowl, 4 In. . . . . . . .3.00
Bowl, 5 1/2 In. . . . . . . . . .3.00
Bowl, 9 1/4 In. . . . . . . . .18.00
Cup & Saucer   . . . . . . . . .4.00
Plate, Bread & Butter,
   6 1/2 In. . . . . . . .1.25 to 2.50
Plate, Dinner, 10 In. . . . . . .9.50

**PINK**
Bowl, 9 1/4 In. . . . . . . . .18.00
Bowl, Fruit, 5 1/2 In. . . . . .3.50
Bowl, Vegetable, Round,
   9 In. . . . . . . . . . . . . . .14.00
Bowl, Vegetable, Round,
   10 In. . . . . . . . . . . . . .16.50

Cake Plate, 2 Handles . . . .15.00
Cup & Saucer . . . . . . . . .4.00
Plate, Bread & Butter,
   6 1/2 In. . . . . . . .2.00 to 2.50
Plate, Dinner, 10 In. . . . . . .4.00
Soup, Dish, Flat, 8 1/2 In. . .6.00
Sugar & Creamer,
   Cover . . . . . . . . . . . . .15.00

**ORANGE POPPY,** see Poppy

## ORGANDIE

Organdie is one of six different plaid patterns made by Vernon Kilns, Vernon, California, in the 1940s and 1950s. It is an overall brown pattern with a yellow and brown plaid border. Other related plaids are Calico (pink and blue), Gingham (green and yellow), Homespun (cinnamon, yellow, and green), Tam O'Shanter (rust, chartreuse, and deep green), and Tweed (yellow and gray-blue ). Organdie was originally the name for a group of plaid designs made in 1937. One of these was Coronation Organdy (gray and rose).

Berry Bowl . . . . . . . . . . .9.00
Bowl, Fruit,
   5 1/2 In. . . . . . . . .3.00 to 5.00

Bowl, Salad, 10 1/2 In. . . .60.00
Bowl, Vegetable, 9 In. . . .20.00
Butter . . . . . . . .22.00 to 30.00
Casserole, 8 In. . . . . . . . .65.00
Chicken Pot Pie, Cover . . .30.00
Chop Plate,
    12 In. . . . . . . .25.00 to 28.50
Chop Plate, 16 5/8 In. . . .425.00
Coffee Server . . . . . . . .25.00
Creamer . . . . . . . . . . . .9.00
Creamer, Tall . . . . . . . . .24.00
Cup . . . . . . . . . . . . . . .8.00
Cup, After Dinner . . . . . .18.00
Cup & Saucer . . . . . . . . .6.00
Eggcup . . . . . . . . . . . .25.00
Flowerpot, 5 In. . . . . . . .40.00
Gravy Boat . . . . . . . . . .18.00
Jug, 2 Qt. . . . . . . . . . . .65.00
Mug . . . . . . . . . . . . . .15.00
Plate, Bread & Butter,
    7 In. . . . . . . . . .4.00 to 10.00
Plate, Dessert, 6 In. . . . . . .3.00
Plate, Dinner,
    9 1/2 In. . . . . . .6.00 to 11.00
Plate, Salad, 7 1/2 In. . . . .5.00
Platter, 12 In. . . .15.00 to 24.00
Platter, 14 In. . . . . . . . .30.00
Salt & Pepper . . .10.00 to 18.00
Saucer . . . . . . . . . . . . .2.50
Server, 2 Tiers . . . . . . . .20.00
Soup, Dish, 8 In. . . . . . . .10.00
Sugar & Creamer, Cover  .18.00
Teapot, Cover . . . . . . . . .40.00
Tumbler . . . . . . . . . . . .28.00

## ·P·

## PETIT POINT

Petit Point was an idea that was used by many makers. The pattern had a center design that looked as if it had been stitched of colored wool. Petit Point patterns were made by Crown Pottery of Evansville, Indiana, in 1941; Leigh Potters of Alliance, Ohio, in 1936 for Montgomery Ward; and Taylor, Smith, and Taylor of Taylor, West Virginia, and East Liver-

pool, Ohio. Other similar patterns with "stitched" designs were called Petit Point Basket, Petit Point House, etc. The prices for all of the patterns are very similar, and so only one price listing is given for all Petit Point patterns.

Bowl, 5 1/4 In. . . . . . . . . .3.50
Bowl, 6 In. . . . . . . . . . . .4.00
Bowl, House, 5 1/4 In. . . . .3.50
Bowl, House, 6 In. . . . . . .4.00
Cake Lifter . . . . . . . . . .20.00
Cake Plate . . . . . . . . . . .30.00
Casserole, Cover,
    8 1/2 In. . . . . . . . . . . .10.00
Casserole, Cover,
    Stacking . . . . . . . . . . .55.00
Creamer, House . . . . . . . .3.00
Plate, Dinner,
    10 In. . . . . . . . .2.00 to 10.00
Plate, Dinner, House,
    10 In. . . . . . . . . . . . . . .2.00
Plate, Salad, House, 6 In. . .3.00
Saucer . . . . . . . . . . . . . .1.00
Saucer, House . . . . . . . . . .1.00

## PLAINSMAN

Plainsman is a pattern made by Frankoma Pottery. It was originally named Oklahoma. The pattern started in 1948 and is still being made. It is available in Autumn Yellow, Black, Brown Satin, Desert Gold, Flame, Peach Glow, Prairie Green, Robin's Egg Blue, White Sand, and Woodland. The 1994 catalog offered 22 pieces of Plainsman with the simplified color names of

Brown, Country Blue, Gold, Green, Forest, and Navy.

### BROWN SATIN
Bowl, Salad, Sapulpa
    Clay . . . . . . . . . . . . . .5.00
Salt & Pepper . . . . . . . . .6.00
Salt & Pepper, Sapulpa
    Clay . . . . . . . . . . . . . .6.00
Sugar & Creamer,
    Cover, On Tray . . . . . . .35.00
Tumbler, 6 Oz. . . . . . . . . .4.00

### DESERT GOLD
Cup, 5 Oz. . . . . . . . . . . .8.00
Cup, Sapulpa Clay, 5 Oz. . .8.00
Cup, Sapulpa Clay, 7 Oz. . .6.00
Lazy Susan, Base,
    Sapulpa Clay . . . . . . . .75.00
Mug, Sapulpa Clay,
    10 Oz. . . . . . . . . . . . . .10.00
Plate, Bread & Butter,
    Sapulpa Clay, 7 In. . . . . .5.00
Plate, Breakfast, 9 In. . . . . .5.00
Plate, Dinner, 10 1/2 In. . .12.00
Plate, Dinner, Sapulpa
    Clay, 10 1/2 In. . . . . . .12.00
Platter, Sapulpa Clay,
    13 In. . . . . . . . . . . . . .20.00

### FLAME
Creamer . . . . . . . . . . . . .5.00

### PRAIRIE GREEN
Casserole, Ada Clay,
    Individual . . . . . . . . . .35.00
Casserole, Sapulpa Clay,
    Large . . . . . . . . . . . . .25.00

Cup, After Dinner . . . . . . . .5.00
Cup, After Dinner,
   Ada Clay . . . . . . . . . . .10.00
Jug, Sapulpa Clay, 3 Qt. . .20.00
Mug, 12 Oz. . . . . . . . . . . .8.00
Platter, 13 In. . . . . . . . . . .8.00
Salt & Pepper,
   Sapulpa Clay . . . . . . . . .6.00
Sauceboat, Ada Clay . . . .25.00
Vase, Pod, Sapulpa
   Clay, 9 In. . . . . . . . . . .24.00

### WHITE SAND
Bowl, Divided, 13 In. . . . . .7.50

### POPPY

Poppy, sometimes called Orange Poppy by collectors, was made by the Hall China Company, East Liverpool, Ohio, from 1933 through the 1950s. The decals picture realistic groups of orange poppies with a few leaves. Another Hall pattern called Red Poppy has bright red stylized flowers with black leaves and trim. Poppy is a name used by at least five companies but listed here are Poppy pattern pieces by Hall. Reproductions using the Poppy decoration, but called Orange Poppy, have been made. These, unlike the originals, are marked "Limited Edition."

Bean Pot . . . . . . . . . . .150.00
Berry Bowl, 5 In. . . . . . .10.00
Bowl, 9 1/4 In. . . . . . . . .25.00
Bowl, 10 In. . . . . . . . . . .50.00
Bowl, Vegetable, Round,
   9 1/4 In. . . . . . .25.00 to 36.00
Cake Plate . . . . . . . . . . .36.00
Cake Safe . . . . . . . . . . .75.00

Canister, Coffee . . . . . . .325.00
Canister Set, 4 Piece . . .1000.00
Casserole, Oval, 8 In. . . . .65.00
Casserole, Oval, 9 In. . . . .55.00
Casserole,
   Sunshine . . . . .35.00 to 40.00
Coffeepot . . . . . . . . . . .45.00
Coffeepot, S-Lid . . . . . . .55.00
Cup & Saucer . . . . . . . .60.00
Custard,
   Individual . . . . .3.00 to 10.00
Gravy Boat . . . . . . . . . .85.00
Plate, Breakfast, 9 In. . . . . .8.00
Plate, Dinner, 10 In. . . . . .60.00
Platter, 9 In. . . . . . . . . . .35.00
Platter, Oval, 14 In. . . . . .36.00
Salt & Pepper, Teardrop . .38.00
Sandwich Server . . . . . . . .8.00
Spoon . . . . . . . . . . . . .130.00
Sugar, Cover . . . . . . . . . .85.00
Teapot, Aladdin . . . . . . .93.00
Teapot, Boston . . . . . . . .350.00
Teapot, Melody,
   Streamline . .240.00 to 300.00
Teapot, Windshield . . . . .300.00
Vase, 6 1/2 In. . . . . . . . .100.00

### POPPY & WHEAT

Poppy & Wheat is a design that was introduced after 1933. It was made by Hall China Company, East Liverpool, Ohio. The design shows a realistic spray of orange flowers and wheat heads. It is sometimes called Wheat or Wild Poppy.

Bean Pot . . . . . . . . . . .225.00
Bowl, 5 In. . . . . . . . . . . .16.00
Coffeepot, Washington,
   10 Cup . . . . . . . . . . . .395.00
Cookie Jar, Banded . . . . .295.00

Creamer, Radiance,
   Large . . . . . . . . . . . . . .40.00
Jug, Cover, No. 6,
   Radiance . . . . . . . . . . .175.00
Plate, 14 In. . . . . . . . . . .36.00
Sugar, Handles . . . . . . . .75.00
Tea Tile, Round, 6 In. . . . .70.00
Teapot, Manhattan,
   6 Cup . . . . . . . . . . . . .395.00
Teapot, New York,
   4 Cup . . . . . . . . . . . . .175.00
Teapot, New York,
   6 Cup . . . . . . . . . . . . .395.00

### POPPY TRAIL

Metlox Potteries of California made many dinnerwares marked with the word Metlox or Poppytrail (Poppy Trail). Solid-colored wares and hand-decorated pieces were made. Listed here are solid mix-and-match pieces marked Metlox Poppy Trail. This is the 1934 pattern known to the company as the 200 Series. The original eight colors were Canary Yellow, Cream, Delphinium Blue, Old Rose, Poppy Orange, Rust, Sea Green, and Turquoise Blue. Later, seven pastel colors were added: Opaline Green, Pastel Yellow, Peach, Petal Pink, Powder Blue, Satin Ivory, and Satin Turquoise.

### CANARY YELLOW
Bowl, 6 In. . . . . . . . . . . .10.00
Bowl, Salad, 9 1/2 In. . . . .17.00
Plate, Bread & Butter,
   6 In. . . . . . . . . . . . . . .5.00
Plate, Dinner, 10 In. . . . . .9.00

### DELPHINIUM BLUE
Bowl, 6 In. . . . . . . . . . . .10.00
Plate, Dinner, 10 In. . . . . .9.00

Platter, Round,
12 1/2 In. . . . . . . . . . . .25.00

**OLD ROSE**

Bowl, 6 In. . . . . . . . . . . .10.00
Plate, Bread & Butter,
6 In. . . . . . . . . . . . . . . .5.00
Plate, Dinner, 10 In. . . . . . .5.00

**TURQUOISE BLUE**

Cup & Saucer . . . . . . . . .7.00
Plate, Bread & Butter,
6 In. . . . . . . . . . . . . . . .5.00
Plate, Dinner,
10 In. . . . . . . . . .8.00 to 9.00

## PROVINCIAL BLUE

Provincial Blue is a Metlox Potteries pattern that was made from 1950 to about 1968. It is decorated with blue scenes of farm life. A similar pattern, Homestead Provincial, has the designs in other colors.

Bowl, Round, 10 In. . . . . .44.00
Coffeepot . . . . . . . . . . .100.00
Creamer . . . . . . . . . . . . .24.00
Plate, 6 In. . . . . . . . . . . .8.00
Plate, 10 In. . . . . . . . . . .14.00
Platter, Casual . . . . . . . .35.00
Salt & Pepper . . . . . . . .24.00

---

**For emergency repairs to chipped pottery, try coloring the spot with a wax crayon or oil paint. It will look a little better.**

---

## QUEEN ESTHER

Queen Esther is a Homer Laughlin China Company pattern. It is on the Liberty shape designed by Frederick Hurten Rhead about 1928. The pattern is decorated with a large pink rose decal.

WARRANTED 22 KARAT
GOLD DESIGN

Bowl, 8 3/4 In. . . . . . . . .14.00
Bowl, Dessert, 5 3/4 In. . .45.00
Creamer . . . . . . . . . . . . .10.00
Cup & Saucer . . . . . . . . .9.00
Plate, Bread & Butter,
6 In. . . . . . . . . . . . . . . .3.00
Plate, Dinner, 9 1/2 In. . . . .7.00
Platter, 13 3/4 In. . . . . . .18.00

## ·R·

### RAFFIA

Raffia is a pattern made by Vernon Kilns about 1950. It is green brushed with brownish-red to give a textured effect. Barkwood and Shantung are the same pattern in different colors.

Butter . . . . . . . . . . . . . .30.00
Casserole, Cover . . . . . . .20.00
Chop Plate . . . . . . . . . . .20.00

Creamer . . . . . . . . . . . . .10.00
Cup & Saucer,
Colossal . . . . . . . . . . . .200.00
Eggcup . . . . . . . . . . . . .20.00
Pitcher, 2 Qt. . . . . . . . . .45.00
Syrup, Dripcut . . . . . . . .45.00

---

## RAYMOR

Many collectors search for pieces in the Raymor pattern. It is a stoneware made by Roseville Pottery Company of Zanesville, Ohio, in 1952 and 1953. It was designed by Ben Siebel. Pieces were made in Autumn Brown, Avocado Green, Beach Gray, and Terra Cotta (rust) in either plain or mottled versions, and in Contemporary White. Some Avocado Green pieces are mistakenly called black. Later, Chartreuse and Robin's Egg Blue were added to the line.

**AUTUMN BROWN**

Bowl, Fruit . . . . . . . . . . .14.00
Cup, After Dinner . . . . . .45.00
Eggcup . . . . . . . . . . . . .22.00
Jam Jar, Cover . . . . . . . .65.00
Platter, Meat, 20 In. . . . .110.00
Sugar & Creamer,
After Dinner . . . . . . . .110.00

**AVOCADO GREEN**

Bowl, Fruit . . . . . . . . . . .12.00
Eggcup, Double . . . . . . .25.00
Plate, Salad, 7 In. . . . . . . .8.00

Soup, Dish, Lug,
No. 155 . . . . . . . . . . . .25.00
Sugar & Creamer,
After Dinner . . . . . . . . .75.00

**BEACH GRAY**
Bowl, Divided, No. 165 . .55.00
Casserole, Cover . . . . . . .145.00
Cup . . . . . . . . . . . . . . .12.00
Pitcher, Water . . . . . . . .125.00
Platter, Oval, 13 In. . . . . .45.00

**CONTEMPORARY WHITE**
Platter, 12 In. . . . . . . . . .50.00
Ramekin, Cover,
Individual, No. 156 . . . .30.00

**TERRA COTTA**
Bowl, Fruit . . . . . . . . . . .12.00
Casserole, Cover . . . . . . .90.00
Creamer, Individual . . . . .18.00
Cup, After Dinner . . . . . .40.00
Plate, Bread & Butter,
6 In. . . . . . . . . . . . . . .6.00
Plate, Breakfast, 9 In. . . . .10.00
Soup, Cream . . . . . . . . . .24.00
Soup, Dish, Lug,
No. 155 . . . . . . . . . . . .25.00

## RED POPPY
Bright red flowers and black leaves were used on this popular Hall China Company pattern called Red Poppy. The pattern, made in East Liverpool, Ohio, from 1930 through 1950, was a premium item for Grand Union Tea Company. Matching metal pieces, such as wastebaskets and bread boxes, were made, and glass tumblers are known. Reproductions using the Red Poppy decoration

have been made since 1993. These, unlike the originals, are marked "Limited Edition."

Baker, French Flute . . . . .35.00
Bowl, Fruit . . . . . . . . . . . .8.00
Bowl, Vegetable, Round,
9 1/2 In. . . . . . . . . . . . .30.00
Casserole,
Cover . . . . . . .39.00 to 45.00
Cup . . . . . . . . . .9.00 to 10.00
Custard . . . . . . . . . . . . .19.00
Drip Jar . . . . . . . . . . . . .30.00
Jug . . . . . . . . . . . . . . . .33.00
Jug, Ball . . . . . . . . . . . . .40.00
Mixing Bowl, Pair . . . . .38.00
Plate, Breakfast, 9 In. . . . . .9.00
Salt & Pepper, Eggdrop,
Pair . . . . . . . . . . . . . . .44.00
Salt & Pepper, Handle,
Pair . . . . . . . . . . . . . . .28.00
Salt & Pepper, Pair . . . . .22.00
Soup, Dish . . . . . . . . . . .15.00
Teapot, New York . . . . . .65.00

## RED RIDING HOOD
One of the easiest patterns of American dinnerware to recognize is Red Riding Hood. Three-dimensional figures of the little girl with the red hood have been adapted into saltshakers, teapots, and other pieces. The pattern was made by the A.E. Hull Pottery Company, Crooksville, Ohio, from 1943 to 1957.

Bank, Wall . . . . . . . . . .2800.00
Butter, Cover . . . . . . . . .425.00
Cookie Jar, Cover . . . . .195.00
Creamer, Open . . . . . . . .150.00
Creamer, Tab Handle . . .300.00
Matchbox Holder . . . . .545.00
Mustard . . . . . . . . . . . .300.00
Pitcher, Top Pour,
8 In. . . . . . . .375.00 to 475.00
Salt & Pepper,
3 1/4 In. . . . . . .65.00 to 95.00
Salt & Pepper, Range,
5 1/2 In. . . . .145.00 to 250.00
Sugar & Creamer . . . . . .300.00
Sugar & Creamer,
Creeping, Rose Decal, Tab
Handle . . . . .650.00 to 700.00
Teapot . . . . .300.00 to 395.00
Wall Pocket . . . . . . . . .450.00

## RED ROOSTER
Red Rooster by Metlox Potteries is one of the Poppytrail line made beginning in 1955. It is easy to identify because the center design is a large red rooster. The same design was made by Metlox in different colors and included Rooster Bleu and California Provincial. Some of the pieces look as if they have rivets.

Ashtray, 8 In. . . . . . . . . .30.00
Basket, Vegetable,
Round, 8 In. . . . . . . . .25.00

Bowl, Cereal,
7 1/4 In. . . . . . .12.00 to 18.00
Bowl, Fruit, 6 In. . . . . . . . .8.00
Bowl, Salad, 11 1/2 In. . . .95.00
Bowl, Vegetable,
Divided, 7 7/8 In. . . . . .38.00
Bowl, Vegetable, Divided,
Handle, 12 In. . . . . . . .48.00
Bowl, Vegetable, Open,
Round, 10 In. . . . . . . . .30.00
Bowl, Vegetable, Stick Handle,
2 Pt., 8 1/2 In. . . . . . . .45.00
Bread Server, 9 1/2 In. . .150.00
Butter, Cover . . . . . . . . . .55.00
Canister Set,
8 Piece . . . . .200.00 to 275.00
Casserole, Kettle, Cover,
Handle . . . . . . . . . . . . . .35.00
Chop Plate,
Round . . . . . . .40.00 to 65.00
Coffeepot,
6 Cup . . . . . . . .60.00 to 95.00
Cookie Jar, Cylinder . . . . .75.00
Cruet Set, 5 Piece . . . . . .225.00
Cruet Set, Oil &
Vinegar . . . . . . . . . . . . .80.00
Cup & Saucer . . .6.00 to 10.00
Eggcup . . . . . . . . . . . . .38.00
Gravy Boat, Handle . . . . .30.00
Mug, 8 Oz. . . . . . . . . . . .22.00
Mug, Handle, 2 Pt. . . . . .30.00
Mustard, Cover . . . . . . . .45.00
Plate, Bread & Butter,
6 In. . . . . . . . . . . . . . . . .6.00
Plate, Dinner, 10 In. . . . .12.00
Plate, Luncheon, 8 In. . . .10.00
Platter,
13 1/2 In. . . . . .20.00 to 25.00
Salt & Pepper . . . . . . . .12.00
Saucer . . . . . . . . . . . . . . .4.00

---

**China can be washed in
warm water with mild
soapsuds. The addition
of ammonia to the
water will add that
extra sparkle.**

---

Soup, Dish, 8 In. . . . . . . .18.00
Soup, Dish, Lug, 5 In. . . .15.00
Soup, Tureen, Ladle . . . .575.00
Sugar . . . . . . . . . . . . . . .19.00
Teapot, 5 Cup . . .60.00 to 80.00
Tumbler, 11 Oz. . . . . . . .15.00

---

## REFRIGERATOR WARE

Refrigerator sets were made by
the Hall China Company, East
Liverpool, Ohio, from the late
1930s. For Westinghouse, the
company made Phoenix (Patrician) in 1938, General (Em-
peror) in 1939, Hercules or
Peasant Ware (Aristocrat) in
1940-1941, and Adonis (Prince)
in 1952. Hall also made King
and Queen ovenware to match
the Refrigerator ware. Sears,
Roebuck; Montgomery Ward;
Hotpoint; and General Electric
also used Hall Refrigerator
ware. In addition, the company
made some pieces sold with the
Hall name: Bingo in the late
1930s, Plaza in the 1930s to the
1960s, and Norris.

**Made Exclusively for
WESTINGHOUSE By
The Hall China Co.
MADE IN U.S.A.**

---

**GENERAL ELECTRIC**
Leftover, Cover, Blue,
Yellow, 4 x 8 In. . . . . . .22.00
Leftover, Cover, Blue,
Yellow, 8 x 8 In. . . . . . .34.00
Water Server, Adonis,
Blue, Yellow . . . . . . . . .55.00
Water Server, Adonis, Gray,
Yellow . . . . . .45.00 to 55.00

**HOTPOINT**
Leftover, Gray, Square,
4 3/4 In. . . . . . . . . . . . . .40.00

**MONTGOMERY WARD**
Leftover, Ivory,
Rectangular . . . . . . . . .60.00

**WESTINGHOUSE**
Butter, General,
Dark Green . . . . . . . . .40.00
Butter, Hercules,
Yellow . . . . . .30.00 to 40.00
Casserole, Cover, Blue . . .40.00
Casserole, Cover, Ridged,
Yellow . . . . . . . . . . . .40.00
Leftover, Delphite . . . . . .16.00
Leftover, General,
Orange . . . . . . . . . . . .30.00
Leftover, General,
Yellow . . . . . . . . . . . .30.00
Leftover, Hercules,
Green . . . . . . . . . . . . .30.00
Leftover, Hercules,
Ivory . . . . . . . . . . . . . .30.00
Leftover, Hercules,
Yellow . . . . . . . . . . . .30.00
Leftover, Phoenix, Blue . .30.00
Pitcher, Donut, Ivory . . . .90.00
Water Server, General,
Green . . . . . . . . . . . . .95.00
Water Server, Phoenix,
Blue . . . . . . . . . . . . . .45.00

---

## RHYTHM

Rhythm is a solid-color dinnerware made by Homer Laughlin
China Company from about
1951 to 1958. It is a pattern
with simple, modern shapes.
The dishes were made in many
of the Harlequin colors, including Chartreuse, Forest Green,
Gray, Maroon, and Yellow.
Other companies also made
patterns named Rhythm, but
only Homer Laughlin Rhythm
is listed here.

**BURGUNDY**
Plate, Dinner, 10 In. . . . . .18.00
Platter, Oval, 11 1/2 In. . . .15.00

Soup .............14.00
Sugar .............18.00

**CHARTREUSE**
Creamer .............6.50
Cup & Saucer ..10.00 to 12.00
Plate, Dinner, 10 In. .....18.00
Salt & Pepper ........22.00

**FOREST GREEN**
Spoon Rest .........310.00

**HARLEQUIN YELLOW**
Teapot ..............60.00

# RING

Ring, sometimes called Beehive, was made by J. A. Bauer Pottery Company, Los Angeles, California, from 1932 to 1962. It was made in many colors including Black, Burnt Orange (orange red), Chartreuse, Chinese Yellow (light yellow), Dark Blue, Gray, Green, Ivory, Jade Green, Light Brown, Maroon, Olive Green, Orange, Pale Blue, Pink, Red Brown, Turquoise, White, and Yellow.

**BLACK**
Bowl, Vegetable, 8 In. ...65.00
Chop Plate,
    12 1/2 In. ...195.00 to 250.00
Creamer ............120.00
Cup & Saucer ........50.00
Mixing Bowl, No. 12,
    9 1/2 In. ...........250.00
Mixing Bowl, No. 36,
    5 In................95.00
Platter, 12 1/2 In. ......225.00
Punch Cup ..115.00 to 125.00
Salt & Pepper,
    Barrel .....250.00 to 295.00

Vase, Cylinder, 8 In. ....180.00

**BURNT ORANGE**
Ashtray, Square, 4 In. ....75.00
Bean Pot, Cover .......45.00
Bowl, Salad, 12 In. .....155.00
Butter, Cover,
    Round ....145.00 to 165.00
Carafe, Copper
    Handle .....65.00 to 125.00
Casserole, 9 1/2 In. ......80.00
Casserole, Cover, Rack ..255.00
Chop Plate, 12 In. .......40.00
Chop Plate, 13 In. .......95.00
Chop Plate, 14 In. .......65.00
Cookie Jar ..800.00 to 995.00
Goblet .............145.00
Grill Plate, 10 1/2 In. ....75.00
Jug ...............295.00
Mixing Bowl, No. 9,
    10 1/2 In. ...........155.00
Mug ...............65.00
Pitcher, 1 Qt. ...75.00 to 125.00
Pitcher, 3 Qt. ........225.00
Plate, Dinner, 10 1/2 In. ..95.00
Plate, Luncheon, 8 In. ....15.00
Sandwich Server,
    17 In. ..............100.00
Sugar, Cover ..........65.00
Sugar &
    Creamer ..100.00 to 125.00
Sugar Shaker, Low ......15.00
Teapot, 2 Cup .........95.00
Teapot, 6 Cup ........125.00
Tumbler, 6 Oz. .........20.00
Tumbler, 12 Oz. ........45.00
Tumbler, Barrel,
    Handle .....125.00 to 225.00

**CHARTREUSE**
Mixing Bowl, No. 9,
    10 1/2 In. ...........110.00
Pitcher, 2 Qt. ........250.00
Punch Bowl, 9 In. ......450.00
Syrup, 1 Pt. ...........120.00

**DARK BLUE**
Butter, Cover, Round ...145.00
Carafe ..............75.00
Chop Plate, 13 In. ......85.00
Goblet .....140.00 to 225.00
Gravy Boat .........125.00
Pickle .............55.00
Punch Bowl, 14 In. ....1295.00

Teapot, 6 Cup ........350.00
Tumbler, 12 Oz. ........45.00
Vase, 6 In. ...........75.00
gray
Berry Bowl, 4 In. .......10.00
Mixing Bowl, No. 36,
    5 In................40.00
Tumbler, 12 Oz. ........75.00

**GREEN**
Berry Bowl, 4 In. .......50.00
Bowl, Vegetable, 8 In. ...55.00
Carafe .............30.00
Chop Plate, 12 In. ......65.00
Chop Plate, 17 In. .....265.00
Coffeepot ...........120.00
Goblet .............225.00
Mixing Bowl, No. 12,
    9 1/2 In. .............50.00
Pie Plate, 10 In. ........45.00
Plate, Dinner, 10 1/2 In. ..95.00
Plate, Salad, 7 1/2 In. ....12.00
Stack Set, Cover .......95.00
Sugar
    Shaker ....350.00 to 395.00
Teapot .............225.00

**IVORY**
Chop Plate, 12 In. .....145.00
Mixing Bowl, No. 36,
    5 In................55.00
Plate, Dinner, 10 1/2 In. ..75.00
Sugar & Creamer .....350.00

**MAROON**
Berry Bowl, 4 In. .......10.00
Chop Plate, 13 In. .....250.00
Gravy Boat .........145.00
Mug ...............40.00
Punch Cup ...........55.00
Teapot .............325.00

**PALE BLUE**
Bowl, Salad, Low,
    9 In................65.00
Butter, Cover,
    Round ....125.00 to 225.00
Carafe, Copper Handle ..275.00
Chop Plate, 13 In. ......60.00
Nappy, Handle, 7 In. ....16.00
Pitcher, 1 Qt. .........165.00
Pitcher, 2 Qt. .........275.00
Plate, Dinner, 10 1/2 In. ..95.00
Plate, Luncheon, 8 In. ....36.00
Punch Cup ...........55.00

Saucer . . . . . . . . . . . . . .15.00
Tumbler, 6 Oz. . . . . . . . .35.00
Vase, Cylinder, 10 In. . . . .80.00

### TURQUOISE
Beater Bowl, 5 In. . . . . .100.00
Vase, Cylinder, 8 In. . . . . .85.00

### WHITE
Bowl, Salad, 12 In. . . . . .375.00
Carafe, Wooden
Handle . . . . . . . . . . . .350.00
Punch Bowl, Pedestal,
14 In. . . . . . . . . . . . .2000.00
Vase, Cylinder, 10 In. . . .110.00

### YELLOW
Bean Pot, 2 Qt. . . . . . . .125.00
Bowl, Fruit, 5 In. . . . . . .55.00
Bowl, Salad, 12 In. . . . . .125.00
Carafe . . . . . . . . . . . . . .65.00
Casserole, Rack,
7 1/2 In. . . . . .70.00 to 125.00
Chop Plate, 12 In. . . . . . .65.00
Creamer . . . . . . . . . . . . . .45.00
Cup & Saucer . . . . . . . . .40.00
Mixing Bowl, No. 9,
10 1/2 In. . . . . . . . . . . .125.00
Mug . . . . . . . . . . . . . . .165.00
Mustard . . . . . . . . . . . .525.00
Nappy, 9 In. . . . . . . . . . .50.00
Plate, Dinner, 10 1/2 In. . .95.00
Punch Bowl, Pedestal,
14 In. . . . . . . . . . . . . . .995.00
Punch Cup . . . . . . . . . . .55.00
Sugar Shaker . . . . . . . . . .15.00
Syrup, 1 Pt. . . . . . . . . . . .85.00
Teapot, 2 Cup . . . . . . . .225.00
Teapot, 6 Cup . . . . . . . . .85.00
Tumbler, Barrel,
Handle . . . . . . . . . . . .300.00

❖

**Bauer Ringware pattern
can be dated from the
mark. "Bauer" or
"Bauer Los Angeles"
were the earliest.
"Bauer Made in USA" or
"Bauer USA" were used
in the mid-1930s.**

❖

## RIVIERA

Riviera was solid-color ware
made by Homer Laughlin
China Company, Newell, West
Virginia, from 1938 to 1950. It
was unmarked and sold exclusively by the Murphy Com-
pany. Plates and cup handles
were squared. Colors were
Ivory, Light Green, Mauve
Blue, Red, Yellow, and, rarely,
Dark Blue.

### DARK BLUE
Platter, Oval,
11 1/4 In. . . .135.00 to 200.00

### IVORY
Bowl, Fruit, 5 1/2 In. . . . . .8.00
Bowl, Oatmeal,
6 In. . . . . . . . . .5.00 to 16.00
Bowl, Utility . . . . . . . . . .40.00
Butter, 1/2 Lb. . . . . . . . .155.00
Casserole . . . . . . . . . . . . .65.00
Creamer . . . . . . .7.00 to 10.00
Cup . . . . . . . . . . . .7.00 to 8.00
Cup & Saucer, After
Dinner . . . . . .45.00 to 95.00
Jug, Batter, Cover . . . . . .160.00
Plate, Luncheon, 9 In. . . . .12.00
Platter, Oval,
11 1/4 In. . . . . .12.00 to 15.00
Soup, Cream . . . . . . . . . .45.00
Sugar & Creamer . . . . . . .65.00
Syrup, Cover . . . . . . . . .125.00

### LIGHT GREEN
Bowl, Oatmeal, 6 In. . . . . .85.00
Bowl, Sugar, Cover . . . . .20.00

Butter, 1/4 Lb. . . . . . . . .65.00
Casserole, Cover . . . . . . . .95.00
Creamer . . . . . . . . . . . . . .9.00
Cup . . . . . . . . . . . . . . . .11.00
Jug, Batter, Cover . . . . . .160.00
Nappy, 9 In. . . . . . . . . . .20.00
Plate, Dessert,
6 In. . . . . . . . . . . .6.50 to 9.50
Plate, Dinner,
10 In. . . . . . . . . . . . . . .95.00
Plate, Luncheon,
9 In. . . . . . . . . . . . . . .12.00
Saucer . . . . . . . . . . . . . .3.00
Shaker . . . . . . . . . . . . . .8.00
Sugar & Creamer,
Cover . . . . . . . . . . . .30.00
Tumbler, Handle . . . . . . .80.00

### MAUVE BLUE
Bowl, Sugar, Cover . . . . .25.00
Casserole,
Cover . . . . . .85.00 to 110.00
Creamer . . . . . . . . . . . . .7.00
Cup . . . . . . . . . .7.00 to 11.00
Cup, Tea . . . . . . . . . . . . .10.00
Nappy, 9 In. . . . . . . . . . .18.00
Pitcher,
Juice . . . . . .325.00 to 350.00
Plate, Dessert,
6 In. . . . . . . . . . . .5.50 to 6.00
Plate, Luncheon,
9 In. . . . . . . . . . . . . . .12.00
Platter, 13 1/4 In. . . . . . .25.00
Saltshaker . . . . . . . . . . . .8.00
Sugar . . . . . . . . . . . . . . .20.00
Tumbler, Handle . . . . . . .75.00

### RED
Bowl, Fruit,
5 1/2 In. . . . . . . . . . . . . .8.00
Bowl, Oatmeal, 6 In. . . . .29.00
Butter, 1/2 Lb. . . . . . . . .135.00
Cup . . . . . . . . . . . . . . . .7.00
Plate, Dessert, 6 In. . . . . . .9.50
Plate, Luncheon,
9 In. . . . . . . . . . . . . . .12.00
Saucer . . . . . . . . . . . . . .5.00
Soup, Cream . . . . . . . . . .32.00
Syrup, Cover . . . . . . . . .150.00
Teapot . . . . . . . . . . . . . .75.00

### YELLOW
Bowl, Fruit, 5 1/2 In. . . . . .8.00
Bowl, Oatmeal, 5 In. . . . . .8.00

Casserole,
Cover . . . . . . .75.00 to 150.00
Cup . . . . . . . . . .7.00 to 10.00
Cup & Saucer . . . . . . . . .11.00
Juice Set, 5 Piece . . . . .500.00
Pitcher, Juice . . .75.00 to 160.00
Plate, Deep . . . . . . . . . . .65.00
Plate, Dessert,
6 In. . . . . . . . . . . . . . . . .6.00
Plate, Dinner,
10 In. . . . . . . .85.00 to 95.00
Plate, Luncheon,
9 In. . . . . . . . . .10.00 to 12.00
Platter,
11 1/4 In. . . . . .15.00 to 22.00
Salt & Pepper . . . . . . . .15.00
Sugar . . . . . . . . . . . . . . .8.00
Teapot . . . . . . . . . . . . .150.00
Tumbler,
Handle . . . . . . .42.50 to 55.00

## ROOSTER WATT

Rooster pattern was introduced by Watt Pottery Company of Crooksville, Ohio, in 1955. It was made until at least 1958. The factory closed in 1965.

Baker, Cover,
No. 67 . . . . . . . . . . . . .160.00
Baker, No. 85,
Rectangular . . . . . . .1400.00
Casserole, Cover,
No. 18, Individual . . . .425.00
Creamer, No. 62 . . . . . .295.00
Crock, Cheese,
No. 80 . . . . . . . . . . .1500.00
Mixing Bowl, No. 5,
Ribbed . . . . . . . . . . . . .80.00
Mug, No. 701 . . . . . . . .1000.00
Pitcher, No. 15 . . . . . . . .150.00
Salt & Pepper, Barrel,
No. 45 & No. 46 . . . .295.00

**Take off your rings and bracelets before you start to wash dishes.**

## ROSE PARADE

The Hall China Company, East Liverpool, Ohio, sometimes made surprising color- and decal-decorated wares. Rose Parade has a solid Cadet Blue body with contrasting Hi-white knobs and handles. A rose decal was added to the white spaces. Sometimes the flower is pink, sometimes blue. The pattern was made from 1941 through the 1950s. Serving pieces, not dinnerware sets, were made. Pert is a shape.

Brown, Mug, Footed . . . . .4.00
Jug, Pert, 5 In. . . . . . . . .32.50
Salt & Pepper . . . . . . . .24.00
Salt & Pepper, Pert,
Pair . . . . . . . .25.00 to 27.50

## ROSE WHITE

Rose White, first made in 1941 by Hall China Company, is similar to Rose Parade. The same shapes were used, but the pieces were all white with a slightly different rose-decal decoration. There is silver trim on many pieces. Pert is a shape.

Bean Pot, Cover . . . . . . .115.00
Pitcher, Pert,
Small . . . . . . . . . . . . . .29.00
Salt & Pepper,
Pert . . . . . . . . . . . . . . .30.00

## ROSEBUD

Rosebud was made by Coors Porcelain, Golden, Colorado, from 1934 to 1942. It is a solid-colored ware with a stylized flower and leaves on the edge of plates or sides of cups. It was made in Blue, Green (turquoise), Ivory, Maroon, Orange, and Yellow.

**BLUE**
Plate, 9 1/4 In. . . . . . . . .30.00
**GREEN**
Plate, 7 In. . . . . . . . . . . .15.00

❖

It is safe to wash most dishes in the dishwasher if they are undamaged and have no gold overlay. For best results, be sure the water temperature is between 140 and 160 degrees and use a rinse agent that causes the water to flow off the dishes in sheets.

❖

**IVORY**
Pitcher . . . . . . . . . . . . .250.00

**MAROON**
Plate, 7 In. . . . . . . . . . . .15.00
Tumbler, Handle . . . . . .145.00

**MAROON & GREEN**
Salt & Pepper . . . . . . . .60.00

**ORANGE**
Baker, Large . . . . . . . . . .85.00
Cake Knife . . .100.00 to 175.00
Cake Plate . . . . . . . . . . .55.00
Cookie Jar . . . . . . . . . . .85.00

**YELLOW**
Honey Pot,
Cover . . . . . . . . . . . .200.00

## ROUNDUP

RoundUp is a hand-painted Red Wing Potteries pattern made from January 1958. It was made on the Casual shape and decorated with cowboys and desert scenes in tones of browns, blues, and greens. It was very similar to Chuck Wagon, which was sold by mail.
Butter, Cover . . .95.00 to 175.00
Cup . . . . . . . . . . . . . . . .25.00
Cup & Saucer . . . . . . . . .40.00
Pitcher,
12 In. . . . . . .185.00 to 250.00
Salt & Pepper . . . . . . . .75.00

**RUSSEL WRIGHT,** see American Modern; Grass; Iroquois; Sterling; White Clover

## SALAMINA

Salamina is an important pattern made by Vernon Kilns in 1939. The pattern pictures a girl from Greenland. Each piece has a different scene. The designs were adapted from the drawings in the book *Salamina* by Rockwell Kent. It is the story of a girl. The dinnerware was hand-colored.

Chop Plate, 12 In. . . . . . .265.00
Chop Plate, 14 In. . . . . . .375.00
Pitcher, 2 Qt. . . . . . . . .825.00
Plate, Dinner, Salamina
Kneeling, 10 1/2 In. . . .125.00

## SCULPTURED DAISY

Sculptured Daisy was made by Metlox Potteries of Manhattan Beach, California, as part of the Poppy Trail line in 1964. The pattern features raised white daisies and green leaves.

Bowl, 12 In. . . . . . . . . . .70.00
Bowl, Handle, 7 In. . . . . .28.00
Bowl, Handle, 8 In. . . . . .35.00
Casserole, Cover,
1 1/2 Qt. . . . . . . . . . . .85.00
Coffeepot . . . . . . . . . . .50.00
Creamer . . . . . . . . . . . . .18.00
Cup & Saucer . . . . . . . .12.00
Gravy Boat, Handle,
1 Pt. . . . . . . . . . . . . . .32.00
Mug . . . . . . . . . . . . . . .18.00
Plate, 7 1/2 In. . . . . . . . . .8.00
Soup, Dish, 7 In. . . . . . . .12.00
Sugar, Cover . . . . . . . . . .24.00

## SCULPTURED GRAPE

Sculptured Grape is a pattern made by Metlox Potteries as part of the Poppy Trail line from 1963 to 1975. The pattern had a raised grapevine colored blue, brown, and green.

Bowl, 9 1/2 In. . . . . . . . .27.00
Bowl, 12 In. . . . . . . . . . .90.00
Bowl, Cereal, 7 3/8 In. . . .15.00
Bowl, Vegetable . . . . . . .23.00
Canister Set, 4 Piece . . . .240.00

Casserole, Cover, 1 Qt. . . .85.00
Cup & Saucer  . . . . . . . .16.00
Gravy Boat  . . . . . . . . . .42.50
Plate, Dinner,
   10 1/2 In. . . . . . . . . . . .17.00
Plate, Luncheon,
   7 1/2 In. . . . . . . . . . . . .10.00
Platter, Oval, 10 In.  . . . .30.00
Platter, Oval, 12 In.  . . . .40.00
Salad Fork, Spoon  . . . . .45.00
Sugar, Cover . . . . . . . . . .22.00
Sugar & Creamer  . . . . . .45.00

## SCULPTURED ZINNIA

Sculptured Zinnia is a pattern
made by Metlox Potteries as
part of the Poppy Trail line
made from 1964 to 1980. The
Sculptured Zinnia shape was
made in three color variations
named Sculptured Zinnia, Lavender Blue, or Memories.

Bowl, 12 In. . . . . . . . . . .48.00
Bowl, Cereal, 7 3/8 In. . . .13.00
Bowl, Fruit, 6 In.  . . . . . .11.00
Bowl, Vegetable, 8 In.  . . .30.00
Cup & Saucer  . . . . . . . .13.00
Plate, Bread & Butter,
   6 In. . . . . . . . . . . . . . . .5.50
Plate, Dinner, 12 In.  . . . .14.00
Plate, Luncheon, 8 In. . . . .10.00
Plate, Salad, 7 1/2 In. . . . .7.00
Platter, 12 In. . . . . . . . . .37.50
Platter, Oval, 11 In.  . . . .28.00
Platter, Oval, 14 In.  . . . .32.00
Salt & Pepper  . . . . . . . .16.00
Saucer  . . . . . . . . . . . . . .1.00
Sugar & Creamer  . . . . . .9.50

## SERENADE

There are three patterns named
Serenade. The Homer Laughlin
China Company dishes made
from 1939 to the 1940s listed
here are plain, made in Blue,
Green, Pink, or Yellow. The
Hall China Company dishes are
decorated with sprigs of orange
flowers. Another pattern called
Serenade was made by Edwin
M. Knowles China Company.

**BLUE**
Casserole, Cover . . . . . . .100.00
Saucer  . . . . . . . . . . . . . .4.00
**GREEN**
Casserole, Cover . . . . . . .100.00
Cup & Saucer  . . . . . . . .16.00
Plate, Bread & Butter, 6 In.  6.00
**PINK**
Bowl, Fruit, 5 1/2 In.  . . . .10.00
Chop Plate, 13 In. . . . . . .40.00
Creamer . . . . . . . . . . . . .12.00
Cup & Saucer  . . . . . . . .16.00
Plate, Dinner, 10 In. . . . . .20.00
Plate, Salad, 7 In. . . . . . . .8.00
**YELLOW**
Cup . . . . . . . . . . . . . . . .10.00
**SHELLWARE,** see Cameo
   Shellware

## SILHOUETTE

Silhouette looks just like its
name. The 1930s pattern shows
a black silhouette of two people
eating at a table and a dog beg-
ging for food in front of the
table. The plates are trimmed in
platinum. The pattern, made by
Crooksville China Company,
Crooksville, Ohio, is similar to
Taverne, but Taverne has no
dog. Matching metal pieces and
glasswares were made. At least
five companies called their patterns Silhouette. Reproductions
called Silhouette but using the
Taverne decal with no dog have
been made since 1993. These,
unlike the originals, are marked
"Limited Edition."

Bowl, Vegetable, Oval  . . .30.00
Plate, Bread & Butter,
   6 In. . . . . . . . . . . . . . . .7.00
Plate, Salad, 7 In. . . . . . . .10.00
Platter, Oval, 11 In.  . . . .35.00
Salt & Pepper  . . . . . . . .58.00

## STANHOME IVY

Stanhome Ivy is a Blue Ridge
pattern made on the Skyline
shape after 1954. It is decorated
with a stylized green ivy sprig.

Cup & Saucer, Skyline  . . . .5.00
Plate, Skyline, 6 In.  . . . . . .2.00
Plate, Skyline, 9 1/2 In.  . . .4.00

## STARBURST

Starburst pattern was made by Franciscan Ceramics of Los Angeles, California, in 1954. The company started in 1934 and became part of what is now Waterford Wedgwood USA in 1979. They stopped making Starburst in 1985.

Ashtray, Football,
  7 1/2 In. . . . . . . . . . . . .80.00
Bonbon . . . . . . . . . . . . .35.00
Bowl, Salad . . . . . . . . . .95.00
Bowl, Vegetable, Divided,
  Round, 8 1/2 In. . . . . . . .38.00
Butter, Cover . . .45.00 to 50.00
Canister, Flour . . . . . . . .200.00
Cruet Set, Oil &
  Vinegar, 2 Piece . . . . .135.00
Cup & Saucer . . . . . . . . . .5.00
Gravy Boat . . . . . . . . . . .38.00
Ladle . . . . . . . . . . . . . . . .35.00
Mug . . . . . . . . . . . . . . .25.00
Pitcher, Milk . . . .75.00 to 82.00
Pitcher, Water, 10 In. . . .115.00
Plate, Bread & Butter,
  6 In. . . . . . . . . . . .4.00 to 5.00
Plate, Dinner,
  11 In. . . . . . . . . .9.00 to 12.00
Plate, Luncheon,
  9 1/2 In. . . . . . . . . . . . . .20.00

Plate, Salad, 7 In. . . . . . . .6.00
Platter, Oval, 15 In. . . . . .55.00
Salad, Crescent . .25.00 to 45.00
Saucer . . . . . . . . . . . . . .4.00
Snack Tray, Cup Rest,
  12 1/2 In. . . . . . . . . . . .65.00

## STARFLOWER

Starflower by Watt Pottery Company was made in the early 1950s in several variations. One type has either 4-petal or 5-petal red flowers with green leaves on a cream background. Other variations have two or three green leaves. Similar patterns with different names were made in several color combinations. There is another pattern named Star Flower by Stangl Pottery.

Baker, Cover, No. 67 . . .160.00
Bowl, Spaghetti,
  No. 24 . . . . . . . . . . . . .100.00
Casserole, Tab Handles,
  No. 18, Individual . . . .100.00
Cookie Jar, No. 21 . . . . .155.00
Creamer,
  No. 62 . . . . .180.00 to 250.00
Jar, Grease, No. 01 . . . . .350.00
Jug, No. 15, 5-Petal . . . . .85.00
Jug, No. 17, 4-Petal, Ice
  Lip . . . . . . . .110.00 to 175.00
Mug, Barrel,
  No. 501 . . . . . .75.00 to 90.00
Mug, No. 121,
  White On Red . . . . . .1100.00
Pepper Shaker, No. 46,
  Barrel . . . . . . . . . . . . .65.00
Plate, Dinner, 10 In. . . . . .13.00
Platter, No. 31, Round,
  15 In. . . . . . . . . . . . . . .50.00

Salt & Pepper, Barrel, No. 45
  & No. 46 . . .135.00 to 185.00
Salt & Pepper, Hourglass,
  No. 117 & No. 118 . . .295.00

## STERLING

Sterling by Russel Wright is a heavy restaurant china made by the Sterling China Company in 1949. It was made in Ivy Green, Shell Pink, Straw Yellow, Suede Gray, and Cedar Brown.

### IVY GREEN
Ashtray . . . . . . . . . . . .125.00
Grill Plate, Child's,
  Astronaut, 8 In. . . . . . .60.00
Platter, Oval, 7 1/2 In. . . .22.00

### SHELL PINK
Plate, 7 1/2 In. . . . . . . . .6.00
Plate, 10 In. . . . . . . . . . .12.00
Plate, 11 1/2 In. . . . . . . .25.00
Platter, Oval, 7 1/2 In. . . .20.00

### STRAW YELLOW
Ashtray . . . . . . . . . . . . .95.00
Plate, 7 1/2 In. . . . . . . . .12.00
Plate, 9 In. . . . . . . . . . . .14.00

## •T•

## TAM O'SHANTER

Tam O'Shanter is one of the many plaid patterns made by Vernon Kilns, Vernon, California. It is a rust, chartreuse, and dark green plaid with forest green border. Other related plaids are Calico (pink and blue), Coronation Organdy (gray and rose), Gingham (green and yellow), Homespun (cinnamon, yellow, and green), Organdie (brown and yellow), and Tweed (yellow and gray-blue).

Bowl, Salad, Individual . .25.00
Bowl, Vegetable,
    Divided . . . . . . . . . . . .18.00
Butter . . . . . . . . . . . . . .40.00
Cup, After Dinner . . . . . . .15.00
Eggcup . . . . . . . .12.00 to 18.00
Plate, Bread & Butter,
    6 In. . . . . . . . . .4.00 to 10.00
Plate, Dinner, 10 1/2 In. . .15.00
Plate, Luncheon, 9 1/2 In. . .8.00
Platter, 14 In. . . . . . . . . .30.00

## TAMPICO

Tampico is a pattern with browns, greens, and pinks picturing watermelon slices. The pattern, on a Futura shape, was made by Red Wing Potteries of Red Wing, Minnesota. This modern design was introduced in 1955. Many other patterns were also made on the Futura bodies.

Bowl, 12 In. . . . . . . . . . .75.00
Creamer . . . . . . . . . . . . .25.00
Gravy Boat . . . .40.00 to 60.00
Nut Bowl, 5 Sections . . .125.00
Pitcher, 2 Qt. . . . .85.00 to 90.00
Plate, Dinner,
    10 1/2 In. . . . . . . . . . . .17.00
Platter, 13 In. . . . . . . . . .90.00

## TAVERNE

Taverne serving pieces were made by the Hall China Company of East Liverpool, Ohio, in the 1930s. Matching dinnerware was made by Taylor, Smith, and Taylor of Chester, West Virginia. A rolling pin was made by Harker Pottery Company. The silhouetted figures eating at a table are very similar to those seen on the pattern Silhouette, but there is no dog in this decal. In some of the literature, Taverne is called Silhouette. Reproductions using the Taverne decoration have been made. These, unlike the originals, are marked "Limited Edition."

Baker, French,
    8 In. . . . . . . . . .30.00 to 45.00
Bowl, Medallion,
    6 In. . . . . . . . . . . . . . . .20.00
Bowl, Salad, 9 In. . . . . . . .25.00
Coffeepot,
    5 Band . . . . .125.00 to 150.00
Drip Jar . . . . . . . . . . . . . .24.00
Drip Jar, Cover . . . . . . . . .40.00
Jug, No. 3 . . . . . . . . . . . . .45.00
Leftover, Square . . . . . . . .75.00
Pretzel Jar, Cover . . . . . .165.00
Saucer . . . . . . . . . . . . . .10.00
Teapot, Medallion . . . . . .125.00

## THISTLE

Thistle, or No. 3847, is a pattern made by Stangl Pottery, Trenton, New Jersey. The hand-painted decoration is a purple thistle and green spiked thistle leaves. The dishes were made from 1951 to 1967. Thistle pattern was made by four companies, but only the Stangl pattern is listed here.

Bowl, 10 In. . . . .40.00 to 45.00
Bowl, 12 In. . . . . . . . . . .50.00
Bowl, Fruit, 5 1/2 In. . . . .10.00
Bowl, Vegetable,
    Divided . . . . . . . . . . . .40.00
Casserole, Individual . . . .10.00
Cup . . . . . . . . . . . . . . . . .6.00

Cup & Saucer ........11.00
Eggcup ..........7.50
Mixing Bowl, 5 1/2 In. ...10.00
Plate, Bread & Butter,
6 In..............5.00
Plate, Luncheon, 8 In. ....10.00
Sugar & Creamer ......22.00

## TICKLED PINK

Tickled Pink is a pattern made by Vernon Kilns from 1955 to 1958. It features small squares and crosses in pink and charcoal on most pieces. Cups, lids, and a few serving pieces are made of solid pink. The pattern and name rights were purchased by Metlox Potteries in 1958 and Tickled Pink continued to be produced. Blue Ridge also made a pattern called Tickled Pink.

Bowl, Vegetable, 9 In. ...22.50
Bowl, Vegetable, Solid
Pink, 7 In. ...........14.00
Coffeepot ...........45.00
Creamer ......12.00 to 14.00
Cup .................9.50
Cup & Saucer ........12.00
Mug ...............38.00
Plate, 13 In. ..........25.00
Plate, Bread & Butter,
7 In.................8.00
Plate, Dinner,
10 In. .........7.00 to 10.00
Platter, 11 In. ...15.00 to 26.00
Platter, 14 In. .........30.00
Platter, Oval, 13 In. .....20.00
Saucer ...............6.50
Teapot ..............65.00
Tumbler,
14 Oz. .......18.00 to 35.00

## TOM & JERRY

Tom & Jerry sets were made to serve the famous Christmas punch. A set was usually a punch bowl and six matching cups or mugs.

### BLACK
Punch Set, Cover,
8 Cup .............200.00
Punch Set, Footed Bowl,
18 5-Oz. Cups .......250.00

### IVORY
Punch Set, Footed Bowl,
Gold Letters,
7 Piece .....100.00 to 120.00

## TOWN & COUNTRY RED WING

Town & Country by Red Wing Potteries was designed by Eva Zeisel in 1947 and was made until 1954. Pieces are decorated with glossy or matte glaze. Sets were sold in mixed colors. Colors include Chalk White, Chartreuse, Dusk Blue, Forest Green, Gray, Metallic Brown, Rust, and Sandy Peach. Town & Country was also made by Stangl.

### DUSK BLUE
Coffeepot ............65.00
Mustard Set, Stopper,
3 Piece .............295.00
Plate, 10 1/2 In. ........25.00
Platter ...............75.00
Sugar, Cover ..........45.00
Syrup ........65.00 to 75.00
Teapot ..............200.00

### FOREST GREEN
Bowl, Dessert ..........12.00
Butter, Cover .........40.00
Casserole, 3 Qt. ........50.00

Cup ................10.00
Jug Set, 4 Mugs,
1 1/2 Pt.............75.00
Pitcher, 2 1/2 Qt. ......37.50

### METALLIC BROWN
Bean Pot ............50.00
Bowl, 7 3/4 In. ........50.00
Bowl, 10 In. ..........50.00
Salt & Pepper ........80.00
Sugar, Cover ..........35.00

### RUST
Mug ...............40.00
Saucer ..............10.00
Teapot .............130.00

## TOWN & COUNTRY STANGL

Stangl Pottery made Town & Country pattern in a variety of colors in the 1970s. The design looks like the sponged stoneware made in the nineteenth century, but the pattern was made in many colors. Black, Blue-Green, Brown, Honey Beige, and Yellow were used. Town & Country was also made by Red Wing Potteries.

### BLUE-GREEN
Pitcher & Wash Basin,
2 Piece ............150.00

### BROWN
Bowl, 7 3/4 In. ........50.00
Butter, Cover .........60.00
Candleholder, 7 1/2 In.,
Pair ...............50.00
Creamer .............20.00
Cup & Saucer ........20.00
Flowerpot, 4 3/4 In. .....25.00
Jello Mold, 7 In. ........35.00
Ladle ...............15.00
Nappy ..............25.00
Plate, Bread & Butter,
6 In.................8.00
Plate, Dinner, 10 1/2 In. ..18.00
Plate, Salad, 8 1/2 In. ....12.00
Platter, Oval, 11 1/2 In. ..60.00

Salt & Pepper ........18.00
Spoon Rest ..........25.00
Sugar, Cover ..........35.00
Tumbler, 8 Oz.,
   3 3/4 In. ...........25.00

### HONEY BEIGE
Bowl, 13 In. ..........125.00

### YELLOW
Bowl, Cereal, 5 1/2 In. ....8.00
Bundt Mold, Swirl,
   7 1/2 In., Pair ........35.00
Casserole, Cover, 3 Qt. ....15.00

## TULIP HALL
Tulip is a 1930s pattern made
by Hall China Company, East
Liverpool, Ohio. It remained
popular until the 1950s. Most
of the pieces were distributed
by Cook Coffee of Cleveland,
Ohio. Pale yellow and purple
tulips were applied by decal.
The ware is trimmed with silver. The same design is found
on a Harker Pottery pattern
called Pastel Tulip.

Bowl, 6 In. ...........27.00
Bowl, 7 1/2 In. ........36.00
Bowl, Fruit, 5 1/2 In. ....10.00
Bowl, Oval, 10 1/2 In. ...35.00

Creamer .............15.00
Mixing Bowl, 6 In. ......27.00
Mixing Bowl, 7 1/2 In. ...36.00
Plate, Dinner, 10 In. .....15.00
Plate, Luncheon, 9 In. ....16.00
Platter, Oval, 13 1/4 In. ..42.00
Sugar, Cover ..........25.00

## TULIP WATT
Watt Pottery Company of
Crooksville, Ohio, made a pattern called Tulip that was sold
in Woolworth's stores. It was
made about 1963. The pattern
featured a red and a blue tulip
with green leaves. Other patterns called Tulip were made
by Hall China Company; Stangl
Pottery; Edwin H. Knowles
China Company; Paden City
Pottery; Universal Potteries;
Leigh Potters; and Royal Pottery. Other patterns called by
the plural name Tulips were
made by Homer Laughlin China
Company; Pottery Guild; Taylor, Smith, and Taylor; and
Blue Ridge.

Baker, Cover, No. 600,
   Ribbed ............340.00
Baker, Cover, No. 601,
   Ribbed ............150.00
Bean Pot, No. 76 ......100.00
Bowl, Salad, No. 73 ....140.00
Bowl, Spaghetti,
   No. 39 ............100.00
Cookie Jar,
   No. 503 ....280.00 to 450.00
Creamer,
   No. 62 ....185.00 to 225.00
Mixing Bowl,
   No. 63 .....65.00 to 110.00
Mixing Bowl, No. 64 ...100.00

**Don't brag about the
value of your collection
to strangers. It might
lead to extra interest by
the local burlgary group.**

Pitcher, No. 16 .......225.00
Pitcher, No. 17,
   Ice Lip .....200.00 to 250.00

## TWEED
Tweed is one of the group of
six plaid patterns made by
Vernon Kilns from 1950 to
1955. The patterns are the same
except that the colors used for
the plaid pattern are different.
Tweed is a yellow and gray-
blue plaid. The other five
related designs are Calico (pink
and blue), Coronation Organdy
(gray and rose), Organdie (yellow and brown), Gingham
(green and yellow), Homespun
(cinnamon, yellow, and green),
and Tam O'Shanter (rust, chartreuse, and dark green).

Cup & Saucer ..........14.00
Creamer, Open .......15.00
Plate, 10 In. ...........16.00

# ·V·

## VILLAGE GREEN
Village Green by Red Wing
Potteries was first made in
1953. It is a heavy pottery set
which is brown on the outside
and green inside. In 1955 they
came out with a related set
called Village Brown, which
was solid brown.

Casserole, Cover ........20.00
Mug, Coffee, 5 In. ......10.00
Pitcher, 7 In. ..........20.00
Salt & Pepper ........15.00

## VIRGINIA ROSE

Virginia Rose is the name of a shape of dishes made by Homer Laughlin China Company, Newell, West Virginia. The shapes were decorated with a variety of decal decorations. The dishes with a design of a spray of roses and green leaves is the pattern most often called Virginia Rose by collectors.

Bowl, Oatmeal . . . . . . . . .5.00
Butter, Cover . . .75.00 to 95.00
Casserole . . . . . . . . . . . .95.00
Pitcher . . . . . . . . . . . . . .98.00
Plate, Luncheon, 8 In. . . . .35.00
Platter, 11 1/2 In. . . . . . . .15.00
Salt & Pepper . . . . . . .140.00
Sauceboat, Liner . . . . . . .25.00
Soup, Coupe . . . . . . . . . .22.00

## VISTOSA

Taylor, Smith, and Taylor of Chester, West Virginia, made a solid-colored dinnerware about 1938 called Vistosa. The plates had piecrust edges, and the other pieces had some bands or ridges. The glaze colors were Cobalt Blue, Deep Yellow, Light Green, and Mango Red. Pieces were marked with the name Vistosa and the initials T.S. & T. Co. U.S.A.

### COBALT BLUE
Bowl, Vegetable . . . . . . .45.00
Creamer . . . . . . . . . . . . .20.00
Cup & Saucer . .15.00 to 18.00
Eggcup . . . . . . . . . . . . .25.00
Plate, Dinner,
   10 In. . . . . . . . .15.00 to 22.00
Sugar . . . . . . . . . . . . . . .15.00
Water Jug . . . . . . . . . . .75.00

### DEEP YELLOW
Cup & Saucer . .15.00 to 17.00
Cup & Saucer,
   After Dinner . . . . . . . .45.00
Salt & Pepper . . . . . . . .22.00
Teapot . . . . . . . . . . . . .100.00

### LIGHT GREEN
Bowl, Salad, Footed,
   12 In. . . . . . . . . . . . .185.00
Chop Plate, 12 In. . . . . . .40.00
Cup & Saucer . .15.00 to 18.00
Plate, Dinner,
   10 In. . . . . . . . .15.00 to 22.00
Plate, Luncheon,
   9 In. . . . . . . . . .15.00 to 20.00
Salt & Pepper . . .20.00 to 30.00
Sauceboat . . . . . . . . . . .125.00
Teapot . . . . . . . . . . . . . .95.00

### MANGO RED
Chop Plate, 14 In. . . . . . .50.00
Cup & Saucer . .16.00 to 20.00
Pitcher, Water . . . . . . . . .85.00
Plate, Bread &
   Butter . . . . . . . .6.00 to 10.00
Plate, Luncheon,
   9 In. . . . . . . . . .15.00 to 20.00
Soup, Coupe . . . .20.00 to 25.00
Sugar, Cover . . . . . . . . . .25.00
Teapot . . . . . . . . . . . . . .85.00

## ·W·

## WAGON WHEEL

Wagon Wheel was made from 1941 to 1983 by Frankoma Pottery. A few pieces are still being made. Many of the pieces in this pattern are shaped like wagon wheels. Most pieces were made in Desert Gold and Prairie Green, a few were made in other colors.

### DESERT GOLD
Baker, Sapulpa Clay,
   3 Qt. . . . . . . . . . . . . .40.00
Bean Pot, Sapulpa Clay,
   Individual . . . . . . . . . .40.00
Bowl, Chili, Ada Clay . . .10.00
Bowl, Dessert,
   Ada Clay . . . . . . . . . . . .8.00
Bowl, Fruit, Ada Clay,
   Small . . . . . . . . . . . . . .10.00
Candleholder, Ada Clay . .25.00
Casserole, Sapulpa Clay . .35.00
Cup . . . . . . . . . . . . . . . .20.00
Cup, Ada Clay . . . . . . . .10.00
Mug, Ada Clay, 16 Oz. . . .12.00
Pitcher, Ada Clay . . . . . .45.00
Plate, Breakfast, Ada
   Clay, 9 In. . . . . . . . . . .13.00
Plate, Dinner, Ada
   Clay, 10 In. . . . . . . . . .10.00
Plate, Dinner, Sapulpa
   Clay, 10 In. . . . . . . . . .10.00
Plate, Luncheon, Ada
   Clay, 8 In. . . . . . . . . . . .8.00
Punch Bowl, Ada Clay,
   10 Qt. . . . . . . . . . . . .100.00
Saucer, Ada Clay . .5.00 to 7.00
Server, Divided, Sapulpa
   Clay . . . . . . . . . . . . . . .25.00
Sugar & Creamer, Sapulpa
   Clay . . . . . . . . . . . . . . .25.00

Teapot, Cover,
   Ada Clay . . . . . . . . . . .35.00

**PRAIRIE GREEN**
Cup . . . . . . . . . . . . . . . . .8.00
Mug, Ada Clay . . . . . . . .15.00
Pitcher, 7 In. . . . . . . . . . .18.00
Plate, Dinner, 10 In. . . . . .20.00
Plate, Salad, Ada Clay,
   7 In. . . . . . . . . . . . . . . . .8.00
Platter, Sapulpa Clay,
   13 In. . . . . . . . . . . . . . .16.00
Salt & Pepper, Ada
   Clay . . . . . . . . .14.00 to 15.00
Sugar, Individual,
   Ada Clay . . . . . . . . . . .10.00
Wall Pocket . . . . . . . . . .30.00

**WHEAT,** see Poppy & Wheat

## WHITE CLOVER

White Clover is a dinnerware that was designed by Russel Wright for Harker Pottery Company of East Liverpool, Ohio. It had the very sleek modern shapes inspired by his other design, American Modern, but a sprig of clover decoration was added. It was made in four colors: Charcoal, Coral Sand, Golden Spice, and Meadow Green. The dinnerware was advertised as ovenproof, chip-resistant, and detergent-resistant. The pattern was discontinued in 1955.

**CHARCOAL**
Plate, Bread & Butter,
   Harker, 6 In. . . . . . . . . .2.50
**GOLDEN SPICE**
Platter, 13 In. . . . . . . . . .50.00
Saltshaker, 4 In. . . . . . . .12.00
**MEADOW GREEN**
Clock Face, Harker . . . . . .12.50
Plate, 9 3/4 In. . . . . . . . . .8.00
Salt & Pepper . . . . . . . .40.00

**WILD POPPY,** see Poppy & Wheat

## WILDFIRE

Great American Tea Company gave Wildfire pattern as a premium. This Hall China Company pattern of the 1950s has a Hi-white body and flower garland decal decoration.

Bowl, 6 In. . . . . . . . . . . . .8.00
Bowl, 8 1/2 In. . . . . . . . . .12.00
Bowl, Oval, 10 1/2 In. . . .20.00
Bowl, Salad, 9 In. . . . . . .12.00
Pitcher, 6 In. . . . . . . . . . . .3.00
Plate, Bread & Butter,
   6 In. . . . . . . . . . . . . . . . .3.00
Plate, Salad, 7 In. . . . . . . .6.00
Salt & Pepper . . . . . . . .50.00
Soup, Dish, 8 1/2 In. . . . . .12.00

## WILDFLOWER

Franciscan made Wildflower pattern in 1942. Other patterns named Wildflower were made by Blue Ridge and Edwin M. Knowles. Pieces listed here are by Franciscan Ceramics.

Ashtray, Mariposa Lily . .100.00
Bowl, 6 1/2 In. . . . . . . . .75.00
Bowl, 8 1/2 In. . . . . . . . .95.00
Casserole . . . . . . . . . . .675.00
Chop Plate, 12 In. . . . . . .275.00

Platter, Oval, 14 In. . . . .425.00
Sugar, Cover . . . . . . . . .250.00

## WILLOW

Willow pattern pictures a bridge, three figures, birds, trees, and a Chinese landscape. The pattern was first used in England by Thomas Turner in 1780 at the Caughley Pottery Works. It was inspired by an earlier Chinese pattern. The pattern has been copied by makers in almost every country. It was made in the United States by Homer Laughlin China Company, Sebring, and others. Pieces listed here are blue unless another color is mentioned. Blue and pink willow was made by the Royal China Company of Sebring, Ohio, from the 1940s through the 1960s.

Bowl, 5 In. . . . . . . . . . . . .3.00
Bowl, Fruit, Royal,
   5 1/2 In. . . . . . . . . . . . . .2.00
Bowl, Royal, 10 1/4 In. . .10.00
Bowl, Vegetable,
   Ridgway . . . . . . . . . . .15.00
Child's Set, 26 Pieces . . .325.00
Chop Plate, Occupied
   Japan . . . . . . . . . . . . . .40.00
Creamer . . . . . . . . . . . . .20.00
Creamer, Angular Handle,
   Royal . . . . . . . . . . . . . . .5.00

Creamer, Occupied Japan,
Medium . . . . . . . . . . . .20.00

Creamer, Pointed Handle,
Royal, 3 In. . . . . . . . . .19.00

Creamer, Round Handle,
Royal . . . . . . . . . . . . .5.00

Creamer, Shenango,
Individual . . . . . . . . . .25.00

Cup & Saucer, Buffalo . . .30.00

Cup & Saucer, Handleless,
Buffalo . . . . . . . . . . . .50.00

Gravy Boat, Double Spout,
Royal . . . . . . . . . . . . . .8.00

Mug . . . . . . . . . . . . . . .15.00

Mug, Inside Decal . . . . . .20.00

Mug, Occupied Japan . . . .15.00

Oil & Vinegar, Stopper,
Tall . . . . . . . . . . . . . . .90.00

Pie Plate, Shallow . . . . . .40.00

Pitcher, Iced Tea, Ice Lip,
Japan . . . . . . . . . . . . .115.00

Plate, Bennett, Brown,
9 In. . . . . . . . . . . . . . . .5.00

Plate, Bread & Butter,
Royal, 6 In. . . . .2.00 to 4.00

Plate, Buffalo, 5 In. . . . . .20.00

Plate, Child's, 4 3/8 In. . . . .9.00

Plate, Dinner, Homer
Laughlin, 10 In. . . . . . . .12.00

Plate, Dinner, Ridgway,
10 In. . . . . . . . .13.00 to 22.00

Plate, Dinner, Royal,
10 In. . . . . . . . . .5.00 to 7.00

Plate, Handle, Royal,
10 1/2 In. . . . . . . . . . . .10.00

Plate, Luncheon, Bennett,
Pink, 8 In. . . . . . . . . . . .4.00

Plate, Luncheon, Ridgway,
9 In. . . . . . . . . . . . . . . .11.00

Plate, Luncheon, Royal,
9 In. . . . . . . . . . . . . . . .5.00

Plate, Salad, 7 In. . . . . . . .5.00

Plate, Salad, Ridgway,
7 In. . . . . . . . . . . . . . .13.00

Plate, Salad, Royal,
7 1/4 In. . . . . . . . . . . . . .3.50

Platter, Oval, Japan,
12 1/2 In. . . . . . . . . . . .24.00

Platter, Rectangular, Bennett,
Brown, 15 In. . . . . . . . .50.00

Platter, Round, Royal,
12 1/4 In. . . . . . . . . . . .10.00

Platter, Round, Royal,
13 1/4 In. . . . . . . . . . . .12.00

Saltshaker, Barrel . . . . . .10.00

Saucer, Buffalo . . . . . . . .10.00

Saucer, Ridgway . . . . . . . .1.00

Shaker, Barrel, Occupied
Japan . . . . . . . . . . . . . .10.00

Soup, Dish, Japan,
7 1/2 In. . . . . . . . . . . . .12.00

Soup, Dish, Ridgway . . . .22.00

Soup, Dish, Royal,
8 3/8 In. . . . . . . . . . . . . .8.00

Soup, Lug, Royal, 7 In. . . .7.00

Sugar, Cover, Pointed
Handle, Royal . . . . . . .24.00

Sugar, Cover, Round
Handle, Royal . . . . . . . .6.00

Sugar & Creamer, Angular
Cover, Royal . . . . . . . . .5.00

Sugar & Creamer, Cover .40.00

Sugar & Creamer, Cover,
Lug, Royal . . . . . . . . .13.00

Sugar & Creamer,
Occupied Japan . . . . . .30.00

Tumbler, Juice, Flat,
3 1/2 In. . . . . . . . . . . . . .6.00

Tumbler, Water . .18.00 to 20.00

Tumbler, Water, Footed,
5 In. . . . . . . . . . . . . . . .9.00

## WINNIE

Winnie is a pattern made in the
1950s by Blue Ridge. It is decorated with off-center red flowers on the Skyline shape.

Berry Bowl . . . . . . . . . . .5.00

Bowl, 9 In. . . . . . . . . . . .18.00

Creamer . . . . . . . . . . . . .10.00

Cup & Saucer . . . . . . . .10.00

Plate, Bread & Butter,
6 In. . . . . . . . . . . . . . . .5.00

Plate, Dinner, 10 In. . . . . .15.00

Platter, 13 In. . . . . . . . . .25.00

Soup, Dish . . . . . . . . . . .10.00

Sugar, Cover . . . . . . . . . .15.00

## ·Z·

### ZEISEL

Eva Zeisel designed the Century and Tomorrow's Classic
shapes for Hall China Company's Hallcraft line in 1952. It
remained popular until the
1960s. The solid white dinnerware, sometimes decorated
with decals, is marked with her
name.

Bowl, 5 3/4 In. . . . . . . . . .5.00

Bowl, Vegetable, Square,
Large . . . . . . . . . . . . . .50.00

Coffeepot . . . . . . . . . . . .170.00

Cup & Saucer . . . . . . . . .8.00

Gravy Boat, Ladle . . . . .100.00

Plate, Bread & Butter,
6 1/2 In. . . . . . . . . . . . . .4.00

Soup, Dish, 7 In. . . . . . . .30.00

Teapot . . . . . . . . . . . . . .245.00

# DINNERWARE FACTORIES, PATTERNS, AND BIBLIOGRAPHY

*Kovels' Depression Glass & Dinnerware Price List* is a concise guide to price and age information. This is a list that will help collectors learn more about dinnerware patterns. Each pottery factory is listed separately with the location and the dates of operation. A list of books that specialize in this type of dinnerware is also included. These books often have many color pictures of dinnerware, reprints of early advertising, and other information. Also included under each factory name is a list of the best-known patterns made by the firm. Not all of these are included in the main body of our book. General reference books on dinnerware are included at the end of this section.

## Abingdon Potteries, Abingdon, Illinois, 1908–1951

### REFERENCE BOOKS
Paradis, Joe. *Abingdon Pottery Artware 1934–1950: Stepchild of the Great Depression.* Atglen, Pennsylvania: Schiffer Publishing Ltd., 1997.
Rehl, Norma. *Abingdon Pottery.* Privately printed, 1981 (P.O. Box 556, Milford, NJ 08848-0556).

### PATTERNS
Abingdon, 1935

## J. A. Bauer Pottery Company, Los Angeles, California, c.1923–c.1958 (Bauer Pottery, 1909–c.1923)

### REFERENCE BOOKS
Chipman, Jack, and Judy Stangler. *Bauer Pottery: 1982 Price Guide.* Privately printed, 1982 (16 E. Holly St., Pasadena, CA 91003).
Tuchman, Mitch. *Bauer Classic American Pottery.* San Francisco, California: Chronicle Books, 1995.

### PATTERNS
Brushes
Cal-Art
California Pottery
El Chico
Hi-Fire, 1930s
La Linda, 1939–1940s

Los Angeles
Monterey, 1934–early 1940s
Modern, 1935
Monterey Moderne, 1948–1962
Moon Song
Ring, 1932–1962

Russel Wright, 1945                          Speck Ware, 1946
Smooth, 1936–1937

## Blair Ceramics, Ozark, Missouri, 1946–1950s

**PATTERNS**

Autumn Leaf                                  Gay Plaid
Bamboo                                       Rick-Rack
Bird                                         Yellow Plaid

## Blue Ridge, see Southern Potteries

## Brusché Ceramics (mark used by J.A. Bauer Pottery Company, c.1950)

**PATTERNS**

Al Fresco, 1950s                             Contempo, 1952

## Buffalo Pottery, Buffalo, New York, established by the Larkin Company after 1902 (Buffalo China Company from 1956, now part of Oneida, Ltd.)

**PATTERNS**

Beverly                                      Dresden
Blue Willow                                  Gaudy Willow
Bungalow                                     Glendale
Coin Gold Band                               Pink Rose

## Caribe-Sterling, Vega Baja, Puerto Rico, early 1950s–1977

**PATTERNS**

Bonita, 1950s–1963                           El Vuelo, 1950s–1963
Caribe Casual, 1950s–1963

## Catalina Pottery, Catalina Island, California, c.1927–1947 (name purchased by Gladding McBean Company in 1937; Catalina name remained in use until 1947)

**REFERENCE BOOKS**

*Catalina Art Pottery Price List and General Sales Instructions, 1942* (catalog reprint). Privately printed, 1982 (Delleen Enge, 912 N. Signal, Ojai, CA 93023).
Fridley, A. W. *Catalina Pottery: The Early Years 1927–1937*. Privately printed, 1977 (P.O. Box 7723, Long Beach, CA 90807).

## PATTERNS

Arabesque, 1935

Art Deco, early 1930s

Octagon, 1930s

Rope Edge, 1936

Trojan, 1930–1940s

## Coors Porcelain, Golden, Colorado, 1910–present (stopped making dinnerware in the 1950s)

### REFERENCE BOOKS

Carlton, Carol and Jim. *Collector's Encyclopedia of Colorado Pottery*. Paducah, Kentucky: Collector Books, 1994.

Schneider, Robert. *Coors Rosebud Pottery*. Privately printed, 1984 (P.O. Box 10382S, Pike Place Station, Seattle, WA 98101).

### PATTERNS

Glencoe, 1920s

Golden, 1930s

Mello-Tone, late 1930s

Rockmount, late 1930s

Rosebud, 1934–1942

Thermo-Porcelain

## Crooksville China Company, Crooksville, Ohio, 1902–c.1960

### PATTERNS

Apple Blossom

Autumn Leaf

Avenue

Black Tulip, 1950s

Blossom Time

Blossoms

Blue Blossoms

Border Bouquet

Border Rose

Brilliance

Calico Chick

Calico Flowers

California James Poppy

Carnival

Country Home

Flamingo

Flower Fair

Gold Drape

Homestead

Hunting

Ivy Vine

Jessie

Kaleidoscope

Little Bouquet

Meadow Flowers

Medallion

Petit Point House

Petit Point Leaf

Pheasant

Pink Border

Posies

Queen Rose

Rose Garden

Rose Garland, 1920s

Roses

Rust Bouquet

Scotch Plaid

Silhouette, 1930s

Southern Belle

Spray

Spring Blossom, 1940s
Swirl
Trellis, 1929

Trotter
Veggies
Willow

## Crown Pottery, Evansville, Indiana, 1882–1962

### PATTERNS

Autumn Leaf
Blue Bird, 1941
Bouquet
Carriage
Croydon, 1941
Dresden, 1941
Garland, 1941
Hawthorne

Laurel, 1941
Navajo
Petit Point, 1941
Poppy
Swedish
Wild Rose, 1941
Windmill

## Franciscan Ceramics Inc., Los Angeles, California, 1934–present (a dinnerware line made by Gladding, McBean & Company, which operated from 1875 to 1984. Franciscan Ceramics has been part of Waterford Wedgwood Group since 1979)

### REFERENCE BOOKS

Enge, Delleen. *Franciscan: Embossed Hand Painted.* Privately printed, 1992 (E. El Roblar Dr., Suite #10, Ojai, CA 93023).

———. *Franciscan Ware.* Paducah, Kentucky: Collector Books, 1981.

Enge, Delleen, and Merrianne Metzger. *Franciscan, Plain & Fancy.* Privately printed, 1997 (121 E. El Roblar Dr., Suite #10, Ojai, CA 93023).

Snyder, Jeffrey B. *Franciscan Dining Services: A Comprehensive Guide with Values.* Atglen, Pennsylvania: Schiffer Publishing Ltd., 1996.

### PATTERNS

Amapola, 1973
Apple, 1940–present
Arcadia, 1941
Autumn, 1955
Canton, 1950
Cherokee Rose, 1941–1942
Coronado, 1936–1956
Coronado Swirl, 1936–1956
Daisy, 1960
Daisy Wreath, 1975

Del Mar, 1937
Desert Rose, 1941–present
Dogwood, 1975
Duet, 1956
Duotone, 1940
El Patio, 1934–1954
Elsinore, 1946
Floral, 1971
Fruit, 1931–1942
Garden Party, 1974

Gingersnap, 1974
Hacienda, 1964
Hawthorne, 1938–1942
Ivy, 1948
Jamoca, 1973
Lorraine, 1946
Mango, 1937–1938
Mariposa, 1949
Maypole, 1974
Meadow Rose, 1977
Mesa, 1950
Mirasol, 1975
Montecito, 1957
Monterey, 1949
Nut Tree, 1970
Oasis, 1955

October, 1977
Palo Alto, 1950
Pebble Beach, 1969
Picnic, 1973
Poppy, 1950
Rancho, 1937–1941
Starburst, 1954
Strawberry Fair, 1979
Tiempo, 1949
Tiger Flower, 1937–1942
Trio, 1954
Wheat, 1951–1953
Wild Flower, 1942
Willow, 1937–1940
Zinnia, 1967

## Frankoma Pottery, Sapulpa, Oklahoma, 1936–present

### REFERENCE BOOKS

Bess, Phyllis and Tom. *Frankoma Treasures.* Privately printed, 1983 (14535 E. 13th
    St., Tulsa, OK 74108).
———. *Suggested Values for Frankoma Treasures.* Privately printed, 1990 (14535
    E. 13th St., Tulsa, OK 74108).
Cox, Susan N. *Collectors Guide to Frankoma Pottery, Book Two.* Privately printed,
    1982 (P.O. Box 2674, La Mesa, CA 92041).
Schaum, Gary V. *Collector's Guide to Frankoma Pottery: 1933–1990.* Gas City,
    Indiana: L-W Book Sales, 1997.

### PATTERNS

Lazybone, 1953
Mayan-Aztec, 1948
Plainsman, 1948

Wagon Wheel, 1941–1983
Westwind, 1962

## French Saxon China Company, East Liverpool, Ohio, 1935 (bought by Royal
China Company in 1964)

### PATTERNS

Aloha
Granada, 1939–1940

Rancho
Thistle

# W. S. George Company, Kittanning, Pennsylvania, 1880–1959

**PATTERNS**

Argosy, 1930

Bird

Blossoms

Blossomtime

Bluebird

Breakfast Nook

Bridle Rose

Country Gentleman

Cynthia

Dogwood

Floral

Flower Rim

Gascon

Iroquois Red

Lido Dalrymple

Mexicana

Mexi-Gren, 1930s

Mexi-Lido

Neville

Peach Blossom

Petalware, late 1930s

Petit Point Rose

Plain-Jane, 1949–present

Poppy

Pussy Willow

Rainbow, late 1930s

Rosita

Rust Floral

Sailing

Shortcake

Springtime, 1940s

Wampum

Wheat

# Gonder Ceramic Art Company, Zanesville, Ohio, 1941–1957

**PATTERNS**

La Gonda, 1950s

# Haeger Potteries, Dundee, Illinois, 1914–present (also called Royal Haeger)

**REFERENCE BOOKS**

Garmon, Lee, and Doris Frizzell. *Collecting Royal Haeger: A Comprehensive Illustrated Price Guide.* Paducah, Kentucky: Collector Books, 1989.

**PATTERNS**

Country Classics

# Hall China Company, East Liverpool, Ohio, 1903–present

**REFERENCE BOOKS**

Cunningham, Jo. *Autumn Leaf Story Price Guide.* Privately printed, 1979 (P.O. Box 4929, Springfield, MO 65808).

Duke, Harvey. *Superior Quality Hall China: A Guide for Collectors.* Privately printed, 1977 (12135 N. State Rd., Otisville, MI 48463).

Miller, C. L. *Jewel Tea Sales and Houseware Collectibles with Value Guide.* Atglen, Pennsylvania: Schiffer Publishing Ltd., 1995.

Miller, C. L. *The Jewel Tea Company: Its History and Products.* Atglen, Pennsylvania: Schiffer Publishing Ltd., 1994.

Whitmyer, Margaret and Kenn. *Collector's Encyclopedia of Hall China.* 2nd edition. Paducah, Kentucky: Collector Books, 1994.

## PATTERNS

Acacia

Adonis, 1952

Airflow Teapot, 1940

Aladdin Teapot, 1939

Albany Teapot, 1930

Albert, 1940s

Alma Teapot

Apple Teapot, 1950s

Automobile Teapot, 1938

Autumn Leaf, 1936–present

Baltimore Teapot, 1930s

Banded, 1937

Basket, 1932–1960

Basketball Teapot, 1938

Basket Teapot, 1938

Bellevue (or Bellvue) Teapot, 1920s–present

Benjamin Teapot, early 1940s

Big Boy

Birch Teapot, early 1940s

Birdcage Teapot, 1939

Bittersweet

Black Beauty, 1935

Blue Blossom, 1939

Blue Bouquet, 1950–1960s

Blue Garden, 1939

Boston Teapot, 1920

Bouquet, 1950s–1960s

Bowknot, early 1940s

Bowling Ball Teapot, late 1930s

Cactus, 1937–1940s

Cameo Rose, 1970s

Caprice, 1952–1957

Carraway

Cattail, 1927

Cleveland Teapot, 1930s

Clover, 1940–1960

Coffee Queen

Colonial Teapot, 1932

Columbia Teapot

Connie Teapot, early 1940s

Coverlet Teapot

Cozy Cover

Crocus, 1930s

Cube Teapot

Cut-A-Way, 1930

Deca-Flip

Disraeli Teapot, 1940s

D-Line, 1936

Donut Teapot, 1938

Eggshell Polka Dot, 1934

English Countryside

E-Style Teapot

Fantasy, 1930s–1940s

Flamingo

Flare Ware Gold Lace, 1960s

Floral Lattice

Flowerpot

Flute, 1935

Football Teapot, 1938–1940

Forman

French Teapot, 1920

Fuji

Fuzz Ball, 1930s

General, 1939

General Electric

Gladstone, 1940
Globe Teapot
Gold Label, 1950s
Grape
Grape Teapot, 1950s
Harlequin
Heather Rose
Hercules, 1940–1941
Hollywood Teapot, late 1920s
Hook Cover Teapot, 1940
Hotpoint
Illinois Teapot, 1920s–early 1930s
Indiana Teapot
Irongate
Johnson Teapot
J-Sunshine
Kansas Teapot
Lipton Teapot
Los Angeles Teapot, 1926
Manhattan Teapot
Marylou
McCormick Teapot, 1907
Meadow Flowers, 1938
Melody Teapot, 1939
Miss Terry
Moderne Teapot, 1930s
Monk's Head
Monticello, 1941–1959
Morning
Morning Glory, 1942–1949
Mountain Flower, 1940
Mt. Vernon, 1940s
Mums, 1930s
Murphy Teapot, early 1940s
Naomi Teapot
Nautilus Teapot, 1939
New York Teapot, 1920
Newport Teapot, early 1930s
Nora, 1950s
Ohio Teapot
Parade Teapot, 1942

Pastel Morning Glory, 1930s
Peach Blossom
Pert Teapot
Petunia, 1932–1969
Philadelphia Teapot, 1923
Phoenix, 1938
Pink Morning Glory
Pink Mums, 1930s
Plain
Plaza, 1930s–1960s
Plum Pudding
Plume Teapot, early 1940s
Polka Dot, 1942
Poppy, 1933–1950s
Poppy & Wheat, 1933
Provincial, 1938
Radiant Ware, 1940s
Rainbow
Red Dot
Red Poppy, 1930–1950
Regal
Regal Teapot, 1950s
Rhythm Teapot, 1939
Richmond, 1941
Ridged
Rio Rose, 1950s
Ronald Reagan Teapot, 1970s
Rose Parade, 1941–1950s
Rose White, 1941
Royal
Royal Rose, late 1940s–early 1950s
Royal Teapot, 1950s
Rutherford Teapot
Saf-Handle Teapot, 1938–1960s
Sani-Grid, 1941
Serenade
Shaggy Tulip, mid-1930s–mid-1940s
Silhouette, 1930s
Sprig Crocus
Springtime
Starlight

Starlight Teapot, 1950s
Star Teapot, 1940
Step-Down
Step-Round
Streamline Teapot, 1937
Sundial Teapot
Sunshine, 1933
Surfside Teapot, 1939
Taverne, 1930s
T-Ball Teapot, 1948
Tea for Two/Tea for Four Teapot
Teataster Teapot, late 1940s
Thistle
Thorley

Tom & Jerry, 1930s
Tritone, 1950s
Tulip, 1930s–1950s
Twinspout Teapot, late 1940s
Twin-Tee Teapot
Victoria, early 1940s
Wildfire, 1950s
Windcrest, 1940s
Windcrest Teapot, 1950s
Windshield Teapot, 1941
World's Fair Teapot
Yellow Rose
Zeisel, 1952–1960s
Zephyr, late 1930s

## Harker Pottery Company, Chester, West Virginia, and East Liverpool, Ohio, 1890–1972

### REFERENCE BOOKS
Colbert, Neva W. *Collector's Guide to Harker Pottery U.S.A.* Paducah, Kentucky: Collector Books, 1992.

### PATTERNS

Amy
Autumn Leaf
Basket
Becky
Birds and Flowers
Blue Rhythm, 1959
Bouquet
Boyce
Brim
Calico Tulip
Cameo Rose, 1940s
Cameo Shellware, 1940s
Cherry
Cherry Blossom
Cherry Trim
Chesterton, 1945–1965
Children's Plates
Colonial Lady
Cottage

Countryside
Deco-Dahlia
Enchantment
Engraved Rooster
Forest Flower
Forever Yours
Fruits
Garden Trail
Heritance
Ivy
Ivy Vine
Jessica
Laurelton
Leaf and Flower
Leaf Swirl
Lotus, 1960s
Mallow
Modern Tulip, 1930s
Pansy

Pastel Tulip
Pate Sur Pate
Petit Point Rose
Pine Cone
Provincial Tulip, 1959
Provincial Wreath
Puritan
Quaker Maid, 1960s
Rawhide, 1960s
Red Apple 1
Red Apple 2
Rooster
Rose Spray
Rosettes
Royal Rose

Ruffled Tulip
Shellridge
Silhouette
Slender Leaf
Springtime
Sun-Glo, 1955
Taverne (Rolling Pin)
Teal Rose, 1952
Vine
Vintage, 1947–1949
Wheat, 1961
White Clover, until 1955
White Rose, 1940s
Wood Song

# Harmony House, see Sears, Roebuck and Co.

# Homer Laughlin China Company, East Liverpool, Ohio, 1877–1929, and Newell, West Virginia, 1905–present

## REFERENCE BOOKS

*Homer Laughlin China Company: A Fiesta of American Dinnerware.* Newell, West Virginia: Homer Laughlin China Co., 1985.

Huxford, Sharon and Bob. *Collector's Encyclopedia of Fiesta.* 7th edition. Paducah, Kentucky: Collector Books, 1992.

Jasper, Joanne. *The Collector's Encyclopedia of Homer Laughlin China: Reference & Value Guide.* Paducah, Kentucky: Collector Books, 1993.

Nossaman, Darlene. *Homer Laughlin China: An Identification Guide.* Revised edition. Privately printed, 1994 (5419 Lake Charles, Waco, TX 76710).

Riederer, LaHoma, and Charles Bettinger. *Fiesta III: A Collector's Guide to Fiesta Dinnerware.* Privately printed, 1980 (P.O. Box 2733, Monroe, LA 71201).

Snyder, Jeffrey B. *Fiesta: Homer Laughlin China Company's Colorful Dinnerware.* Atglen, Pennsylvania: Schiffer Publishing Ltd., 1997.

## PATTERNS

Amberstone, 1967
American Provincial
Apple Blossom, 1935–1955
April
Aristocrat
Bermuda, 1977–1978

Bimini, 1977–1978
Blue Dresden, 1949
Blue Medallion, 1920
Blue Symphony
Bolero, 1977–1978
Briar Rose, 1933

Brittany, 1936–1950s
Call Rose
Capri
Carnation Beauty, 1920
Carnival, late 1930s–early 1940s
Cashmere
Casualstone, 1970
Cavalier, 1950s–1970s
Century, 1931–present
Chateau
Chinese Buddha, 1950s
Clive
Columbine, 1950s
Conchita, 1938
Conchita Kitchen Kraft, 1930s
Coronet, 1935
Country Road, 1977–1978
Crazy Quilt, 1977–1978
Currier & Ives, 1950s
Daisy, 1962–1968
Debutante, 1948–early 1960s
Dick Tracy, 1950
Dogwood, 1960s
Duraprint, 1950s
Early American, 1960s
Eggshell, 1930s–1950s
Eggshell Georgian, 1933–1960s
Eggshell Nautilus, 1937–1950s
Eggshell Theme, 1940s
Elegant Modern
Empress, 1919–1940s
English Garden, 1933
Epicure, 1955
Fiesta, 1936–1972
Fiesta Ironstone, 1970–1972
Fiesta Kitchen Kraft, 1939–early 1940s
Fiesta Wood
Fleur de Lis
Flight of the Swallows, 1930s
Flower Power, 1977–1978
Flowers of the Dell, 1930s

Flying Bluebird, 1920
Fruit Basket, 1977–1978
Gold & Cobalt, 1920
Gold Floral Band, 1920
Gold Garland, 1920
Gold Lace over Cobalt Blue, 1920
Golden Wheat, 1953–1958
Green Valley, 1977–1978
Hacienda, 1938
Harlequin, 1938–1964; 1979
Hollyhock
Jubilee, 1948; 1977–1978
June Rose, 1935
Kitchen Bouquet
Kitchen Kraft, 1930s
Kwaker, 1901–1940s
Lady Alice
Lady Greenbriar
Lady Stratford
Lexington
Liberty, 1928–1950s
Lido, 1977–1978
Louise
Madrid, 1977–1978
Magnolia
Margaret Rose
Marigold, 1930s–1960s
Max-i-cana, 1930s
Mexicana, 1930s
Mexicana Kitchen Kraft, 1938
Mirador, 1977–1978
Nassau
Nautilus, 1930s–1950s
New Art, 1930s
Newell, 1927–1937
Nordic, 1977-1978
Norway Rose
Old English
Orange Tree
Orbit, 1960s
Organdy

Paradise
Petitpoint, 1960s
Piccadilly, 1940s–1950s
Pinecone Spray
Pink Moss Rose, 1920
Pink Rose, 1920
Pink Rose & Daisy, 1920
Priscilla, 1940s–1950s
Queen Esther, 1928
Rambler Rose
Ravenna
Raymond, 1926
Red Tulip
Republic, 1900–1940s
Rhythm, 1951–1958
Rhythm Rose, mid-1940s–1950s
Riviera, 1938–1950
Romance
Rose & Lattice, 1920
Rose Garland Border, 1920
Rosetta
Royal Harvest
Serenade, 1939–1940s
Silver Rose, 1960s
Skyblue, 1977–1978
Skytone
Snowflake, 1920
Sonesta, 1977–1978
Sorrento, 1977–1978

Spring Song
Stardust, 1940s–1950s
Sun Gold, 1953
Sun Porch
Swing, 1938–1950s
Tango, 1930s
Theme, 1939–1990s
Tom Thumb & the Butterfly
Tulip Tree, 1977–1978
Tulip Wreath
Tulips, 1930s
Violet Spray, 1920
Virginia Rose, 1935–1960
Waverly, 1977–1978
Wells, 1930–1935
White & Gold, 1920
White & Gold Carnation, 1920
White & Green Persian, 1920
Wild Bouquet, 1977–1978
Wild Rose
Wild Rose & Flower, 1920
Willow, 1942
Winged Streamliner
Yellow Carnation, 1962–1968
Yellow Matte Gold, 1920
Yellow Matte Gold Band, 1920
Yellowstone, 1927
Zinnia, 1977–1978

## A. E. Hull Pottery Company, Crooksville, Ohio, 1905–1986 (Hull Pottery Company, 1952–1986)

### REFERENCE BOOKS

Hull, Joan Gray. *Hull Shirt Pocket Price List.* Privately printed, 1994 (1376 Nevada SW, Huron, SD 57350).

————. *Hull: The Heavenly Pottery.* 2nd edition. Privately printed, 1992 (1376 Nevada SW, Huron, SD 57350).

Roberts, Brenda. *Roberts' Ultimate Encyclopedia of Hull Pottery.* Privately printed, 1992 (Rt. 2, Highway 65 S., Marshall, MO 65340).

————. *Collectors Encyclopedia of Hull Pottery.* Paducah, Kentucky: Collector Books, 1980.

————. *Companion Guide to Roberts' Ultimate Encyclopedia of Hull Pottery.* Privately printed, 1992 (Route 2, Highway 65 S., Marshall, MO 65340).

**PATTERNS**

Crestone

Red Riding Hood, 1943–1957

---

## Iroquois China Company, Syracuse, New York, 1905–1969

**PATTERNS**

Carrara Modern, 1955
Casual China (Russel Wright), 1946
Impromptu, 1956

Intaglio
Iroquois, 1959–mid 1960s

---

## James River Potteries, Hopewell, Virginia, 1922–1938

**PATTERNS**

Isle of Palms

Pocahontas

---

## Jewel Tea Company, see Hall Autumn Leaf

---

## Johnson Brothers, Ltd., Hanley, England 1883–present (now part of Waterford Wedgwood Group)

**REFERENCE BOOKS**

Finegan, Mary J. *Johnson Brothers Dinnerware Pattern Directory & Price Guide.* Privately printed, 1993 (Marfine Antiques, P.O. Box 3618, Boone, NC 28607).

**PATTERNS**

Friendly Village, 1953–present

---

## Edwin M. Knowles China Company, Chester, West Virginia, 1900–1931, and Newell, West Virginia, 1913–1963. (The trademark was sold to another company in Chester, West Virginia, that makes "collector plates," 1975–present)

**PATTERNS**

Allure, 1960
Ambassador, 1948
Bench
Berkeley, 1955
Black-Eyed Susan, 1959
Blossomtime, 1958
Blue Bells, 1954
Border Rim

Botanica, 1955–1962
Breath O'Spring, 1960
Brown Leaf, 1954
Buttercup, 1948
Caprice, 1954
Carlton, 1955
Carmen, 1958
Cattails, 1955

Celeste, 1961–1963
Celestial, 1955
Chalet, 1955
Choreography, 1955
Classic, 1954–1955
Columbia, 1948
Coral Pine, 1954
Cornflower Blue, 1930s
Coronado, 1948
Corsage, 1954
Country Fair, 1955
Daisies
Damask Rose, 1954
Dawn Rose, 1958
Deanna
Debussy, 1961–1963
Delft, 1957
Dubarry, 1948
Dubonnet, 1955
Duet, 1961–1963
Ebonite, 1954
Eldorado, 1948
Equation, 1955
Evening Song, 1960
Fantasy, 1955
Feather Fantasy, 1955
Festival, 1955; 1957
Fjord, 1959
Fleur de Lis, 1955
Fleurette, 1959
Flight, 1957
Flora, 1948–1955
Florence, 1933–1934
Florida, 1948
Flower Basket
Foliage, 1961–1963
Four Seasons White, 1959–1963
Frosted Leaves, 1955
Fruits
Garden Magic, 1960
Garland, 1948

Golden Foliage, 1960–1963
Golden Laurel, 1930
Golden Wheat, 1936
Golden Wreath, 1960
Gourmet, 1956
Grass, 1957–1962
Green Wheat
Greenbriar, 1959
Happy Days, 1957
Hen Party, 1954
High Sierra, 1955
Highlands, 1957
Hors-d'Oeuvres, 1955
Ingrid, 1954
Isobella, 1948
Jamestown, 1961–1963
Knowles, 1955
Lacquer Blossom, 1957
Leaf Ballet, 1953–1954
Leaf Dane, 1960–1963
Leaf Spray
Lido, 1948
Lucerne, 1960
Mantilla, 1961–1963
Mayfair, 1957
Mayflower, 1957–1963
Meadow Gold, 1954
Ming Tree, c.1954
Mini Flowers
Modern Classic, 1960–1963
Moss Rose, 1954
Navarra, 1955
Nordic Flower, 1959
Oakleaf, 1955
Oslo, 1954
Palm Tree
Pantry Shelf
Park Lane, 1955
Peach Blossom, 1955
Penthouse
Picket Fence

Pink Dogwood, 1960
Pink Pastel
Poppy, 1948
Pretty Pinks, 1957
Provincial Bouquet, 1961–1963
Queen Anne's Lace, 1955–1962
Rambler Rose, 1930s
Reflection, 1960–1963
Rhonda, 1958
Ribbon, 1954
Ring-A-Round, 1959–1963
Romance, 1955
Rose
Rose Bouquet, 1933–1934
Rose Tree, 1955
Rosemont, 1948
Royal Brocade, 1957
Scandia, 1954
Scroll, 1955
Sea Fare, 1957
Seeds, 1956–1962
September Song, 1959
Sequoia, late 1930s
Serenade, 1960
Silver Spray, 1954
Simplicity, 1955
Skiffs
Skylark, 1959
Sleeping Mexican
Snowflower, 1956
Solar, 1957–1966
Southwind, 1959
Star Bright, 1957

Stratosphere, 1955–1957
Suburbia, 1956
Sun Glow, 1958
Sunburst, 1959
Sunnybrook Farm, 1957
Symmetry, 1959
Tea Rose, 1954
Tia Juana
Tiffany, 1955
Tradition, 1948
Tulip
Tuliptime, 1961–1963
Twin Oaks, 1954
Vestal Rose, 1930s
Victoria, 1959
Vintage, 1953–1954
Vistosa, 1936
Water Lily
Weather Bloom, 1933–1934
Weathervane, 1957
Wheat, 1954
Wheat Sheaf, 1955
Wild Oats, 1955
Wild Rose, Regent shape, 1948
Wild Rose, Floral Edge shape,
    1933–1934
Wildflower, 1933–1934
Williamsburg, 1961–1963
Wood Echo, 1957
Wood Violets, 1954
Wrightwood, 1930s
Yellow Trim Poppy
Yorktown, 1936

## Leigh Potters, Inc., Alliance, Ohio, 1926–1938 (Crescent China Company, 1920–1926)

### PATTERNS

Basket
Clio
Fuchsia

Glenedon
Green Wheat
Housetops

Indian Tree
Iris Bouquet
Madison
Manhattan

Mayfair
Petit Point, 1936
Tower
Tulip

**Limoges,** see Sebring Pottery Company

## Metlox Potteries, Manhattan Beach, California, 1935–1989

**REFERENCE BOOKS**
Gibbs, Carl, Jr. *Collector's Encyclopedia of Metlox Potteries.* Paducah, Kentucky: Collector Books, 1996.

**PATTERNS**

Antique Grape, 1964
Blue Dahlia, 1969
Blueberry Provincial, 1962
Blues, 1978
Bottle Brush, 1979
Calico, 1977
California Contempora, 1955
California Apple, 1949
California Aztec, 1955
California Brownstone, 1976
California Confetti, 1955
California Del Rey, 1955
California Freeform, 1954
California Fruit, 1949
California Geranium, 1958
California Golden Blossom, 1953
California Ivy, 1946–1980
California Mobile, 1954
California Palm, 1958
California Peach Blossom, 1952
California Provincial, 1950–1980
California Rose, 1959
California Strawberry, 1961–1980
California Tempo, 1960s
California Whitestone, 1975
Camellia
Cape Cod, 1961

Central Park, 1953
Chantilly Blue, early 1980s
Colonial Heritage, 1956
Colorbands, 1979
Colorstax, 1978–1984
Country Side, 1950s
Della Robbia, 1965
Dill, 1979
Eucalyptus, 1979
Fleur-de-lis, 1964
Floralace, 1975
Geranium, 1976
Gold Dahlia, 1968
Golden Fruit, 1960
Golden Scroll, 1962
Grape Arbor, 1975
Happy Time, 1950s
Homestead Provincial, 1950–1980
Impression Series, 1971
Indiana Summer, 1953
Iris, 1978
Jamestown, 1957
Lavender Blue, 1980
Lotus, 1974
Luau, 1959
Macrame, 1977
Mardi Gras, 1955

Marguerite, 1978
Matilija, 1974
Mayan Necklace, 1964
Memories, early 1980s
Mission Gold, 1966
Mission Verde, 1966
Navajo, 1956
Oh' Susanna, 1975
Painted Desert, 1960
Palm Springs, 1962
Pepper Tree, 1957
Pink Lady, 1965
Pintoria, c. 1937
Pomegranate, 1976
Poppy Trail, 1934–1942
Primary Blue, 1977
Primary Blue Daisies, 1978
Primary Red, 1977
Primary Red Daisies, 1978
Primary Yellow, 1978
Primary Yellow Daisies, 1978
Provincial Blue, 1950–1968
Provincial Flower, 1962
Provincial Fruit, 1961–1980
Provincial Rose, 1958

Provincial Whitestone, 1977
Red Rooster, 1956–1980
Rhythm, 1978
Rooster Bleu, 1966
Sculptured Daisy, 1964
Sculptured Grape, 1963–1975
Sculptured Zinnia, 1964–1980
Shoreline, 1953
Silver Dollar, 1979
Strawflower, 1977
Street Scene, 1956
Tiffany, 1976
Tiffany Yellow, 1976
Tropicana, 1960
True Blue, 1965
Vine Yard, 1965
Vintage Pink, 1965
Wicker Strawberry, 1982
Wicker White, 1982
Wild Poppy, 1972
Wildflower, 1977
William, 1977
Winter Scene, 1950s
Woodland Gold, 1959
Yorkshire, 1939

## Montgomery Ward (sold by Montgomery Ward)

### PATTERNS

Blueberry, 1921
Cascade, 1936
Chartreuse, 1936
Corn Gold, 1921
Emerald, 1921
Fashion White, 1936
Floral Border, 1936
Gold Band, 1920–1936
Gold Initial, 1921

Gold Stripe, 1936
Petit Point, 1936
Pink Print, 1936
Red & Gold, 1936
Snowflake, 1936
Spring Bouquet, 1936
Ward's Garland, 1936
White and Embossed, 1920

# Noritake China, Japan, 1904–present

## REFERENCE BOOKS

Melvin, Florence, and Rodney and Wilma Bourdeau. *Noritake Azalea China: A Reference in Color for Collectors.* Privately printed, 1975 (Red White and Blue Shop, 2 Starr St., Danbury, CT 06810).

Stevenson, Ferne and David. *Noritake Azalea China,* Privately printed, 1987 (730 North 5th St., Hamburg, PA 19526).

## PATTERNS

Azalela, 1918–1941 (made for Larkin Company)

# Paden City Pottery, Paden City, West Virginia, 1914–1963

## PATTERNS

| | |
|---|---|
| Acacia Flowers | Morning Glory |
| American Beauty | Nasturtium, 1940s |
| Arabian Night | Orange Blossom |
| Autumn Leaf | Paden Rose |
| Blossoms | Patio, 1907–1950s |
| Bluebell | Poppy |
| Caliente, 1940s | Posies |
| Capri, 1933 | Red Rose |
| Corn | Rhythm, 1936 |
| Corn Is Green | Rite of Spring |
| Duchess, 1942 | Rococo, 1933 |
| Far East | Rust Tulip |
| Flaming Rose | Sea Shell |
| Floral | Springblossom |
| Grandiose, 1952 | Strawberry |
| Highlight, 1948 | Touch of Black |
| Ivy | Tulip |
| Jonquil | Wild Rose |
| Modern Orchid | Yellow Rose, 1952 |

# Pope-Gosser China, Coshocton, Ohio, 1902–1958

## PATTERNS

Florence, 1940s
Rose Point

## Pottery Guild, New York, New York, 1937–1946

### PATTERNS

| | |
|---|---|
| Apples | Peach |
| Calico Flower | Pear |
| Calico Fruit | Sombrero |
| Hostess Pantry Ware, 1954 | Tulips |

## Purinton Pottery, Wellsville, Ohio, 1936–1941; Shippenville, Pennsylvania, 1941–1951

### REFERENCE BOOKS

Bero-Johnson, Jamie, and Jamie Johnson. *Purinton Pottery with Values*. Atglen, Pennsylvania: Schiffer Publishing Ltd., 1997.

Dole, Pat. *Purinton Pottery*. Privately printed, 1984 (P.O. Box 4782, Birmingham, AL 35206).

———. *Purinton Pottery Book II*. Privately printed, 1990 (142 W. Salisbury St., P.O. Box 308, Denton, NC 27239-0308).

Morris, Susan. *Purinton Pottery*. Paducah, Kentucky: Collector Books, 1994.

### PATTERNS

| | |
|---|---|
| Apple, 1940s–1959 | Normandy Plaid, 1950s |
| Chartreuse, 1949–1959 | Palm Tree, 1936–1959 |
| Crescent | Palm Tree Intaglio |
| Fruit, 1940s | Peasant Garden |
| Harmony, 1949–1959 | Pennsylvania Dutch, 1936–1959 |
| Heather Plaid, 1950s | Petals, late 1940s–1959 |
| Intaglio, 1950–1959 | Provincial Fruit, 1950s |
| Maywood, 1950–1959 | Saraband, early 1950s–1959 |
| Ming Tree, 1950s | Seaform, mid-1950s–1959 |
| Mountain Rose, 1940s–1959 | Tea Rose, mid-1950s–1959 |

## Red Wing Potteries, Inc., Red Wing, Minnesota, 1878–1967

### REFERENCE BOOKS

Bougie, Stanley J., and David A. Newkirk. *Red Wing Dinnerware*. Privately printed, 1980 (Rt. 3, Box 141, Monticello, MN 55362).

Dollen, B. L. *Red Wing Art Pottery Identification & Value Guide, 1920s–1960s*. Paducah, Kentucky: Collector Books, 1997.

Newkirk, David A. *Guide to Red Wing Prices*. Privately printed, 1982 (Rt. 3, Box 146, Monticello, MN 55362).

Reiss, Ray. *Red Wing Art Pottery, Including Pottery Made for RumRill: Classic American Pottery from the 30s, 40s, 50s, & 60s*. Chicago: Property Publishing, 1996.

————. *Red Wing Dinnerware Price and Identification Guide.* Chicago: Property Publishing, 1997.

Simon, Dolores. *Red Wing Pottery with Rumrill.* Paducah, Kentucky: Collector Books, 1980.

## PATTERNS

Adobestone, 1967

Ardennes, 1941

Blossom Time, 1941

Blue Shadows, 1964

Bob White, 1956–1967

Brittany, 1941

Brocade, 1964

Bud, 1941

Capistrano, 1953–1967

Caprice, 1952

Charstone Bleu, 1967

Chevron, 1935

Chrysanthemum, 1941

Chuck Wagon, 1955

Colonnes, 1960

Country Garden, 1953

Crazy Rhythm, 1960

Crocus, 1960

Daisy Chain, 1960

Damask, 1964

Delta Blue, 1951

Desert Sun, 1962

Driftwood, 1953

Ebb Tide, 1965

Fantasy, 1941

Flight, 1962

Fondoso, 1938

Frontenac, 1960

Fruit, 1941

Golden Viking, 1960

Granada, 1960

Greenwichstone, 1967

Harvest, 1941

Hearthside, 1955

Hearthstone, 1961

Heatherstone, 1967

Heatherstone Beige, 1967

Heatherstone Orange, 1967

Iris, 1941

Ivanhoe, 1937

Kashmir, 1964

Kermis, 1957

Labriego, 1942

Lanterns, 1941

Lexington, 1942

Lotus, 1941

Lupine, 1960

Lute Song, 1960s

Magnolia, 1941

Majestic, 1960

Mediterrania, 1960

Merrileaf, 1960

Midnight Rose, 1953

Montmartre, 1960

Morning Glory, 1941

Nassau, 1941

Normandy, 1941

Northern Lights, 1960

Orleans, 1941

Pepe, 1963

Picardy, 1951

Pink Spice, 1953

Plain, 1935

Plum Blossom, 1949

Pompeii, 1962

Provincial, 1951

Quartette, 1941

Random Harvest, 1961

Red Wing Rose, 1960

Reed, 1935

RoundUp, 1958

Smart Set, 1955

Spring Song, 1941
Spruce, 1956
Tahitian Gold, 1962
Tampico, 1955
Tip Toe, 1955
Town & Country, 1947–1954
Turtle Dove, 1962
Tweed Tex, 1953

Two Step, 1951
Village Brown, 1951
Village Green, 1951
Vintage, 1960
White and Turquoise, 1956
Willow Wind, 1941
Zinnia, 1941

## Roseville Pottery Company, Zanesville, Ohio, 1892–1954

### REFERENCE BOOKS
Huxford, Sharon and Bob. *The Collectors Encyclopedia of Roseville Pottery.* Paducah, Kentucky: Collector Books, 1976. Updated 1993 values.

### PATTERNS
Raymor, 1952–1953

## Royal China Company, Sebring, Ohio, 1933–1986

### REFERENCE BOOKS
Aupperle, Eldon R. *A Collector's Guide for Currier & Ives Dinnerware.* Privately printed, 1996 (29470 Saxon Rd., Toulon, IL 61483).

### PATTERNS
Bluebell, 1940s
Brentwood
Casa del Sol
Casablanca
Clear Day
Colonial Homestead, 1950–1952
Currier & Ives, 1940s–1986
Dynasty
Hidden Valley
Medici

Memory Lane
Middlebury
Night Song
Old Curiosity Shop, 1940s
Overture
Sunny Day
Triple Treat
Tulip
Willow, 1960s

## Sabin Industries, McKeesport, Pennsylvania, 1946–1979

### PATTERNS
Floral Birdsong, 1946
Golden Crown
Jacobean, 1946
Pastel Garden

Pompadour, 1946
Regal Rings, 1946
Tudor Rose

## Salem China Company, Salem, Ohio, 1898–1967

**PATTERNS**

Anniversary, 1943
Aristocrat
Basket
Basket of Tulips
Basket Petit Point
Bluebird
Breeze, 1948
Bridge
Bryn-Mawr
Cadet Series
Cherry, 1951
Colonial
Commodore
Dominion
Dutch Petit Point
Formal
Fruit Basket
Garden Design, 1940s
Goldtrim, 1952
Indian Tree
Jane Adams, 1950s
Jeanette
Jonquil
Landscape, 1940s
Mandarin Red
Mandarin Tricorne

Maple Leaf
Midsummer
Monogram
Moon Flower
Parsley
Petit Point Basket
Polo
Red Berry
Rio, 1943
Rose-Marie
Royal Windsor, 1950s
Rust Tulip
Sailing
Sampler
Sandra, 1950s
Sheffield, 1943
Standard
Summer Day
Tricorne, 1934
Tulip
Victory
Vienna, 1940s
Windmill
Woodhue
Woodland
Yellowridge

## Scio Pottery Company, Scio, Ohio, 1932–1985

**PATTERNS**

Currier & Ives
Dorset

Hazel

## Sears, Roebuck and Company (sold by Sears, Roebuck and Company; pieces usually marked Harmony House or Sunrise)

**PATTERNS**

Acorn
Cat-Tail, made by Universal Potteries, 1934–1956

Colonial Homestead, made by Royal China Company, 1960s

Monticello, made by Hall China
Company, 1941–1959

Mt. Vernon, made by Hall China
Company, 1940s

## Sebring Pottery Company, Sebring, Ohio, 1887–1955 (Sebring Pottery Company, American Limoges China Company, and Salem China Company combined under same management, c.1940)

### PATTERNS

Asbury, 1940s
Blue Willow
Buddah
Casino, c.1954
Chateau-France
Doric
Federal, 1942
Gadroon
Heirloom
Jade Ware, 1940s
Joan of Arc
Karen, 1940
Meerschaum, c.1940s
Midsummer, 1940
New Princess
Old Dutch
Old Mexico

Old Virginia Fashionware, 1942
Posey Shop, 1944–1945
Red Poppy Head
Red Sails, c.1940s
Rose Marie
Royal Marina, 1944–1945
Ship Ahoy, 1940s
Square
Tahiti, 1938
Thin Swirl
Toledo Delight, 1941–1942
Triumph
Trojan
Vermillion Rose
Waldorf, 1939
Wheatfield
White Gold Ware, 1940s

## Shawnee Pottery Company, Zanesville, Ohio, 1936–1961

### REFERENCE BOOKS

Curran, Pamela Duvall. *Shawnee Pottery: The Full Encyclopedia with Value Guide.* Atglen, Pennsylvania: Schiffer Publishing Ltd., 1995.

Mangus, Jim and Bev. *Shawnee Pottery: An Identification & Value Guide.* Paducah, Kentucky: Collector Books, 1994.

Simon, Dolores. *Shawnee Pottery.* Paducah, Kentucky: Collector Books, 1977.

Supnick, Mark E. *Collecting Shawnee Pottery.* Revised edition. Gas City, Indiana: L-W Book Sales, c.1989. Revised 1997 price guide.

Vanderbilt, Duane and Janice. *The Collector's Guide to Shawnee Pottery.* Paducah, Kentucky: Collector Books, 1992.

### PATTERNS

Corn King, 1954
Corn Queen, 1954–1961

Lobster Ware, 1954–1956

# Southern Potteries, Inc. (Blue Ridge), Erwin, Tennessee, 1917–1957

## REFERENCE BOOKS

Keillor, Winnie. *Dishes What Else? Blue Ridge of Course!* Privately printed, 1983 (5731 Gorivan Rd., Frankfort, MI 49635).

Newbound, Betty and Bill. *Southern Potteries Incorporated: Blue Ridge Dinnerware.* 3rd edition. Paducah, Kentucky: Collector Books, 1989.

Ruffin, Frances and John. *Blue Ridge China Today: A Comprehensive Identification and Price Guide for Today's Collector.* Atglen, Pennsylvania: Schiffer Publishing Ltd., 1997.

## PATTERNS

Abundance
Alexandria
Alleghany
Aloaha, 1950s
Amarylis
Amherst
Anemone
Antique Leaf
Appalachian Spring
Apple & Pear, 1950s
Apple Crisp, 1950s
Apple Crunch, 1948
Apple Jack, 1950s
Arlene
Arlington Apple, 1950s
Ashland
Astor Fruit
Atlanta, 1950s
Aurora
Autumn Apple, 1941
Autumn Breeze, 1950s
Autumn Laurel
Bamboo, 1950s
Barbara
Bardstown, 1950s
Basketweave, 1950s
Beaded Apple
Beatrice, 1950s
Becky
Belle Haven, 1950s

Bellemeade
Berea Blossom
Berry Patch, 1950s
Berryville
Bethany Berry, 1950s
Betty, 1950s
Big Apple
Bittersweet, 1950s
Black Ming, 1950s
Blackberry Lily
Bleeding Heart
Blossom Tree, 1950s
Blue Bouquet
Blue Flower
Blue Heaven
Blue Moon
Blue Tango
Blue Willow
Bluebell Bouquet
Bluefield
Bonsai, 1950s
Bosc
Bountiful
Bouquet
Bourbon Rose
Bow Knot
Bramwell
Breckenridge
Briar Patch
Bridal Bouquet

Bristol Bouquet
Bristol Lily
Brittany
Brownie
Brunswick
Buttercup
Butterfly and Leaves
Cactus
Cadenza, 1948
Caladium, 1950s
Calais
Calico
Calico Farm, 1950s
California Poppy, 1950s
Callaway, 1948
Camelot, 1948
Candied Fruit
Cantata, 1948
Carlise
Carnival
Caroline, 1950s
Carretta Cattail, 1950s
Cassandra
Cattails, 1950s
Champagne Pinks, 1940s–1950s
Chanticleer, 1950s
Cheerio, 1950s
Cherokee Rose, 1950s
Cherries Jubilee
Cherry Blossom
Cherry Cobbler
Cherry Coke
Chicken Feed, 1950s
Chicken Pickins, 1950s
Chickory
Chintz
Christmas Doorway, 1950s
Christmas Tree
Chrysanthemum
Cinnabar
Clairborne

Clover, 1947–1954
Cock o' the Morn, 1950s
Cock o' the Walk, 1948
Cock-a-Doodle, 1950s
Cocky-Locky
Colonial Birds No. 1
Colonial Birds No. 2
Colonial Rose
Color Stitch
Columbine, 1950s
Concorde
Confetti
Constance
Coreopsis
Corsage
Cosmos, 1950s
Country Fruit, 1950s
Country Garden
Country Road
County Fair
Cowslip
Crab Apple, 1930–1957
Crab Orchard
Cradle
Crocus
Cross Stitch
Cumberland, 1948
Cynthia, 1949
Daffodil, 1948
Dahlia, 1948
Dandridge Dogwood, 1950s
Daydream
Deep Purple
Delft Rose
Delicious
Della Robbia, 1948
Desert Flower, 1950s
Dewberry
Dixie Harvest (No. 3913), 1949
Dogwood, 1950s
Dream Flower

Dreambirds
Dresden Doll
Duff
Dutch Bouquet
Dutch Iris
Dutch Tulip
Edgemont
Eglantine
Evening Flower, 1950s
Eventide, 1950s
Fairmede Fruits
Fairmount, 1950s
Fairy Bells
Fairy Tale
Falling Leaves
Falmouth, 1950s
Fantasia, 1950s
Fantasy Apple, 1950s
Farmer Takes a Wife
Farmhouse, 1950s
Farmyard, 1950s
Fayette Fruit
Feathered Friends, 1950s
Festive, 1950s
Field Daisy
Fireside, 1950s
Fisherman
Flight, 1950s
Flirt, 1950s
Flounce
Flower Bowl
Flower Fantasy, 1954
Flower Ring
Flower Wreath
Floweret, 1950s
Flowering Berry
Fluffy Ruffles
Forest Fruits, 1950s
Fox Grape
Foxfire, 1950s
Frageria, 1950s

French Peasant
Fruit Cocktail
Fruit Fantasy
Fruit Punch
Fruit Ring
Fruit Salad
Fruit Sherbet
Fruitful
Fuchsia
Full Bloom
Gaity
Garden Flowers
Garden Lane
Garden Pinks, 1950s
Garland
Gingham Fruit, 1950s
Gooseberry
Grandfather's Clock
Grandmother's Garden
Granny Smith Apple, 1950s
Grape Salad
Grass Flower, 1950s
Green Briar, 1948
Green Eyes, 1950s
Greensville, 1950s
Gumdrop Tree
Gypsy
Gypsy Dancer
Ham 'n Eggs
Harvestime, 1950s
Hawaiian Fruit, 1948
Heirloom
High Stepper
Highland Ivy, 1949
Hilda
Hollyberry
Hollyhock
Homeplace, 1950s
Homestead, 1950s
Honolulu
Hopscotch

Jan
Jellico, 1950s
Jessamine, 1948
Jessica
Jigsaw, 1950s
Joanna
Jonquil
Joyce
June Apple, 1950s
June Bouquet
June Bride
June Rose
Karen
Kate
Kimberly, 1950s
Kingsport
Kitchen Shelf
Language of Flowers
Laura
Laurie
Lavalette, 1950s
Lavender Fruit
Leaves of Fall, 1950s
Ledford
Lenore
Lexington
Little Violet
Liz
Louisiana Lace
Love Song
Madras
Magic Flower
Magnolia, 1948
Manassas
Maple Leaf, 1950s
Mardi Gras, 1943
Mardi Gras Variant
Mariner
Mary
Mayflower, 1950s
Meadow Beauty

Meadowlea, 1950s
Medley
Memory Lane
Memphis
Meylinda
Mickey
Ming Blossom, 1950s
Ming Tree (No. 4387), 1950s
Mod Tulip
Moss Rose (No. 4486), 1950s
Mountain Aster
Mountain Bells
Mountain Cherry, 1951
Mountain Ivy, 1951
Mountain Nosegay
Mountain Sweetbriar, 1950s
Muriel
Nadine
Nautical
Night Flower, 1952
Nocturne
Norma
Normandy, 1950s
North Star Cherry
Obion
Orchard Glory
Oriental Poppy
Orion
Painted Daisy
Pandora
Paper Roses
Partridge Berry, 1950s
Pastel Poppy
Patchwork Posy
Patricia, 1950s
Pauline
Pembrooke
Penny Serenade
Peony
Peony Bouquet
Periwinkle

Petunia
Picardy
Piedmont Plaid
Pilgrims, 1950s
Pinecone, 1950s
Pink Dogwood, 1950s
Pink Petticoat
Pinkie, 1950s
Pippin, 1950s
Plantation Ivy, 1950s
Plum
Plum Duff
Plume
Poinsettia, 1950
Polka Dot
Pom Pom
Potpourri
Primrose Path
Priscilla
Pristine
Queen Anne's Lace, 1950s
Quilted Fruit, 1950s
Quilted Ivy, 1950s
Rainelle
Razzle Dazzle, 1950s
Red Apple
Red Bank
Red Barn, 1950s
Red Cone Flower
Red Rooster
Red Tulip
Red Willow
Rhapsody
Ribbon Plaid, 1950s
Ridge Rose
Ring-O-Roses, 1948
Roan Mountain Rose
Roanoke
Rock Castle, 1950s
Rock Garden, 1950s
Rock Rose
Rockport Rooster

Rooster (or Game Cock), 1950s
Rooster Motto
Rosalinde
Rose Hill
Rose Red
Rosette
Rosey, 1950s
Roundelay (No. 4499)
Ruby
Rugosa
Rustic Plaid, 1950s
Rutledge
Sampler, 1948
Saratoga, 1952
Sarepta
Shadow Fruit, 1950s
Sherry
Shoo Fly
Showgirl
Signal Flags, 1948
Silhouette, 1950s
Skyline Songbirds, 1950s
Smoky Mountain Laurel
Snappy
Soddy-Daisy, 1950s
Sonata, 1950s
Songbirds
Southern Camellia, 1948
Southern Dogwood, 1950s
Sowing Seed
Spiderweb, 1950s
Spindrift
Spray, 1950s
Spring Glory
Spring Hill Tulip
Square Dance
Squares, 1950s
Stanhome Ivy, 1954
Stardancer
Still Life
Strathmoor
Strawberry Patch

Strawberry Sundae, 1950s
Streamers, 1950s
Sun Drops
Sunbright
Sundance
Sundowner
Sunfire
Sunflower, 1947
Sungold
Sunny
Sunrise, 1950s
Sunshine
Susan, 1950s
Susannah
Sweet Clover
Sweet Pea
Sweet Rocket, 1950s
Symphony
Tanglewood
Tazewell Tulips
Tempo, 1948
Texas Rose
Thanksgiving Turkey, 1950s
Think Pink
Thistle, 1954
Tic Tack, 1948
Tickled Pink
Tiger Lily
Tropical, 1920–1957
Tulip Trio
Tuliptime
Tuna Salad, 1950s
Turkey with Acorns, 1950s

Unicoi
Valley Violet
Vegetable Patch, 1950s
Veggie, 1950s
Verona
Veronica
Victoria
Vintage
Violet Spray, 1950s
Waltz Time
Waterlily
Weathervane (No. 4277), 1950s
Wheat, 1950s
Whirligig, 1950s
Wild Cherry No. 1, 1950s
Wild Cherry No. 2, 1950s
Wild Cherry No. 3, 1950s
Wild Irish Rose
Wild Rose
Wild Strawberry
Wildfire
Wildwood
Windflower, 1940s
Windjammer
Winesap, 1950s
Winnie, 1950s
Wishing Well, 1950s
Wren
Wrinkled Rose
Yellow Poppy
Yorktown
Zinnia

## Stangl Pottery, Flemington and Trenton, New Jersey, 1930–1978

### REFERENCE BOOKS

Duke, Harvey. *Stangl Pottery*. Radnor, Pennsylvania: Wallace-Homestead, 1993.
Rehl, Norma. *Collectors Handbook of Stangl Pottery*. Privately printed, 1979 (P.O. Box 556, Milford, NJ 08848).
———. *Stangl Pottery, Part II*. Privately printed, 1982 (P.O. Box 556, Milford, NJ 08848).

## PATTERNS

ABC, mid-1940s–1974
Adrian, 1972–1974
Amber Glo, 1954–1962
Americana, 1930s
Antiqua, 1972–1974
Apple Delight, 1965–1974
Aztec, 1967–1968
Bachelor's Button, 1965
Bella Rosa, 1960–1962
Bit Series, mid-1940s–1974
Bittersweet
Blossom Ring, 1967–1970
Blue Bell, 1942
Blue Carousel, mid-1940s–1974
Blue Daisy, 1963–1974
Blue Elf, mid-1940s–1974
Blue Tulip                    .
Blueberry, 1940
Bo Peep, mid-1940s–1974
Bonita
Brown Satin
Bunny Lunch, mid-1940s–1974
Carnival, 1954–1957
Cat and the Fiddle, mid-1940s–1974
Cherry, 1940
Chicory, 1961
Circus Clown, mid-1940s–1974
Colonial, 1926
Colonial Dogwood
Colonial Rose, 1970–1974
Colonial Silver, 1970
Concord, 1957
Cookie Twins, mid-1940s–1971
Cosmos
Country Garden, 1956–1974
Country Life, 1956–1967
Cranberry
Crocus
Dahlia, 1970–1974
Daisy, 1936–1942

Deco-Delight
Delmar, 1972–1974
Diana, 1972–1974
Dogwood, 1965
Ducky Dinners, mid-1940s–1974
Fairlawn, 1959–1962
Festival, 1961–1967
Field Daisy, 1941–1942
First Love, 1968–1973
Five Little Pigs, mid-1940s–1974
Flora, 1941
Floral, 1941–1942
Floral Plaid, 1940–1942
Florentine, 1958
Florette, 1961–1962
Frosted Fruit, 1957
Fruit, 1942–1974
Fruit & Flowers, 1957–1974
Galaxy, 1963–1970
Garden Flower, 1947–1957
Garland, 1957–1967
Ginger Boy, mid-1940s–1974
Ginger Cat, mid-1940s–1974
Ginger Girl, mid-1940s–1974
Golden Blossom, 1964–1974
Golden Grape, 1963–1972
Golden Harvest, 1953–1973
Grape, 1973–1974
Green Grapes
Harvest
Heritage
Holly, 1967–1972
Humpty Dumpty, mid-1940s–1974
Indian Campfire, mid-1940s–1974
Inspiration, 1967–1968
Jack in the Box, mid-1940s–1974
Jonquil
Kitten Capers, mid-1940s–1974
Kumquat
Laurel, 1942

Laurita
Lime, 1950
Little Boy Blue, mid-1940s–1974
Little Quackers, mid-1940s–1974
Lyric, 1954–1957
Magnolia, 1952–1962
Maple Whirl, 1965–1967
Mary Quite, mid-1940s–1974
Mealtime Special, mid-1940s–1974
Mediterranean, 1965–1974
Monterey, 1967–1968; 1970
Morning Blue, 1970
Mother Hubbard, mid-1940s–1974
Mountain Laurel, 1947–1957
Newport, 1940–1942
Norma
Old Orchard, 1941–1942
Olivia
Orchard Song, 1962–1974
Our Barnyard Friends
Paisley, 1963–1967
Peter Rabbit
Petite Flowers, 1970–1974
Pie Crust, 1969
Pink Carousel, mid-1940s–1974
Pink Cosmos, 1966
Pink Dogwood
Pink Fairy, mid-1940s–1974
Pink Lily, 1953–1957
Playful Pups, mid-1940s–1974
Plum, 1940
Pony Tail, mid-1940s–1974
Posies, 1973
Prelude, 1949–1957

Provincial, 1957–1967
Ranger
Ranger Boy, mid-1940s–1974
Red Ivy, 1957
Rialto
Ringles, 1973–1974
Rooster, 1970–1974
Roxanne, 1972–1974
Rustic, 1965–1974
Rustic Garden, 1972–1974
Sculptured Fruit, 1966–1974
Sesame, 1972–1974
Sierra, 1967/1968–1970
Spun Gold, 1965–1967
Star Flower, 1952–1957
Stardust, 1967
Sunshine
Susan, 1972–1974
Terra Rose, 1941–1942
Thistle, 1951–1967
Tiger Lily, 1957–1962
Town & Country, 1970s
Trinidad, 1972–1974
Tulip, 1942–1973
Water Lily, 1949–1957
White Dogwood, 1965–1974
White Grape, 1967
Wild Rose, 1955–1973
Wildwood
Windfall, 1955–1957
Wizard of Oz, mid-1940s–1974
Woman in the Shoe, mid-1940s–1974
Wood Rose, 1973–1974
Yellow Flower, 1970

## Sterling China Co., East Liverpool, Ohio, 1917–present

### REFERENCE BOOKS

*Sterling Vitrified China.* Catalog. East Liverpool, Ohio: Sterling China Company, 1991.

## PATTERNS

Russel Wright, 1948                    Sterling, 1947

---

# Steubenville Pottery Company, Steubenville, Ohio, 1879–c.1960

## PATTERNS

Adam                                   Rhea
American Modern, 1939–1959             Rose Bud
Aztec                                  Shalimar
Aztec on Desert Sand                   Spring
Jean                                   Susan
Lenore                                 Tyrol
Monticello                             Violet
Pate-Sur-Pate                          Woodfield
Remembrance

---

**Sunrise,** see Sears, Roebuck and Company

---

# Syracuse China Corporation, Syracuse, New York, 1871–present

## PATTERNS

Edmonton
Rose Leaf
Traveler, 1937–1969
Vogue

---

# Taylor, Smith and Taylor, Chester, West Virginia, and East Liverpool, Ohio, 1901 (sold to Anchor Hocking Corporation in 1972; production ended in 1981)

## REFERENCE BOOKS

Meehan, Kathy and Bill. *Collector's Guide to Lu-Ray Pastels.* Paducah, Kentucky: Collector Books, 1995.

## PATTERNS

Alia Jane, 1933–1934                   Coffee Time, 1950s
Autumn Harvest                         Conversation, 1951
Beverly, 1940                          Coral-Craft, 1939
Blue Crocus, 1940                      Daisy
Boutonnier, 1958–1965                  Design 69
Bridal Flower                          Dianthus, 1958–1965
Center Bouquet, 1930–1940              Dogwood, 1942
Chinese Temple, 1937                   Dutch Tulip, 1940

Dwarf Pine, 1950
Emma Susan, 1933–1934
Ever Yours, 1958–1965
Fairway, 1934–1940s
Floral Bouquet, early 1930s
Garland, 1933–1942
Green Dots, early 1930s
Happy Talk, 1958–1965
Heathertone, 1930–1940
King O' Dell, 1950s
Laurel, 1930s
Leaf
Lu-Ray, after 1938
Mexican Fantasy, 1940
Morningside, late 1920s
Moulin Rouge, 1958–1965
Mums
Pebbleford, 1958–1965
Peppermint Roc, 1960–1972

Petit Point
Petit Point Bouquet, late 1920s
Platinum Blue, 1960s
Red Wheat, 1938
Reveille, 1958–1965
Rooster, 1950–1960
Rose Lattice, 1930–1940
Shasta Daisy, 1960s
Sirocco, 1960s
Sweet Pea
Taverne
Touch of Brown
Tulips
Twilight Time, 1958–1965
Versatile, 1950
Vine Wreath, 1933–1934
Vistosa, 1938
Wood Flower, 1960s

## Universal Potteries, Inc., Cambridge, Ohio, 1934–1956

**PATTERNS**

Autumn Fancy
Ballerina, 1947–1956
Ballerina Mist, 1950s
Bird in the Heart
Bittersweet, 1942–1949
Calico Fruit, 1940s
Cat-Tail, 1934–1956
Fountain, 1950
Fruit & Flowers
Hazelnut
Hollyhock
Iris

Largo
Mermaid, 1950
Moss Rose, 1953–1955
Painted Desert, 1950
Passy, 1950
Rambler Rose
Roxanna
Thistle
Tulip
Windmill
Woodvine

## Vernon Kilns, Los Angeles and Vernon, California, 1912–1958 (name and molds purchased by Metlox Potteries)

**REFERENCE BOOKS**

Nelson, Maxine. *Collectible Vernon Kilns: An Identification & Value Guide.* Paducah, Kentucky: Collector Books, 1994.

————. *Versatile Vernon Kilns.* Privately printed, 1978 (P.O. Box 1686, Huntington Beach, CA 92647).

————. *Versatile Vernon Kilns Book II.* Paducah, Kentucky: Collector Books, 1983.

## PATTERNS

Abundance, 1939

After Glow, 1935–1937

Anytime, 1955–1958

Aquarium, 1938

Arcadia, 1942; 1950–1955

Autumn Ballet, 1940

Banana Tree, 1937

Banded Flower, 1935–1937

Barkwood, 1953–1958

Beige, 1935–1937

Bel Air, 1940; 1955

Bellflower, 1939

Beverly, 1942

Bird Pottery, early 1930s

Bird's Eye

Blend No. 4, 1938

Blend No. 10, 1938

Blossom Time, 1942

Blossoms, 1937

Blue Bow, 1938

Blue Feather, 1938

Blue Star (Constellation), 1938

Blueberry Hill, 1957–1958

Bouquet, 1938

Briar Rose, 1944

Brown Eyed Susan, 1938–1958

Calico, 1949–1955

California Originals, 1947; 1954

California Series, 1930s

California Shadows, 1953; 1955

Carmel, 1942–1950

Casa California, 1938

Casual California, 1947–1956

Chatelaine, 1953

Chinling, 1950

Chintz, 1942; 1950

Choice, 1939

Coastline, 1937

Colleen, 1939

Coral Reef, 1940

Coronado, 1935–1939 (grocery promotion)

Cosmos, 1942

Cottage Window, 1937

Country Cousin, 1957–1958

Country Side, 1950

Dainty, 1935–1947

Delight, 1940

Desert Bloom, 1944; 1955

Desert Mallow

Dewdrop Fairies, 1940

Dis 'N Dot, 1957–1958

Disney, 1940–1941

Dolores, 1942–1947

Dreamtime, 1950

Duo-Tone, 1938

Early California, 1935–1947

Early Days, 1944; 1950–1955

Ecstasy, 1940

Enchantment, 1940

Evening Star, 1935–1937

Fairyland, 1940

Fantasia, 1940

Five Fingers, 1938

Fleur de Lis

Flora, 1938

Floral Series, 1935–1937

Floret, 1939

Flower Ballet, 1940

Four Winds, 1950

Frolic, 1955

Frontier Days, 1950; 1954

Fruitdale, 1942–1947

Garden Plates, 1938

Gayety, 1948; 1954
Gingham, 1949–1958
Glamour, 1938
Golden Maple, 1935–1937
Good Earth
Grace, 1939
Harvest, 1938
Hawaii, 1942
Hawaiian Coral, 1952; 1956
Hawaiian Flowers, 1938
Heavenly Days, 1956–1958
Heyday, 1954–1958
Hibiscus, 1944; 1954
Hilo, 1938
Homespun, 1949–1958
Honolulu, 1938
Imperial, 1955–1956
Joy, 1940
Lei Lani, 1938–1942; 1947–1955
Linda, 1940
Little Mission, 1937
Lollipop Tree, 1957–1958
Lotus, 1950
Marine, 1937
Mariposa Tulip
May and Vieve Hamilton
May Flower, 1942–1955
Meadow Bloom, 1947
Melinda, 1942
Mexicana, 1950–1955
Michigan Coastline, 1937
Milkweed Dance, 1940
Moby Dick, 1939
Modern California, 1937–1947
Mojave, 1955
Montecito, 1935
Monterey, 1942; 1950–1954
Montezuma-Aztec, 1937
Morning Glory
Multi Flori California, 1935–1937
Native American, 1935–1937

Native California, 1942–1947
North Wind, 1948
Nutcracker, 1940
Olinala (Olena)-Aztec, 1937
Orchard, 1937; 1939
Organdie, 1940s & 1950s
Our America, 1939
Palm Brocade, 1950
Pan American Lei, 1950
Pear Turnpike
Pedro & Conchita, 1937
Peppers, 1937
Phacelia
Philodendron, 1942; 1950–1954
Polychrome A, 1935–1937
Pomegranate, 1935–1937
R.F.D., 1951–1953; 1954
Raffia, 1950
Raisin
Rio Chico, 1938
Rio Verda, 1938
Rio Vista, 1938
Rosa, 1938
Rose-A-Day, 1958
Rosedale, 1950
Salamina, 1939
Santa Anita, 1942
Santa Barbara, 1939
Santa Clara, 1939
Santa Maria, 1939
Santa Paula, 1939
Seven Seas, 1954
Shadow Leaf, 1954–1955
Shantung, 1953
Sherwood, 1955–1958
Sierra Madre, 1938
Southern Rose, 1942
Spice Islands, 1950
Style, 1939
Sun Garden, 1953
Tahiti A, B, C

Tam O'Shanter, 1939
Taste, 1939
Tickled Pink, 1955–1958
Trade Winds, 1954–1956
Trailing Rose, 1939
Trellis, 1935–1937
Tweed, 1950–1955
Two-Some, 1938
Two-Tone, 1938
Ultra California, 1937–1942
Vera, 1938

Vernon 1860, 1944; 1955
Vernon Rose, 1944; 1950–1954
Victoria, 1939
Vintage, 1950
Walt Disney, 1941
Wheat, 1942
Winchester '73, 1950
Year 'Round, 1957–1958
Young in Heart, 1958
Zodiac, 1937

**Vernonware,** division of Metlox Potteries, Manhattan Beach, California, 1958–
1989; bought and produced some Vernon Kilns patterns

## REFERENCE BOOKS

Gibbs, Carl, Jr. *Collector's Encyclopedia of Metlox Potteries.* Paducah, Kentucky:
Collector Books, 1996.

## PATTERNS

Accents, 1961
American Heritage, 1980
American Heritage-Gourmet Set, early
    1980s
Antique Blue, 1975
Autumn Berry, 1978
Autumn Leaves, 1960
Big Sur, 1978
Blue Fascination, 1967
Blue Zinnias, 1963
Brookside, 1976
Butterscotch, 1960
Capistrano, 1978
Caprice, 1967
Castile, 1964
Catalina, 1978
Cinnamon, 1973
Cinnamon Green, 1976
Classic Antique, 1963
Classic Blue, 1977
Classic Flower, 1964
Classic Roma, 1964

Classic Wheat, 1977
Cognac, 1978
Colonial Garden, 1967
Fancy Free, late 1950s
Flower Basket, 1976
Fruit Basket, 1961
Gigi, 1978
Golden Amber, 1968
Golden Garden, 1967
Happy Days, 1978
Hermosa-Dos, 1978
Hermosa-Mucho, 1978
Hermosa-Tres, 1978
Hermosa-Uno, 1978
Italian Delight, 1979
LaMancha Gold, 1968
LaMancha Green, 1968
LaMancha White, 1971
Laura, early 1980s
Lemon Tree, 1975
Lime Tree, 1975
Margarita, 1969

Marigold, 1980
Marissa, 1980
Meadow, 1980
Mesa, 1976
Monterey, 1977
Morning Glory, 1980
Mount Whitney, 1978
Old Cathay, 1976
Painted Desert, 1977
Patrician White, 1959
Petalburst, 1968
Pink Lady, 1960
Quail Ridge, 1979
Rattan, 1979
San Fernando, 1966
Sculptured Berry, 1973
Sierra Flower, 1962
Sorrento, 1980
Spring Garland, 1979

Springtime, 1961
Sun 'N Sand, 1962
Tisket-a-Tasket, late 1950s
Town & Country, 1961
Tradition White, 1967
True Blue, 1959
Vernon Antiqua, 1966
Vernon Bouquet, 1974
Vernon Calypso, 1971
Vernon Della Robbia, 1965
Vernon Florence, 1969
Vernon Gaiety, 1970
Vernon Nasturtium, 1972
Vernon Pacific Blue, 1971
Vernon Pueblo, 1972
Vernon Rose, 1965
Vernon Tulips, 1971
Vineyard, 1960
White Rose, 1977

## Waterford Wedgwood Group, Burslem, England, 1759–present. See Franciscan Ceramics Inc.; Johnson Brothers, Ltd.

## Watt Pottery Company, Crooksville, Ohio, 1922–1965

### REFERENCE BOOKS

Morris, Sue and Dave. *Watt Pottery: An Identification and Value Guide.* Paducah, Kentucky: Collector Books, 1993.

Thompson, Dennis, and W. Bryce Watt. *Watt Pottery: A Collector's Reference with Price Guide.* Atglen, Pennsylvania: Schiffer Publishing Ltd., 1994.

### PATTERNS

Apple, 1952–1960s
Autumn Foliage, 1959–1965
Cherry, mid-1950s
Cut-Leaf Pansy, 1950s
Daisy, 1949–1953
Dogwood, 1949–1953
Dutch Tulip, 1956
Eagle, 1950–1960
Esmond, 1950–1960

Floral
Moonflower, 1949–1953
Morning Glory, late 1950s
Old Pansy, 1950s
Orchard Ware, 1949–1959
Pansy (also called Cross Hatch), 1950
Raised Pansy (also called Wild Rose), 1950s
Rooster, 1955–1958

Royal Danish, 1965
Silhouette, early 1950s
Starflower, 1950s
Tear Drop, mid-1950s

Tulip, mid-1950s
Valencia, 1937–1940
White Daisy, 1950–1960

## Enoch Wedgwood, Ltd., Hanley and Stoke, England (now part of Waterford Wedgwood Group)

**PATTERNS**

Liberty Blue, 1977

# General Reference Books

Chipman, Jack. *Collector's Encyclopedia of California Pottery.* Paducah, Kentucky: Collector Books, 1992.

Cunningham, Jo. *Collector's Encyclopedia of American Dinnerware.* Paducah, Kentucky: Collector Books, 1982.

———. *The Best of Collectible Dinnerware.* Atglen, Pennsylvania: Schiffer Publishing Ltd., 1995.

Derwich, Jenny, and Mary Latos. *Dictionary Guide to United States Pottery & Porcelain (19th and 20th Century).* Privately printed, 1984 (P.O. Box 674, Franklin, MI 48025).

Duke, Harvey. *Official Price Guide to Pottery and Porcelain.* 8th edition. New York: House of Collectibles, 1995.

*Eva Zeisel: Designer for Industry.* Chicago: University of Chicago Press, 1984.

*From Kiln to Kitchen: American Ceramic Design in Tableware.* Springfield, Illinois: Illinois State Museum, 1980.

Gates, William C., Jr., and Dana E. Ormerod. "The East Liverpool, Ohio, Pottery District: Identification of Manufacturers and Marks." *Historical Archaeology* 16 (1982). Washington, D.C.: The Society for Historical Archaeology.

Hayes, Barbara, and Jean Bauer. *California Pottery Rainbow.* Privately printed, 1975 (1629 W. Washington Blvd., Venice, CA 90291).

Kerr, Ann. *Collector's Encyclopedia of Russel Wright Designs.* 2nd edition. Paducah, Kentucky: Collector Books, 1998.

———. *Russel Wright and His Dinnerware.* Privately printed, 1981 (P.O. Box 437, Sidney, OH 45365).

———. *Russel Wright Dinnerware: Designs for the American Table.* Paducah, Kentucky: Collector Books, 1985.

———. *Steubenville Saga.* Privately printed, 1979 (P.O. Box 437, Sidney, OH 45365).

Klein, Benjamin. *Collector's Illustrated Price Guide to Russel Wright Dinnerware.* Smithtown, New York: Exposition Press, 1981.

**Kovel, Ralph and Terry.** *Kovels' Antiques & Collectibles Price List.* **30th edition. New York: Crown Publishers, 1998.**

———. *Kovels' Guide to Selling, Buying, and Fixing Your Antiques and Collectibles.* **New York: Crown Publishers.**

———. *Kovels' Know Your Collectibles.* **New York: Crown Publishers, 1981, updated 1992.**

———. *Kovels' New Dictionary of Marks—Pottery & Porcelain: 1850 to the Present.* **New York: Crown Publishers, 1986.**

Lehner, Lois. *Complete Book of American Kitchen and Dinner Wares.* Radnor, Pennsylvania: Wallace-Homestead Book Co., 1980.

————. *Lehner's Encyclopedia of U.S. Marks on Pottery, Porcelain & Clay.* Paducah, Kentucky: Collector Books, 1988.

Newbound, Betty. *Gunshot Guide to Values of American Made China & Pottery.* Privately printed, 1981 (4567 Chadsworth, Union Lake, MI 48085).

————. *Gunshot Guide to Values of American Made China & Pottery, Book 2.* Privately printed, 1984 (4567 Chadsworth, Union Lake, MI 48085).

Piña, Leslie. *Pottery: Modern Wares 1920–1960.* Atglen, Pennsylvania: Schiffer Publishing Ltd., 1994.

*Pottery 1880–1960.* Encino, California: Orlando Gallery, 1973.

# KOVELS' LIBRARY

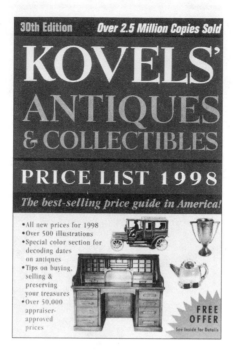

# Kovels' Antiques and Collectibles Price List
## 30th Edition

*Kovels' Antiques & Collectibles Price List* is the premier source of prices for both amateur and serious collectors. This year's 30th edition features a 16-page color insert packed with information about decoding dates on antiques. The price list includes more than 50,000 reliable, all-new prices gathered from shops, markets, sales, and auctions nationwide; hundreds of factory marks and logos; plus hints on buying, selling, and preserving antiques and collectibles. *Kovels' Antiques & Collectibles Price List* includes information on classic 18th- and 19th-century antiques as well as the hot 20th-century favorites. And the computer-generated, cross-referenced index is the most complete of its kind available.

0-609-80142-2

896 pages / $14.95 paperback

## KOVELS'
## Quick Tips
### 799
### Helpful Hints
### on How to
### Care for Your
### Collectibles

**Ralph & Terry Kovel**

## Kovels' Quick Tips
799 Helpful Hints on How to
Care for Your Collectibles

Wearing their hats as the Heloise of the antiques world, the
Kovels give you quick and handy tips on how to care for all
the treasures in your home, from your favorite jewelry, heirloom silver, and childhood toys to your Coca-Cola bottle collection, kitchen collectibles, books, and family photographs.
Organized by subject matter and charmingly illustrated, this
book includes 799 tips collected by the Kovels over the past
twenty years.

0-517-88381-3
176 pages / $12.00 paperback

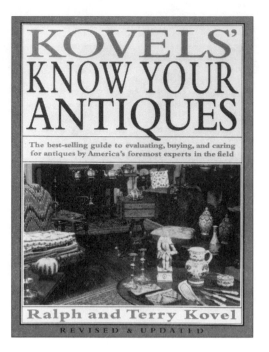

## Kovels' Know Your Antiques
### Revised & Updated Edition

The best guide in print today for beginning collectors. Learn how to recognize, evaluate, and purchase virtually any type of antique—large or small—like an expert. There is detailed advice about caring for your antiques, identifying fakes, and finding bargains. This best-seller is used by collectors and college classes alike.

0-517-57806-9

368 pages / $16.00 paperback

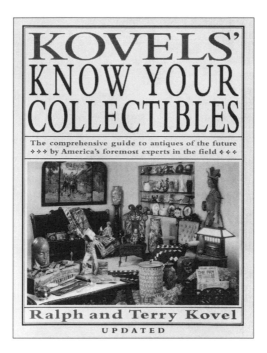

## Kovels' Know Your Collectibles
### Updated Edition

The guide to what's selling in shops and at shows today. The collectibles category covers items made since 1890, including the coveted Depression glass, Tiffany lamps, Mission furniture, and advertising items. Marks, catalog reprints, and photographs make every category clear. An in-depth study of jewelry includes names, dates, and artists information.

0-517-58840-4
416 pages / $16.00 paperback

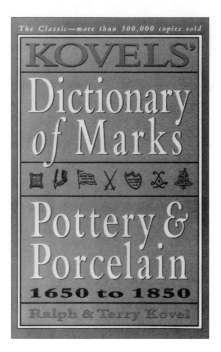

## Kovels' Dictionary of Marks
### Pottery & Porcelain (1650–1850)

A classic in the field, *Kovels' Dictionary of Marks* is a comprehensive guide to more than 5,000 American and European pottery and porcelain marks. It shows at a glance the geographical location of the factory, family name or manufacturer's name, type of ware, color of mark, and the date the mark was used.

0-517-70137-5

288 pages / $17.00 hardcover

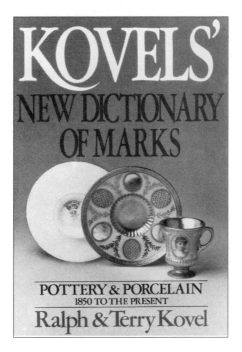

## Kovels' New Dictionary of Marks
Pottery & Porcelain (1850–Present)

*Kovels' New Dictionary of Marks* provides the quickest and easiest way to identify more than 3,500 American, European, and Oriental marks from 1850 to the present. The perfect companion to the Kovels' original best-seller *Kovels' Dictionary of Marks—Pottery & Porcelain,* this is the most comprehensive reference manual for the nineteenth- and twentieth-century marks.

0-517-55914-5

304 pages / $19.00 hardcover

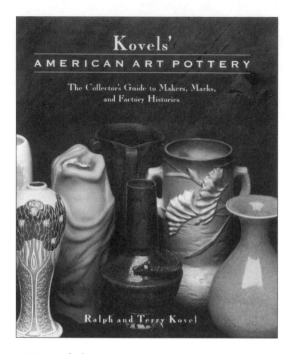

## Kovels' American Art Pottery
The Collector's Guide to Makers, Marks,
and Factory Histories

*Kovels' American Art Pottery* contains alphabetical listings
and information on 104 potteries and 95 tile factories. More
than 700 fabulous color and black-and-white photographs
show details of design, lists of makers with the identifying
marks, factory marks with dating information, and hundreds
of clues to help the beginner or serious collector identify all
types of art pottery.

0-517-58012-8
336 pages / $60.00 hardcover

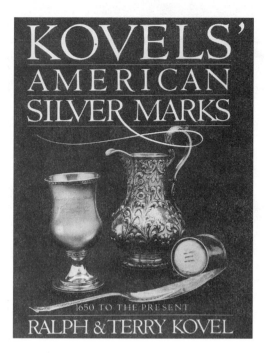

## Kovels' American Silver Marks
### (1650–Present)

*Kovels' American Silver Marks* is a simple-to-use guide to identifying marks and monograms that appear on silver. Collectors and professional dealers can quickly determine the maker of a piece of silver. Each listing includes working dates, location, mark (if known), and bibliographic references to more than 200 books and articles. More than 10,000 silversmiths are listed in alphabetical order, with a cross-indexing system for monograms and pictorial marks.

0-517-56882-9
432 pages / $40.00 hardcover

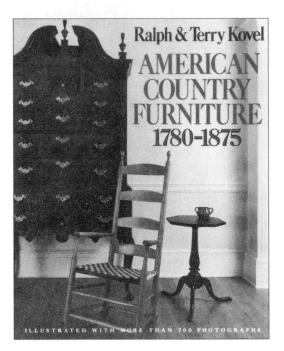

## American Country Furniture
### 1780–1875

More than 700 photographs identify styles, construction,
woods, finishes, hardware, and other details. Here is all the
information you need to be an expert on American country
furniture. There are special sections on Pennsylvania, Shaker
furniture, spool furniture, and furniture construction, plus an
illustrated glossary of accessories and terms.

0-517-54668-X
256 pages / $16.95 paperback

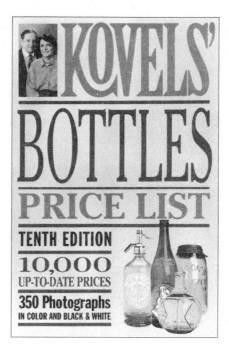

# Kovels' Bottles Price List
## 10th Edition

*Kovels' Bottles Price List* is the complete guide to collecting bottles of all types. More than 10,000 current pieces are included in this, the most complete bottle book available. More than 200 illustrations in full color and black and white aid in identification of bottles. Included are old and new bottles, bitters, perfumes, figurals, flasks, Avons, Beams, and a host of others. Notes on styles of manufacturers, lists of bottles magazines and clubs, recommended reading, and a bibliography for the serious collector make *Kovels' Bottles Price List* the best listing of current bottle prices available.

0-517-88435-6
240 pages / $16.00 paperback

# The Label Made Me Buy It:

## From Aunt Jemima to Zonkers—the Best-Dressed Boxes, Bottles & Cans from the Past

Filled with over 300 beautiful and often humorous color labels from the past 150 years, this new Kovels' book takes readers on a visual journey through the history of labels and early advertising. Drawing on their collection of more than 10,000 labels, the Kovels reveal the histories of companies, printers, and label designs. Labels are grouped by image such as Famous Men & Women, Dogs & Cats, Sports, and Patriotic Symbols. Learn how to decode the mysteries of patent numbers and legal wording. A book for collectors of labels, lovers of graphic art, and students of history.

AVAILABLE IN NOVEMBER 1998

0-609-60168-7
224 pages / $40.00 hardcover

# K O V E L S

SEND ORDERS & INQUIRIES TO: **Crown Publishers, Inc.**
**c/o Random House, 400 Hahn Road**
**Westminster, MD 21157**

ATT: ORDER DEPT.

SALES & TITLE INFORMATION
1-800-733-3000
FOR ORDER ENTRY
FAX# 1-800-659-2436
INTERNET http://www.randomhouse.com

NAME_____

ADDRESS _____

CITY & STATE _____ZIP _____

*PLEASE SEND ME THE FOLLOWING BOOKS:*

| ITEM NO. | QTY. | TITLE | | PRICE | TOTAL |
|----------|------|-------|---|-------|-------|
| 0-609-80142-2 | _____ | Kovels' Antiques & Collectibles Price List, 30th Edition *New!* | PAPER | $14.95 | _____ |
| 0-517-58012-8 | _____ | Kovels' American Art Pottery | HARDCOVER | $60.00 | _____ |
| 0-517-54668-X | _____ | American Country Furniture 1780 –1875 | PAPER | $16.95 | _____ |
| 0-517-70137-5 | _____ | Kovels' Dictionary of Marks— Pottery & Porcelain | HARDCOVER | $17.00 | _____ |
| 0-517-55914-5 | _____ | Kovels' New Dictionary of Marks (1850-present) | HARDCOVER | $19.00 | _____ |
| 0-517-56882-9 | _____ | Kovels' American Silver Marks | HARDCOVER | $40.00 | _____ |
| 0-517-88435-6 | _____ | Kovels' Bottles Price List, 10th Edition | PAPER | $16.00 | _____ |
| 0-609-80310-7 | _____ | Kovels' Depression Glass & Dinnerware Price List, 6th Edition | PAPER | $16.00 | _____ |
| 0-517-57806-9 | _____ | Kovels' Know Your Antiques, Revised & Updated | PAPER | $16.00 | _____ |
| 0-517-58840-4 | _____ | Kovels' Know Your Collectibles, Updated | PAPER | $16.00 | _____ |
| 0-517-88381-3 | _____ | Kovels' Quick Tips: 799 Helpful Hints on How to Care for Your Collectibles | PAPER | $12.00 | _____ |

_____ TOTAL ITEMS          TOTAL RETAIL VALUE_____

CHECK OR MONEY ORDER ENCLOSED
MADE PAYABLE TO CROWN PUBLISHERS, INC.
or telephone 1-800-733-3000
(No cash or stamps, please)
Charge: ☐ Master Card    ☐ Visa    ☐ American Express
Account Number (include all digits) Expires MO._____YR._____

Shipping & Handling Charge
$2.00 for one book;
50¢ for each additional book.
Please add applicable sales tax.   _____

TOTAL AMOUNT DUE _____

_____

Signature _____
Thank you for your order.

PRICES SUBJECT TO CHANGE
WITHOUT NOTICE. If a more recent
edition of a price list has been published at
the same price, it will be sent instead of the
old edition.

# We Want to Send You a Gift.

Because you love antiques, we know you will be interested in our monthly newsletter, *Kovels on Antiques and Collectibles*, a nationally distributed, fully illustrated publication now in its 24th year.

- Current prices, collecting trends, landmark auction results for all types of antiques and collectables

- Tax, estate, security, and other pertinent news for collectors

- Fakes and foibles of the market place

- All in 12 information-packed pages each month, plus a free yearly index

For a free sample copy of the newsletter, just fill in your name and address on this order form and mail to:  **Kovels on Antiques and Collectables**
**P.O. Box 420349**
**Palm Coast, Florida 32142-9655**

[  ] **YES!**  Please send me a FREE sample of *Kovels On Antiques and Collectibles.*

Name _____

Address _____

City _____ State _____ Zip _____

67KKPL